TOPOSCOPIC STUDIES
OF LEARNING

TOPOSCOPIC STUDIES
OF LEARNING

By

DONALD W. DeMOTT, Ph. D.

Department of Psychology
University of Rochester
Rochester, New York

CHARLES C THOMAS • PUBLISHER

Springfield • Illinois • U.S.A.

Published and Distributed Throughout the World by
CHARLES C THOMAS · PUBLISHER
BANNERSTONE HOUSE
301-327 East Lawrence Avenue, Springfield, Illinois, U.S.A.
NATCHEZ PLANTATION HOUSE
735 North Atlantic Boulevard, Fort Lauderdale, Florida, U.S.A.

With THOMAS BOOKS *careful attention is given to all details of
manufacturing and design. It is the Publisher's desire to present books
that are satisfactory as to their physical qualities and artistic possibilities
and appropriate for their particular use.* THOMAS BOOKS *will be true
to those laws of quality that assure a good name and good will.*

Printed in the United States of America
Y-2

To
PAT

A *Cebus albifrons* of great dignity and independence of spirit,
who died for a cause not of her choosing

PREFACE

This book is primarily a report of my investigations into the cortical mechanisms of learning in primates, conducted under the auspices of the National Institute of Mental Health, at the University of Rochester. More than that, however, I have attempted to give some insight into the pleasures and frustrations of research in a little known area. I hope that the book may prove useful to graduate and undergraduate students as well as to scientists in the field of psychobiology. I also hope that, in addition to being useful, it may prove to be relatively painless reading.

If, at times, I seem to berate the National Institute of Mental Health for their lack of patience, it is with full realization that their patience lasted far longer than I really had any right to expect. I wish to express my gratitude to the administrators of that institute for making this research possible. I also wish to thank Dr. G. R. Wendt of the Department of Psychology, University of Rochester, for his great assistance during my graduate training at that institution and his continued interest in my research since then. Above all, I am grateful to Dr. R. M. Boynton, now of the Center for Visual Science, University of Rochester, who took a camel into his tent.

Most of the credit for this research, of course, must go to the monkeys who gave their tolerance, their lives, and their undying curiosity to the advancement of human knowledge.

D. W. DeMott

CONTENTS

ix

Contents

TOPOSCOPIC STUDIES
OF LEARNING

Chapter *I*

INTRODUCTION

Some of my closest friends have suggested that I chose toposcopy as an approach to the study of cortical function because I
am not overly fond of historical research, and toposcopy has about
as short a history as any electrophysiological technique. Such un-
kind sentiments are only partly true. I cannot deny that stack
grubbing is not my favorite form of recreation, but my rationaliza-
tions for plunging into the field of toposcopy can be made to sound
much nobler than a distaste for dusty volumes.

The most obvious anatomical fact about the cerebral cortex is
its basic two-dimensional shape. The increasing convolutions of
the organ as we ascend the phylogenetic scale, with no concomitant
increase in thickness, point up the fact that it is not the volume of
cerebral cortex which is the significant measure of its potential,
but rather its surface area. It would seem to follow that, if we are
to understand the functioning of a basically two-dimensional structure, we should study it in two dimensions. This is the justification
for the existence of toposcopy, which may be most generally defined as the study of the cortex in two dimensions of space. To be
technically correct, I should modify my term to *cortical toposcopy*,
since similar two-dimensional methods have been applied to other
organs. This book, however, will be exclusively concerned with
the cerebral cortex, so the modifier need not be continually repeated.

Two reviews of the history of toposcopy have been published,
the first by Antoine Rémond in 1955, the second, an introductory
chapter to a book entitled *Electroencephaloscopy* by Livanov
and Anan'ev in 1960. The former review is in French, the latter in
Russian, but an English translation is available. I will repeat only

the highlights of these two reviews, then try to evaluate the main trends in toposcopy at the present time.

Since history is not the primary topic of this book, I will confine myself to those developments which either lay in the main line of development of toposcopy or which produced a sizable body of data. Many semitopological techniques will be omitted. Much of the exquisite mapping of Woolsey and his collaborators may be considered toposcopy, since the data are presented in a two-dimensional format. The techniques used, however, are those of conventional nonspatial electrophysiology, the spatial element being introduced only by the addition of measures borrowed from geometricians and cartographers. The very detailed mapping of the spinal cord by Howland and collaborators is omitted for the same reason.

Techniques which include only a single spatial dimension, such as the multivibrator toposcope of Marko and Petsche (1960) or the time-space recording of Rémond and his collaborators (Rémond, 1960), are omitted because they have been adequately covered in the reviews mentioned and are only peripherally related to the development of two-dimensional toposcopy. Finally, the techniques attempted by Cohn (1950) and by Goldman *et al.* (1948) for two-dimensional toposcopy will not be covered, as they are adequately described by Livanov, and the techniques were never developed to the point of actually producing usable data.

Of the three general approaches to topological presentation and analysis of cortical electrical activity described by Rémond, we are primarily concerned with the method which permits the description of two-dimensional spatial gradients of electrical potential at a particular instant in time. By this definition the first real toposcope was developed by J. C. Lilly in the late 1940's (Lilly, 1949). Lilly termed his device a Bavatron, and the photographic records "electro-iconograms." It consisted of twenty-five electrodes arranged in a square array, each one driving a separate amplifier, the output of which was displayed as the brightness of a glow modulator tube (see Fig. 1). These output tubes were arranged in spatial correspondence to the electrode array, and photographed at 128 frames per second. Patterns of electrical potential on the cortex under the electrode array are thus recorded as patterns of photographic density on the film.

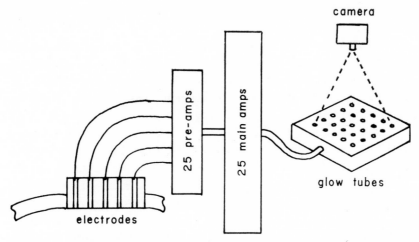

Figure 1. J.C. Lilly's 25-channel Bavatron, 1949.

Lilly used an electrode spacing of 2 mm between centers, so that the array covered one square centimeter of cortex. Most of his published data are of auditory evoked potentials in the cat, although he also recorded some sensory evoked potentials as well as motor cortex activity in monkeys. He found that the auditory evoked potential was spatially organized and appeared to propagate across the cortical surface. This phenomenon was very carefully analyzed in a series of publications in collaboration with Cherry (Lilly and Cherry, 1951-1955).

The major limitation of Lilly's approach to toposcopy was the difficulty of converting the photographic records into numerical form, which requires densitometric measures on the film. Actually, this is not nearly as serious a drawback as it may seem at first. Most of us are accustomed to electrophysiological data in the format of the EEG, that is, a continual graph of voltage versus time. In ordinary EEG recording, of course, time and voltage are the only variables available. In toposcopic recordings two dimensions of space are also part of the data. Toposcopic data may be analyzed in terms of voltage versus space, which is the shape of instantaneous patterns, space versus time, which is the propagation of wave fronts, for voltage versus time, which is the conventional EEG, or for voltage versus space versus time, which is a change in patterns. Although voltage is a factor in all of these analyses, it is only the conventional EEG that requires an accurate voltage measure. For analysis of patterns, the voltage variable is usually reduced to about a five-part scale. Too fine a voltage analysis in this case merely confuses the presentation, actually obscuring the spatial shape of the patterns which is the datum of primary interest. The human visual system is quite capable of making sufficiently accurate discriminations of density to permit direct analysis of the film data without quantification of the voltage variable. Spatial and temporal variables are already quantified in the film records, assuming that electrode spacing and camera speed are uniform. Voltage quantification is generally necessary only for those frames of film intended for publication or if the data are to be analyzed by computer. In the former case, the densitometry may be done by underpaid undergraduates; in the latter case, it is a simple matter to program the computer to do its own voltage quantification. In short, if one wants an EEG, he should use an EEG recorder. If he is primarily interested in spatial factors, he should use a toposcope, which presents data with the spatial dimensions much more accurately quantified than can be achieved by the usual hand measurements used to locate the electrode position in conventional EEG work.

The next significant development in toposcopy was the publication in 1951 by Walter and Shipton of a description of a 24-channel toposcope using an array of cathode ray tubes (CRT) as its display. The CRT beams were swept circularly around the tube face, with voltage displayed as brightness, so that voltage excursions appeared as radial bands on the tubes. Again, voltage was not directly quantified; the toposcope was intended to display frequencies in terms of the number of radial bands per revolution, and phase relationships as the relative angles of the bands. This was later modified to a helical scan presentation, which gives a clearer picture of drifting phase relationships. Since it was not intended to permit direct analysis of instantaneous spatial patterns, it does not lie on the main phylogenetic line of toposcopy.

In 1955, Livanov and Anan'ev published the first results obtained with Livanov's 50-channel electroencephaloscope. This device used a commutation principle, switching the fifty inputs successively into a single amplifier, the output of which was then used to modulate the brightness of the beam of a cathode ray tube. The

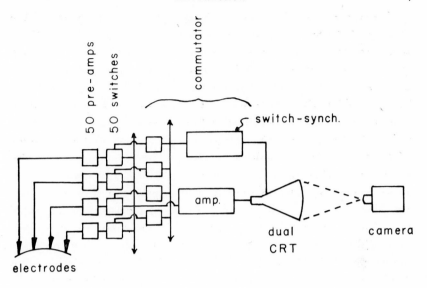

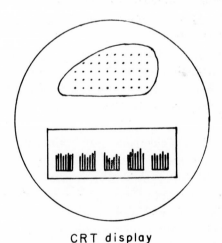

CRT display

FIGURE 2. M.N. Livanov's 50-channel electroencephaloscope.

CRT beam was moved across the tube face in a spatial pattern corresponding to the electrode array, and a temporal rate was locked to the commutator, so that the fifty signals were rearranged in the spatial format of the electrodes (Fig. 2).

If we compare this toposcope with Lilly's Bavatron, it has the obvious advantage of having twice as many channels. The use of a single main amplifier also provides a simple gain control. The savings in electronics, however, is only apparent, since Livanov's toposcope had a preamplifier for each channel before the signal was commutated. The added complexity of the synchronizing circuits more than makes up the difference. Furthermore, the inherent limitations of commutation restrict the speed at which the entire array of electrodes can be sampled. Although the commutator operates at 250 sweeps per second, the tube face is typically photographed at 24 frames per second, which is obviously too slow to record anything but alpha activity. As this type of toposcope is expanded to more channels, the requirements on the commutator become impossibly severe, and the difficulties in synchronizing the commutator and display system similarly multiply. The relative complexity of the commutated and parallel channel systems may be estimated from their power requirements. Although exact figures are difficult to derive from Livanov's description, it appears that his 50-channel electroencephaloscope requires between 2 and 3 kW of power. My own 400-channel Kinetak, which also used vacuum tubes (see below), drew less than 1 kW.

The only significant advantage of the Livanov apparatus over Lilly's approach is that, having commutated the inputs, it was a simple matter to display the commutator output in a single sweep across a cathode ray tube (or the same tube, using either a dual beam or a rather complex beam splitter), thus preserving the precise voltage of each electrode in the familiar format of Y axis representation (see Fig. 1).

Even this advantage, however, is partly vitiated by another error inherent in the commutator approach. The voltage measured for electrode 1 is taken at a different time from that measured for electrode 50. A commutated toposcope can never give an accurate picture of the spatial pattern at an instant in time, since it requires a finite length of time to sample all the electrodes. This problem can be minimized by commutating at such a rate that the pattern changes only very slightly between frames, but in the current state of the art this remains only a theoretical possibility.

The commutation principle has also been used in a toposcope developed by Tunturi (1958). His toposcope is quite similar to Livanov's, except that it was designed primarily for computer analysis of the output. Since Livanov has since added this feature to his electroencephaloscope (Livanov *et al.*, 1965), the two devices are very similar.

My own toposcope, which I refer to as Kinetak, was first operated in 1960, using 160 channels. The first vacuum tube model was simply an extension of Lilly's approach, and eventually reached a size of four hundred channels (see Fig 8). It shared with the Bavatron the difficulty of voltage quantification, and, in addition, had the limitation of a fixed gain. Individual gain controls for four hundred channels would be impractical even for a team of octopuses. This difficulty was overcome in the solid state successor to the first Kinetak, also a 400-channel model, by providing built-in levels of gain in each channel which could be selected by applying a signal to all channels simultaneously. The amplifiers were also built in separate stages, connected by identical plug-in cables, so that an entire stage or stages may be bypassed. By applying different gain control signals and/or bypassing stages, the gain of the system may be varied in 6 dB steps from a usable signal of 10 mV to about 500 mV (see Fig. 11).

At this writing, the only toposcopes in active use, to the best of my knowledge, are my own, Livanov's (I believe several models are in use, all very similar), Tunturi's, and Walter's. I have had personal communication with several people who were planning toposcopes, but none has yet written me of a successful operation.

Projecting this "history" into the foreseeable future, always a risky venture, we may compare the potentials for further development of the Lilly, or parallel channel toposcope, with that of the Livanov, or commutated toposcope. Further development will depend largely upon increasing the number of channels, utilization of computer analysis, and in the case of the Livanov toposcope, increasing recording speed. Naturally, I have greater enthusiasm for the Lilly type of apparatus, or I would not have adopted it. Those Russians with whom I have been in contact are equally enthusiastic about the commutation principle.

A commutated system could overcome the temporal spread of recordings only by some technique for instantaneously sampling all electrodes and then holding this information until the commutator completes its sweep. This would appear to be much more difficult than parallel amplification. It appears likely, therefore, that this will continue to be a limitation of this method. It becomes less crucial as commutator frequencies increase, and rapid progress in this direction is being made. Rapid and noise-free commutation, however, is still a very expensive matter and is technically so complex as to present serious maintenance problems. Where the signals are individually preamplified in order to avoid contamination by a noisy commutator as in Livanov's present toposcope, the problems of many parallel channels are added to the problems of commutation and synchronization of display. Indeed, such a device is really no different from a parallel channel toposcope with a commutator added to the end.

In 1964, I constructed a computerlike system to quantify the toposcope films for publication. The film was projected onto a bank of cadmium sulphide photocells. The outputs of these cells were then commutated and printed out in numerical form on teletype paper in a spatial format corresponding to the electrode array (see Fig. 16). With this addition the Lilly type of toposcope becomes rather similar to the Livanov type, except for the sequence of operations. In Livanov's device, the signals are preamplified, commutated, displayed, and photographed. In my system, the signals are amplified, displayed, and photographed, then commutated and rerecorded. The change in sequence avoids the inherent temporal spread of the commutated toposcope and also defers the commutation to a time when the data are safely stored on film. If my computer breaks down, as it rather frequently does, I have not lost any data. I assume that Livanov's commutator and display system are more reliable than my computer, but it nonetheless adds maintenance problems on top of the difficulty of keeping many channels of amplifiers all working, which we both share.

Maintenance problems in the two divisions of the toposcope are of a different nature. If an amplifier breaks down, you lose only $1/N$ of your data, where N is the number of channels. If the commutator or display system break down, you lose everything. I feel much more comfortable having my commutator connected only to imperishable film rather than a perishing preparation.

In addition, when commutation is done from the film records, the demands on the commutator are less severe, since speed is only a convenience, not a necessity. My present computer takes almost sixty seconds to commutate information from four hundred channels, which gives me enough time to fix a cup of coffee. When the commutator is connected to a preparation, one millisecond is a long time.

It would appear, then, that the commutated toposcope is limited in the number of channels that may practicably be used by both the difficulties of maintaining a large number of preamplifiers and the speed of a workable commutator. The parallel channel system is limited only by the former problem. Maintenance problems in the parallel portion of the apparatus are somewhat ameliorated by the fact that one can tolerate a small percentage of nonfunctional channels. Further, the parallel channel system avoids the temporal spread artifact, which appears to be unavoidable in the commutator.

If the data are to be analyzed by a computer, Livanov's technique has some advantage over mine. The commutated signal can be fed directly into the computer with a minimum of interfacing, and analyzed in real time so that an experiment can be guided by the data as they emerge. In my system, the computer would have to be fed commutated data from the film record, which means that the experiment is necessarily ended before the data are analyzed. This disadvantage is somewhat offset by the fact that the analysis need not be done in real time, which removes a serious limitation as to what one can reasonably ask of the computer. At present, I have not used any computer analyses, partly because of financial limitations, but largely because that oldest of all computational systems, the human brain and sense organs, produces such an embarrassing wealth of information from the toposcopic data that I have not felt the need for more.

References

Cohn, R.: A simple method for cerebral toposcopy. *Electroenceph. Clin. Neurophysiol.*, 2:97-98, 1950.

Goldman, St., Vivian, W.E., Chien, Ch.K., and Bowes, H.N.: Electronic mapping of the activity of the heart and the brain. *Science, 108*:720-723, 1948.

Lilly, J.C.: A method of recording the moving electrical potential gradients in the brain: the 25-channel Bavatron and electroiconograms. Conference on electric instruments in nucleonics and medicine. New York, 1949 (American Institute of Electrical Engineering).

LILLY, J.C., and CHERRY, R.B.: Traveling waves of action and of recovery during responses and spontaneous activity in the cerebral cortex. *Amer. J. Physiol., 167*:806, 1951.

LILLY, J.C., and CHERRY, R.B.: Criteria for the parcellation of the cortical surface into functional areas. *Electroenceph. Clin. Neurophysiol., 4*:385, 1952.

LILLY, J.C., and CHERRY, R.B.: Surface movements of click responses from acoustical cerebral cortex of cat: leading and trailing edges of a response figure. *J. Neurophysiol., 17*:521-532, 1954.

LILLY, J.C., and CHERRY, R.B.: Surface movements of figures in spontaneous activity of anesthetized cerebral cortex. Leading and trailing edges. *J. Neurophysiol., 18*:18-32, 1955.

LIVANOV, M.N., and ANAN'YEV, V.M.: An electrophysiological study of spatial distribution of activity in the cerebral cortex of a rabbit. *Sechenov J. Physiol., USSR, 41*:461-469, 1955.

LIVANOV, M.N., and ANAN'YEV, V.M.: *Electroencephaloscopy.* Moscow, 1960. (English translation from OTS No. TT61 27274.)

LIVANOV, M.N., GAVRILOVA, N.A., EFREMOVA, T.M., KOROLKOVA, T.A., and ASLANOV, A.S.: The application of electronic computing techniques to the analysis of cortical biopotentials in man and in animals with multichannel toposcopic recording. *Med. Electron. Biol. Engin., 3*:137-144, 1965.

MARKO, A., and PETSCHE, H.: The multivibrator toposcope; an electronic polygraph. *Electroenceph. Clin. Neurophysiol., 12*:209-211, 1960.

RÉMOND, ANTOINE: Directions and trends in topographic methods in the study of electrical activity of the brain. *Rev. Neurol. (Paris), 93*:399-432, 1955.

RÉMOND, A.: Search for meaning in the EEG. I: The problem of spatial reference. *Rev. Neurol. (Paris), 102*:412-415, 1960.

TUNTURI, A.R.: Localized responses in auditory cortex to brief tones in high level noise. *Amer. J. Physiol., 195*:779-786, 1958.

WALTER, W.G., and SHIPTON, H.W.: A toposcopic display system applied to neurophysiology. *J. Brit. IRE, 2*:260-284, 1951.

WALTER, W.G., and SHIPTON, H.W.: A new toposcopic display system. *Electroenceph. Clin. Neurophysiol., 3*:281-292, 1951.

Chapter II

HISTORY OF THIS RESEARCH PROJECT

Fᴏʀ those who are less than fascinated with historical detail, this chapter may be skipped with no loss to the continuity of the remainder of the book. For those, however, who may be interested in knowing why one small contribution to knowledge should require twelve years of a man's life, this chapter may provide an answer. Searching for a needle in a haystack takes time, but if one does not know in advance that it is a needle he is looking for . . .

As a graduate student, I had read the Millbank symposium on the *Biology of Mental Health and Disease* (Lilly, 1952). In it, Lilly described his 25-channel toposcope together with a few data on evoked potentials. It struck me as being the most promising technique for study of cortical mechanisms that I had yet seen. It was rather like opening a window on the brain, through which one could watch it in action, although with only twenty-five channels it was more akin to a keyhole.

I was particularly interested in the mechanisms underlying learning. If, as Lilly's data seemed to indicate, stimuli were represented on the cortex as two-dimensional moving pictures, then these pictures should change in some way as the animal learned new ways of perceiving. I determined to build my own toposcope. Of course, I knew nothing whatsoever about electronics, or about surgery either for that matter. There are times when ignorance is a powerful ally.

I had done my dissertation research under Dr. R. M. Boynton, measuring stray light in excised steer eyes. The apparatus for that research was built into two adjacent plywood booths with a total floor space of about eighty square feet. In the fall of 1956, armed with an NIH fellowship, a soldering iron, the *Radio Amateur's Handbook*, and Dr. Boynton's generous permission to continue using part of his laboratory, I proceeded to turn those plywood booths into Rube Golbergian death traps. My amplifiers were designed around the 6AC7 pentode because it was capable of high gain and was available free from the Department of Electrical Engineering. In order to get the gain I needed without too much distortion, I ran them at 1500V B+. Recording was through a row of two-inch cathode ray tubes with 5000V on the anodes. Since my amateurish wiring had a tendency to explode into clouds of acrid blue smoke at unpredictable intervals, I soon acquired a reflex flinch when reaching for the main power switch.

Nine electrodes were placed in a straight line across the preparation's cortex at 1.5 mm spacing. They drove nine amplifiers (I had planned ten, but never got that last one working) which drove the horizontal deflection plates of nine cathode ray tubes, arranged in a horizontal row. These were imaged by a single lens onto a vertically moving strip of film. The effect was that of a 9-channel EEG machine, except that the upper frequency limit was much higher than in a conventional ink recorder, and the whole thing cost less than four hundred dollars. Its application to unidimensional toposcopy, if such a term makes any sense, was very similar to that of the Marko and Petsche multivibrator toposcope.

I was looking for propagated potentials such as reported by Lilly. I knew, of course, that you cannot really tell anything about two-dimensional movement from a one-dimensional array, but the practice in electronics and surgery would give me a start in toposcopy, and the data might tell me something about frequencies, voltages, and possible propagation. Actually, considering the primitive apparatus used, the data were surprisingly good.

My preparation was the *encèphale isolé* cat. I learned surgery by cadging some overaged rats from the animal room (they would have been destroyed anyway) and working through the procedure mistake by mistake. This experience did not really prepare me for the crimson tide that accompanies any attempt to penetrate the cat's cranium, but I was able to get my data without wasting any lives. The electrodes were straight silver wire sliding in a plastic guide so that the array of nine electrodes could be lowered onto

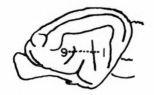

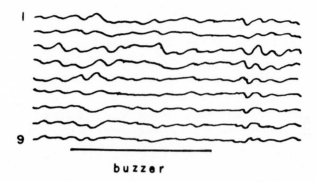

b u z z e r

.I sec

FIGURE 3. Sample recording from the author's 9-channel toposcope, 1957. The location of the electrode array on auditory cortex of an acutely prepared cat is shown above.

the brain at any desired locus and orientation and would adapt itself to the convolutions. By sampling a given locus at several orientations, I could search for evidence of propagated waves.

With an animal under barbiturate narcosis, I could usually find examples of spontaneous or evoked waveforms that appeared to propagate uniformly (Fig. 3). Without anesthesia, however, the picture was much more complicated. I suspected that the simple picture presented by Lilly's preliminary data was rather misleading.

The following year, still under the NIH fellowship, I decided to try for a two-dimensional toposcope of forty-nine channels, with high-speed motion picture recording. Since the total research funds in the fellowship amounted to five hundred dollars, this was a fairly ambitious undertaking. However, my wife assures me that I am the world's champion penny pincher, and I had discovered the $12AX7$, a twin triode which gives more gain per dollar than any other tube made and has a very satisfactory noise figure. I had also found a way to circumvent the high cost of displaying amplifier output in a recordable form. In studying the literature on neon glow tubes, I found that in the ionized state their brightness is a linear function of current. In those days, an NE-2 cost only eight cents, so that a matrix of forty-nine tubes was a very inexpensive display device. Furthermore, DuPont makes a fast emulsion, "Superior 4," which is particularly sensitive to the red light of neon.

I built a high-speed camera based on the rotating prism principle, with parts salvaged from the junk box of a camera repair shop. When the camera actually ran and produced recognizable pictures, I was so pleased that I wanted to give it a trademark. "Kodak" was already taken. A graduate student working with Dr. Boynton, who was something of a philologist, suggested the Greek roots "cine" and "tacho." Stealing George Eastman's idea of the initial and terminal "k," I produced the word "Kinetak," subsequently applied to all my major inventions.

This first Kinetak apparatus recorded from a square array of forty-nine electrodes which rested gently on the cortex of an acutely prepared guinea pig. I used this species rather than the cat for several reasons. One, I was concentrating on apparatus development rather than data collection, and the use of guinea pigs greatly simplified housing, handling, and surgery. Two, I could cover most of the brain with my forty-nine electrodes at 1.5 mm spacing. Three, the simpler mentality of the guinea pig improved the chances of my being able to make some sense of the data.

The forty-nine amplifiers had a fixed gain, fixed frequency spectrum, in fact a fixed everything except for the zero-signal brightness of the neon tubes. Actually, the amplifier gain was a bit high, so that the distribution of film densities tended to pile up at each end of the H and D curve of the film; but for visual identification of patterns, this makes for easy analysis. The camera ran at about 250 frames per second for most recording, although it was capable of more than twice that speed. The film was developed by wadding it up into a spaghettilike mass and sloshing it around in a ten-quart bucket of chemical. The only gain adjustment in the system was the choice of D-76 (low gain) or D-11 (high gain) in the bucket.

The most interesting fact emerging from these 49-channel re-

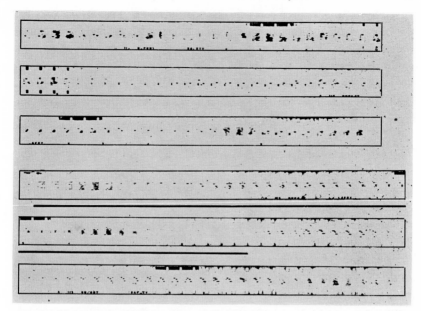

Figure 4. Sample data from 49-channel toposcope. Camera speed was 220 frames per second. Black areas are electrically negative. Time runs left to right, top to bottom. Samples are of spontaneous activity (first three strips) and response to buzzer (duration shown by black line) in cortex of unanesthetized guinea pig.

cordings was that the cortical activity consists of a sequence of discrete patterns, each one maintained for a period of time, and then the entire pattern replaced by a new one. Of course, this says nothing more than the statement that electrical activity maintains fixed phase relationships over most of the guinea pig cortex, but seeing this activity as two-dimensional movies is a much more compelling presentation of the fact and gives one a feeling as to why it should be so. Furthermore, each pattern is a recognizable entity, and when a pattern reappears, as they do under some conditions, the repetition can be noted. This would not be possible with less than a two-dimensional recording system. Examples of such recordings are shown in Figure 4.

Crude as these data were, in that summer of 1958 they were the best toposcopic recordings available anywhere, and they showed enough to demonstrate that the technique was well worth pursuing. I applied to NIH for a research grant to develop a real toposcope, planning a final size of two thousand channels. The study section agreed to fund the project for three years to see what I might produce. While waiting for this decision, I took a temporary job with the University's atomic energy project, where I collaborated with physicist Tom Davis, measuring the amount of light (from a simulated atomic flash) it took to burn holes in a rabbit's retina. (De-Mott and Davis, 1959).

In December of 1958, I began work under research grant M-2413 from the National Institute of Mental Health. The first year was spent in constructing housing for 2000 channels, behavioral apparatus, surgery, and so forth. I also built 160 channels of amplifiers and display. Naturally, nothing worked.

The second year was devoted largely to debugging. One of the nastiest problems was plugging an animal into the toposcope input. I was planning for 2000 channels, but even with the 160 channels I actually had, individually wired plug connections were impracticable. After several miscarriages, I produced the scheme shown in Figure 5A. With this arrangement, the electrodes on the cortex could be randomly arranged, simply by close packing, and the desired array of recording sites would be selected by the arrangement of probe contacts. Part B of the same figure shows the present evolutionary status of the probe. It has become somewhat fancier and a great deal more expensive, but not really much better. I refer to the electrode arrangement as a "stainless steel cortex" because it is electrically equivalent to a plane projection of the cortical surface. One can record from this surface by any conventional technique and can stimulate through it as well. Details of the preparation and implantation techniques are given in Chapter III.

Several times during 1960 I thought I had finally recorded some data, only to discover that it was some new exotic form of noise or artifact. Finally, on November 9, 1960, I recorded one roll of film from an acutely prepared guinea pig, which contained a response evoked by a flash of light. For the next few weeks everything worked perfectly. Each day a few hundred feet more data ran through my jury-rigged film processor. The 160 channels were quite adequate to give a detailed picture of the activity over the entire surface of the guinea pig brain. I plied my preparations with lights and sounds and jabs, I doped them with an assortment

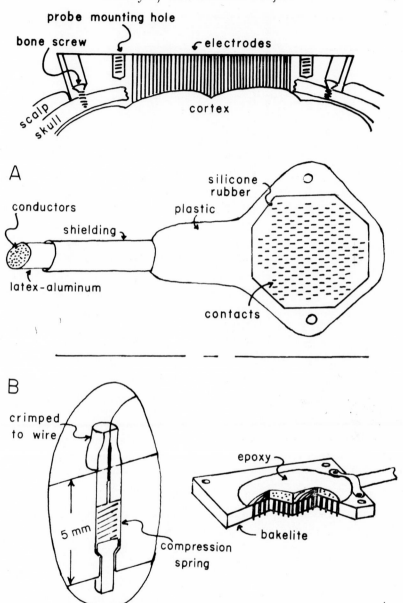

FIGURE 5. Details of recording probes used to connect toposcope input to chronic preparations. *A*, 160 channels. *B*, Present 400-channel probe.

of drugs, and every afternoon I sat in my darkened laboratory watching movies.

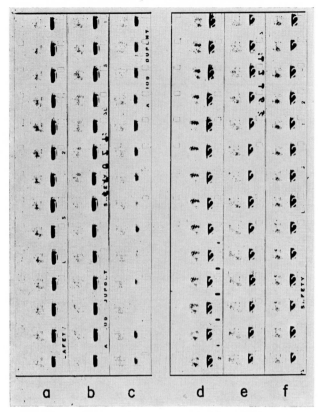

FIGURE 6. Sample recordings from 160-channel Kinetak, Camera speed 250 frames per second. Read from the top down: *a*, spontaneous; *b*, response to light flash in right eye; *c*, response to 2000-cycle tone; *d* through *f*, same as *a* through *c* except preparation had received 50 mg/kg sodium pentobarbital.

J. C. Lilly had seen "forms and figures" in the output of his 25-channel Bavatron. I could see whole epic dramas in the motion pictures produced by my 160-channel Kinetak (Fig. 6). The majestic sweep of massive waveforms in the anesthetized brain, the rapid flickering of detailed patterns in the normal, the redundant response to a simple flash of light, the quick, nervous patterns in an animal under epinephrine; I became frantically eager to get a chronic monkey in there and start observing a primate brain as it learned. First, however, I devoted two months to recording the effects of a variety of drugs on my guinea pigs, and another month to analyzing and writing the results for publication. The journal editor very tactfully suggested that I probably did not really want to publish such preliminary results, and perhaps when I had a little more to offer. . . . (I had published five articles on phases of physiological optics, in which the combined information content was less significant than these toposcopic data from guinea pigs.) In later years some editors and referees became more frank and admitted that they did not want the data because they were "difficult to compare with conventional results;" in other words, scientific journals do not like to publish anything unconventional. The editor did, however, accept a short note on the apparatus (DeMott, 1961). This proved rather embarrassing to me because, expecting the two articles to appear in the same issue, I had not included any literature references in the apparatus note. This oversight apparently did not bother the editor, and did not even occur to me until I received a very gentle note from Lilly, pointing out that he had done some rather similar work, and enclosing reprints of all the articles with which I was so familiar. My personal apologies at that time can now be supplemented by this more public apology.

Since then, when articles have been turned down for "poor scholarship," I remember the article that was happily published with no scholarship at all as long as it contained only innocuous wiring diagrams. I even had the very well-known editor of an august journal reject a paper, largely on the grounds that I had referred to Lilly as the originator of toposcopy when "Livanov actually originated the technique." Livanov's first publication came six years after Lilly's.

Filing the unwanted manuscript well back in the drawer, I pressed on toward my major goal of obtaining records from monkeys undergoing training procedures. My ignorance of our primitive cousins was nearly complete. By great good fortune I early acquired a *Cebus albifrons* (cinnamon ring-tail) who genuinely liked people, although she was keenly aware of their inferior phylogenetic position. She was named Pat, partly because of some uncertainty as to her sex. (The genital anatomy of the Cebus monkey is so confusing that I do not see how they ever know what they are doing.) She taught me a great deal about the construction of indestructible and escape-proof cages, effective restraint procedures, to what sorts of problems Cebus monkeys apply themselves, and for what rewards. Together we worked out a simple operant conditioning task in which the monkey pulls a string in order to obtain a grape. The apparatus can be wired so that the string works only during some distinctive cue, such as a tone. I refer to this basic paradigm as the "one-tone, one-string" problem. The Cebus monkey typically learns it in ten to thirty trials.

As she learned this operant response, Pat's toposcopic data showed a very distinctive pattern in the region of the parieto-occipital sulcus. As the habit became firmly established, this pattern sharpened, shrank, then disappeared. Now I introduced a different, operationally neutral tone (thus, the "two-tone, one-string" problem), forcing Pat to discriminate the two. The distinctive pattern promptly reappeared, then as the discrimination was learned, again sharpened, shrank, and disappeared. Elated at having struck pay dirt so soon, I termed the pattern a *learning-specific response* and ordered more monkeys. Between training sessions I was collecting other data from Pat. I discovered that the cortical activity evoked by an auditory stimulus is fairly easily identified in toposcopic data by the two-dimensional shape of the evoked pattern. With conventional EEG recording, of course, one generally has to average several hundred responses to a stimulus in order to tease out the evoked waveform from all the other activity of an unanesthetized brain. With toposcopy, however, three or four repetitions of a stimulus enable one to identify the particular pattern which is uniquely associated with it. In this way I was able to obtain a tonotopic map of Pat's auditory cortex in about thirty minutes, data which would have required many days to acquire by conventional techniques. I was also able to record, almost effortlessly, the effects of intermodality sensory conditioning, habituation of evoked responses, responses evoked by complex stimuli, and so forth. In a few days, I knew more about the manner in which Pat's auditory cortex handled a variety of acoustic stimuli than had ever before been known about a single individual.

Pat developed an infection around her electrode implant. After trying for several days to clear it up with antibiotics, I decided to remove the implant, resect the area of infection and while I was there, create an epileptogenic lesion with dry ice. Unfortunately, either the infection had gone too far or my freezing was too extensive, because Pat never recovered from the anesthetic.

I am always sorry when an animal dies, but Pat was more than just another preparation. A great deal of what I know I owe to this diminutive primate, whose epitaph is the dedication of this book.

During the fall of 1961, I built a 400-connector probe and associated input wiring, so that additional channels could be inserted as the amplifiers were completed. With technical help from Mike Ungerman, an undergraduate, we set up a production line, aiming toward a temporary plateau of four hundred channels. Meanwhile, I repeated the auditory operant conditioning on more monkeys, Cebus and Saimiri (squirrel monkey), confirming the existence of the learning-specific response found in Pat. As more data accumulated, however, I was forced to reorganize my concepts. Operant conditioning involving visual cues did not produce a learning-specific response. In cats, a simple two-cup delayed-response problem, which is a test of short-term memory, produced patterns which were clearly related to the distinctive pattern I called the learning-specific response, but which seemed to differ depending on whether the cat was orienting toward the left- or the right-hand food cup, and which did not disappear as the habit became well practiced. Obviously, the learning-specific response was both more and less specific than I had thought.

I wasted most of the summer of 1962 trying to get a Cebus monkey to learn a delayed response. The Cebus has many virtues, but patience is not one of them. As soon as any delay was introduced, the animal became highly emotional and generally refused to play the game at all. I considered using a more patient genus of monkey, such as the macaque, but the relatively unconvoluted cortex of the Cebus seemed to have been designed with toposcopists in mind. This accessibility of cortex, plus a high level of intelligence, fairly human motivational system, and reasonably cooperative disposition, makes the Cebus unmatched for this type of work.

During the fall and winter of 1962-1963 I collected data from Cebus and from cats on a somewhat more complex type of learning problem which I refer to as the hypothesis problem (see Fig. 32). The monkey is presented with four handles of different shapes and different colors (selected to avoid the possible color-blindness of the Cebus). The correct response may be to a particular position, regardless of shape or color, to a particular shape, regardless of color or position, or to a particular color. The animal has no way of knowing in advance which dimension contains the critical cue. In this situation, the monkey appears to form hypotheses: he will respond to a particular position for one or two sessions, then to a particular shape for a time, then to a particular color. Eventually, a Cebus can learn this problem, but only the most intelligent ones can tolerate a change in criterion of correct response after they have once learned. A simpler form of this problem, with only two handles in black and white with highly distinctive shapes, was used with cats.

The results were very interesting but did not lead to any simple generalizations. Patterns looking very much like the learning-specific response would appear and fade in various cortical regions, but with no simple relationship to behavior that I could find.

During this same period of time, I was making a systematic study of sensory evoked potentials in cats and in primitive primates, such as the marmoset and tamarin, and collecting some very striking toposcopic records of chronically induced epileptic activity (De-Mott, 1966).

By spring of 1963, I had begun to wonder whether the original appearance of the learning-specific response in those first monkeys had been just my imagination or coincidence. I repeated the one-tone, one-string problem, and the two-tone, one-string problem. There was the learning-specific response right over the parieto-occipital sulcus, every parameter just as before. I spent the next week in a darkened room, running backward and forward through movies of monkey brains learning visual problems. On a few animals whose electrode arrays extended somewhat further lateral than usual, I could see a small region of activity over the sylvian fissure during the critical training sessions which had the electrical and spatial characteristics of the learning-specific response. This region was right on the edge of the normal electrode array. Knowing where to look, I was able to go back over the data from the other animals and found the learning-specific activity during every visual learning problem, in any animal whose electrodes extended far enough laterally.

It was now obvious that the learning-specific response occurred in parieto-occipital cortex during learning involving an auditory cue, and on the anterior lip of the sylvian fissure during learning involving visual cues. What would happen if both modalities were involved? I set up a problem in which string-pulling was reinforced only when a tone and light were both on, but not for either one alone. When learning this contingency, my monkeys showed either the auditory learning pattern or the visual learning pattern, depending on which aspect of the stimulus was least familiar to them. A monkey who had recently completed the one-tone problem, but had never, or at least not recently, done the one-light problem, would show a typical visual learning pattern as he acquired the response to the simultaneous cue.

These preparations also demonstrated a very interesting phenomenon which I had seen before but not reliably enough to understand. A typical area of learning-specific activity appeared in frontal cortex, just medial to the arcuate sulcus, as the animal learned not to respond to a light or tone alone. I had previously seen this sort of activity in premotor cortex and suspected that it had something to do with suppressing responses, but it was not very constant. The difficulty seems to be that while I can structure a situation so as to specify rather narrowly what the animal must do to obtain a reward, I cannot specify precisely what he should not do. Some animals may suppress a tendency to pull the string continually, others may suppress tendencies to tie knots in the recording cable or to turn somersaults in the chair, and some uninhibited monkeys appear never to use their premotor cortex at all.

At this point in my research, late May of 1963, I had all the basic information on the learning-specific response. I knew that it appeared in different cortical areas for different classes of stimuli, in premotor cortex during suppression of behavior, and (in the cat) during the delay period of a short-term memory problem. It appeared to be closely related to the psychological phenomenon of selective attention. Before I published any of this material, however, I wanted to increase the reliability of certain aspects of the data, particularly the simultaneous light-tone problem, have another try at making sense out of the hypothesis problem, and devise a method for quantifying the film records. I had also become very highly involved in microtoposcopy (DeMott, 1966), which has nothing to do with this story of the search for learning mechanisms, although some day I hope to relate the two areas.

Another important reason for my reluctance to publish the learning data at this point was the subjectivity of the criterion of the learning-specific response. I could recognize the learning-specific activity, and a technician, Marilyn Mayou, who had been working with me for almost two years, could also recognize it, but I knew I could not describe the phenomenon in sufficiently precise terms that a computer, or a nontoposcopist could recognize it. I was not particularly concerned that the whole structure might be a self-delusion, since I had been baffled for several months by my inability to find the activity where I had expected it. In order to be scientifically useful, however, a phenomenon should not require a year's training for its identification.

A final point that made me reluctant to publish at this point was a feeling that I did not really understand the phenomenon. The toposcopic data looked different in a particular brain region during a particular phase of learning a particular type of problem. So what did this indicate beyond itself? The learning-specific response appeared to be merely symptomatic of more basic changes in the state of the cortical tissue.

The focal nature of the phenomenon suggested a relationship with the Russian work on the dominant focus. If the learning-specific response was actually the toposcopic manifestation of a dominant focus, it would be much more meaningful than just another quirk of the EEG. Furthermore, since the dominant focus appeared to be a d.c. phenomenon, this line of investigation might lead to a much simpler and more objective means of identifying the learning-specific activity.

In the fall of 1963 I made the decision to map the d.c. fields of a monkey undergoing training before publishing any of the data on the learning-specific response. This decision eventually cost me my job. I had now been working on toposcopy for seven years, and had produced only one publication, a short note on apparatus. My patrons at NIH were becoming restive. Nonetheless, I did not wish to publish data I did not really understand. I was fairly confident of the psychological correlates of the learning-specific response, but it needed more physiological relatives to become a respectable variable in physiological psychology.

During the winter of 1963-1964 I began the appalling task of designing a d.c. amplifier, stable to within a fraction of a millivolt with no compensating adjustment, for about ten dollars per channel. Furthermore, it had to be completely solid state (I was getting awfully tired of keeping the tube circuits of the present toposcope functional) and have an input impedance of several megohms to minimize the problem of polarization with d.c. electrodes. The electrical engineering department threw up its collective hands and sent the problem back to me with all best wishes. Since Kinetak was getting in rather sad condition, I decided to design a circuit that could be used for either a.c. or d.c. recording and scrap the old toposcope as soon as the new one was finished.

During this time, I was still collecting data on microtoposcopy and on several learning problems, particularly the hypothesis problem. I was also building a computer to quantify the film data.

Construction of a new toposcope was made more urgent in the spring of 1964 when the University decided to renovate the storeroom in which my lab was located and make from it two laboratories, installing such luxuries as lights, ventilation, running water, even tiled floors. Unfortunately, Kinetak, too bulky to move, would have to be dismantled. I had no illusions about the chances of ever reassembling it successfully.

The situation was made somewhat worse in August when the University's head electrician, who was in the lab planning the electrical service to the new facilities, looked over Kinetak and decided that it did not conform to the Underwriters' Code (which it did not). He announced truculently that I could no longer use it, and he would have to pull the plug. Since I was leaving on vacation, anyway, I resisted the temptation to eject him from the window (the lab is on the fifth floor) and told him to go ahead and pull the plug. When I returned from vacation, I discovered that he had gone around the apparatus, randomly cutting wires. It took me about three hours to splice them all back together again. If the municipal sewage disposal plant at Point Barrow ever needs an electrician, I know one I will recommend.

During the fall of 1964 I finished collecting enough data on microtoposcopy to make what I considered to be a reasonably complete publication, and I wrote an article on that topic as well as one on the epilepsy data. Both of these articles were rejected by the journals to which I submitted them, the epilepsy article on grounds that it was rather incomplete, which it was, the microtoposcopy article on the most illogical and emotional grounds that I have ever been privileged to encounter. A few months later, the same manuscript was accepted by the *American Journal of Medical Electronics* on the basis of very favorable comments by two reviewers. This is the only article containing toposcopic data that I have yet had accepted by a scientific journal. I would assume that the fault was mine, except for the fact that I had several papers in physiological optics accepted with no questions or criticism before I took up toposcopy. My methods of conducting and reporting research and my habits of scholarship have not changed, only the subject matter of the reports. This bias on the part of journal editors and referees against unexplored areas of research constitutes a rather serious hindrance to the development of science in this country. Since funding agencies tend to judge research projects on the basis of articles published, and journal editors are reluctant to publish exploratory research, it is obvious that financial security lies in the well-trodden path.

Autumn of 1964 also saw the writing of a major progress report on the learning data and a proposal for a continuation of the research grant as well as the testing of the fourteenth prototype of a d.c. amplifier. This one seemed to work.

The basic concept for the d.c. amplifier was to use a photocell chopper on the input, but bias the reference so that all channels would be negative to the reference value. Thus all channels had the same polarity, differing only in amplitude of the chopped signal. By using the film threshold as a rectifying device, the electronics became essentially just an a.c. amplifier. The resulting circuit is shown in Figure 7.

With the help of an unusually skillful graduate student, John Duda, I constructed a 32-channel prototype of the new solid state, a.c.-d.c. toposcope. This has since been referred to as Kinetak 32 or K-32. I had naively assumed that, once the electronic problems of the d.c. recording were solved, I had merely to place some silver-

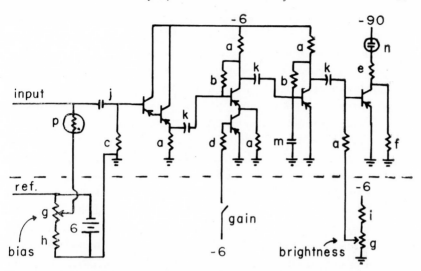

FIGURE 7. Schematic diagram for a toposcope amplifier that does not work: *a*, 2.2 k; *b*, 150 k; *c*, 8.2 meg; *d*, 3.9 k; *e*, 1.0 k; *f*, 1.0 meg; *g*, 10 ohms; *h*, 10 k; *i*, 100 ohms; *j*, 6.8 mF; *k*, 20 mF; *m*, .1 mF; *n*, NE-2; *p*, RCA 4402; transistors 2N1305 except last stage 2N398.

silver chloride electrodes on the surface of a brain and start recording. In surveying the literature, however, I soon discovered that there was one vital difference between what I planned to do and what other scientists had measured in the way of steady potentials or slow potentials or d.c. from chronic preparations. I needed to record absolute d.c. potentials, whereas everyone else had recorded only changes from some arbitrary base line. This meant that fixed offset potentials, of no concern in most experimental situations, were disastrous to me. The only investigator who had solved this problem was Wurtz (1965-1967), and his technique was impracticable for large numbers of electrodes.

During the spring and summer of 1965 I demonstrated to my own satisfaction that any kind of half-cell electrode had either an unreliable offset potential, a fatal degree of toxicity, or both, and that the circuit for Kinetak 32 would not work anyway. I started work on a 48-channel prototype of a modified circuit, K-48, and completed an exhaustive search through the periodic table for a pure metal that would not polarize to a degree which made it unusable.

Concomitantly with the evolution of electrode and amplifier design, my basic concept of d.c. recording evolved from the naive, continuous recording approach to what may be termed the *pulse-sampling* concept. This is treated in some detail in Chapter III, the section on the 48-channel d.c. toposcope.

To permit recording while the toposcope was under construction, I built a simple commutator, operating at 4 rpm, to multiplex forty-eight signals into a Bausch and Lomb V.O.M. 5 chart recorder. From this record, the two-dimensional pattern could easily be reconstructed. As it turned out, this simple commutator has proved to be my main weapon in attacking the problem of d.c. potential fields, while the toposcopes have gathered dust.

On the grounds of toxicity or of high impedance to d.c. currents, I had eliminated the entire periodic table aside from nickel and gold. Both of these had characteristics that I did not understand, the chief of which was the fact that they indicated high voltage d.c. patterns emanating from the brain of an animal that had been dead for two or three days (and presumably longer, although I did not try it). The potentials recorded from the living brain were of higher voltage (50-100 mV) than I was prepared to believe, and the appearance of the patterns showed less change from day to day than I would have expected.

Despite these stumbling blocks to faith, the data did show the effect I had predicted. When an animal learned the one-tone, one-string problem, a positive shift, of 5 to 10 mV, appeared over his parieto-occipital sulcus. Similarly, a visual problem produced a positive shift over the sylvian fissure. I was in the frustrating position of having the confirmation of my hypothesis in hand, yet being unable to believe it.

The clue which enabled me to remove one serious artifact from the recordings was produced by my own clumsiness. In December, 1965, while removing the electrodes from a dead squirrel monkey, part of the skull tore loose and remained firmly stuck to the electrode array. I inserted the electrodes in Ringer's solution, as usual, for a final recording. I found that those electrodes in contact with the bone were about 50 mV negative to the others. This accidental observation recalled to my mind an article by Bassett (1965) which had not really registered at the time I first read it. It appears that injured bone generates d.c. fields. Where my electrodes were inserted in holes drilled into the skull, these d.c. potentials apparently remained as a permanent characteristic of the riddled bone. In my next preparations I removed the bone over the cortex from which I intended to record and held the electrodes in position with a plastic matrix, rather similar to the arrangement I had used for chronic a.c. toposcopy with the old toposcope. The baffling postmortem "ghost" patterns no longer haunted me! When an animal died, his d.c. fields died with him.

The potentials my gold or nickel electrodes recorded from the living brain, however, were still too large to believe. The potential difference between two cortical points sometimes exceeded 100 mV, which is physiologically impossible. There was no question, however, but that the potentials were real and were a function of the brain tissue. Not only did the potentials disappear when the animal died, but they changed from day to day in a manner which appeared to be related to the monkey's psychological state. Most significant of all, the patterns were symmetrical about the midsagittal fissure.

A graduate student in the department, Mr. Monjan, suggested that I try creating a spreading depression (or more accurately, perhaps, a static depression, since in primates this reaction does not spread) to see if the measured voltages would respond to this manipulation, which is known to affect d.c. potentials. For this experiment, I implanted an array of forty-eight nickel electrodes in a plastic matrix over both hemispheres of a squirrel monkey, then cut a hole through plastic, bone, and dura over the left frontal lobe. This hole was temporarily plugged with silicone rubber. Two days later, while the monkey sat in the restraining chair eating grapes, I removed the plug and sprinkled a few crystals of potassium chloride on her cortex. She showed no sign of paralysis, convulsion, or anything much except boredom and a slight overindulgence in grapes. Her d.c. potential fields, however, as recorded by the array of nickel electrodes, developed a striking pattern with a maximum range of 198 mV which appeared over a period of about forty minutes, then gradually subsided to its pretreatment state during the next four hours (see Fig. 57). Control experiments eliminated any possibility that this was a direct effect of potassium chloride on nickel, or a normal fluctuation of the potentials in response to some other aspect of the experimental situation. There could no longer be any doubt that the nickel electrode potentials were directly related to some aspect of the physiology of the brain tissue. However, it was now even less possible to believe that they were simply d.c. potentials. There is certainly no structure in the brain that could provide an e.m.f. of almost 200 mV.

I spent a few months investigating the effect of pH on nickel and gold electrodes in saline solutions. Both metals proved quite sensitive to the pH of the solutions. Apparently they tend to adsorb hydrogen ions or some other substance that makes them act like hydrogen electrodes. This phenomenon appeared adequate to account for the behavior of gold electrodes on the cortex, but the calibration curves showed that I would need a brain pH of about 1.5 in some areas to account for the pattern of potentials recorded from the nickel electrodes. Since this would undoubtedly coagulate the brain, it seemed an unlikely explanation. Furthermore, nickel electrodes that had been implanted for a few days were not sensitive to pH. Such electrodes have a gray coating, presumably some nickel salt, so that they apparently had become half-cells.

The nature of this coating is an interesting question which has not yet been definitely settled. It is discussed at some length in Chapter IV.

I was set off on another false trail by the observation that the potentials from nickel electrodes dropped to a more believable 10 to 15 mV range about two weeks after implantation. I assumed that this marked the completion of the half-cell formation and that subsequent data were genuine d.c. potentials. Pursuing this delusion, I spent several weeks during the fall of 1966 recording from arrays of combination electrodes in which a nickel core was surrounded by an insulated spiral of gold. The expectation was that after two weeks the nickel would reflect true d.c. potentials while the gold would measure pH, contaminated, of course, by direct current. The nickel voltages would be used to correct the gold, thus deriving an accurate measure of pH for comparison with direct current. This logical structure was based on very shaky empirical foundations.

Another unfortunate attempt during fall and winter of 1966-

1967 concerned my behavioral measure. I had been using the one-string problem with either light or tone as a cue almost exclusively. This problem has the rather serious disadvantage of requiring a subjective judgment of the progress of learning. This point is discussed at some length in Chapter III. In order to eliminate this subjective factor, I sought a simple learning problem that would yield an objective, numerical index of learning. The situation I tried was termed the *two-string* problem.

The animal faced a panel from which hung two strings, about 15 cm apart. The apparatus was programmed so that at any moment one or the other of these strings would operate the grape dispenser; the cue stimulus indicated which string was correct. The monkey never had to wait for reinforcement, but could earn his grapes as fast as he could eat. I could use a wide variety of visual or auditory cues to indicate the correct string, and the percentage of correct responses should be a good measure of learning.

I expected the percentage of correct responses to start fairly low, because if the animal first tried the correct string, he would respond only once, but if he tried the incorrect string, he would probably pull it two or three times before switching to the other. As the animal learned the cue contingency, his percent correct should rise rather abruptly to near one hundred.

As usual, the subjects proved smarter than the experimenter. They very quickly learned that one string would always work, then either pulled both strings at once, or else tried one string, then the other. They never paid any attention to my cues. By adopting a simple alternation response, the monkey could achieve 67 percent correct without worrying about stimulus contingencies. I considered punishing wrong responses, but the Cebus is quick to go on strike when dissatisfied with working conditions, so I went back to the old one-string problem instead.

Meanwhile, further recording from nickel electrodes showed that my previous observation of reduced voltages after two weeks *in situ* was a more or less chance effect. There is a tendency for the recorded potentials to decrease as the animal becomes adapted to the experimental situation, but the voltages may increase again or may stay high. It eventually became obvious that nickel would not measure true direct current, no matter how long it might be left in place. It did, however, measure something very interesting. The incidental discovery of waveforms from the nickel electrodes, with amplitudes of several millivolts and periods locked to the intertrial interval of the learning problem in use, was followed by the equally fascinating discovery of localized fluctuations of up to 100 mV over a period of less than five minutes, confined to regions near the arcuate sulcus in a monkey poorly adapted to the experimental situation. I also found that these nickel waveforms and the more static nickel potential fields could be measured just as well through the intact skull as they could from the surface of the cortex. This fact has important implications for the chemical system which is reacting with the nickel, but also had implications of more immediate value for the recording of d.c. potentials.

In my first round of tests of various d.c. electrodes, silver-silver chloride was rejected because of its unpredictable offset potential and its unacceptable toxicity. The experience I had gained from working with nickel electrodes suggested means of overcoming both problems. By placing the electrodes outside the skull, the toxicity of silver was not a serious drawback, and by implanting plain silver, permitting it to form its chloride coating *in situ* with all electrodes connected to a common point through several megohms resistance, the unpredictable offset voltages and drift were prevented.

The potentials recorded from these electrodes were in the range of 1 to 2 mV, which is about what I had expected the d.c. fields to be. Under certain conditions, however, larger potential differences were recorded. A repetition of the "spreading depression" experiment, in which potassium chloride crystals were applied to the cortex anterior to the electrode array, produced a total shift of 25 mV in a few minutes (see Fig. 51). In an animal learning the one-tone, one-string problem, a positive region of 8 to 10 mV appeared over the parieto-occipital sulcus, precisely as predicted, except that it appeared on the left hemisphere only. This did not actually conflict with any of my previous data on the learning-specific activity, but it seemed unlikely. I had been assuming that the critical activity was bilaterally symmetrical.

A few days later while browsing in the library, I discovered an article by Gazzaniga (1963), demonstrating that macaques use only one hemisphere in the acquisition of a simple visual discrimination.

During the winter and spring of 1967, I had also been running an ablation experiment. A series of Cebus and squirrel monkeys had been given bilateral ablations of either auditory or visual learning-specific response areas and then trained on the one-tone and one-light, one-string problems. I expected to find a deficit in learning either the visual or the auditory problem, depending on the locus of ablation. By May of 1967, enough data were in to demonstrate that the ablations caused a serious learning deficit, although the details were by no means clear. However, the demonstration that these cortical regions, identified as learning foci by toposcopic recording, were indeed critical for learning, added strong confirmation to the toposcopic data.

Now, at last, everything was falling into place. Additional data from the silver electrodes showed the visual learning-specific response to consist of a 10 mV positive shift exactly where and when predicted, except that it, too, was confined to the left hemisphere. All the d.c. data, in fact, showed much greater patterning in the left than in the right hemisphere.

The nickel electrodes, on the other hand, were recording something quite different. The data were always symmetrical, and the most distinctive areas appeared in the frontal lobes. The activity seemed to be associated with the emotional state of the animal, a conclusion which was strengthened by the very dramatic effects of chlorpromazine on these nickel potentials. In collaboration with Richard Jaffe, a student in the chemistry department, I started the search for the chemical system to which the nickel was responding. That search is not yet concluded, although it appears probable that it is an enzyme system associated with oxidative metabolism.

By late April, 1967, I had begun the process of collating data and reviewing literature for this book. On May 7, I received word that the National Institute of Mental Health would not renew my research grant. The grant therefore ended on August 31, 1968, ten years after it had begun, and twelve years after I had begun the search for cortical mechanisms accompanying the learning process.

References

BASSETT, C.A.L.: Electrical effects in bone. *Sci. Amer.*, *213(4)*:18-25, 1965.

DeMOTT, D.W.: An inexpensive, multi-channel, electrophysiological recording system. *Electroenceph. Clin. Neurophysiol.*, *13*:467-470, 1961.

DeMOTT, D.W.: Cortical micro-toposcopy. *Med. Res. Engin.*, *5(4)*:23-29, 1966.

DeMOTT, D.W., and DAVIS, T.P.: Irradiance thresholds for chorioretinal lesions. *Arch. Ophthalmol. (Chicago) 62*:653-656, 1959.

GAZZANIGA, M.S.: Effects of commissurotomy on a preoperatively learned visual discrimination. *Exp. Neurol.*, *8*:14-19, 1963.

LILLY, J.C.: Forms and figures in the electrical activity seen in the surface of the cerebral cortex. In Millbank Memorial Fund: *The Biology of Mental Health and Disease: Twenty-seventh Annual Conference of the Millbank Memorial Fund*. New York: Hoeber, 1952.

WURTZ, R.H.: Steady potential shifts during arousal and deep sleep in the cat. *Electroenceph. Clin. Neurophysiol.*, *18*:649-662, 1965.

WURTZ, R.H.: Steady potential correlates of intracranial reinforcement. *Electroenceph. Clin. Neurophysiol.*, *20*:59-67, 1966.

WURTZ, R.H.: Steady potential fields during sleep and wakefulness in the cat. *Exp. Neurol.*, *15*:274-292, 1966.

WURTZ, R.H.: Physiological correlates of steady potential shifts during sleep and wakefulness. II. Brain temperature, blood pressure, and potential changes across the ependyma. *Electroenceph. Clin. Neurophysiol.*, *22*:43-53, 1967.

Chapter III

APPARATUS AND TECHNIQUES

400-CHANNEL A.C. TOPOSCOPE: VACUUM TUBE

THE apparatus most central to this research project is the original 400-channel Kinetak, completed on November 7, 1961, and destroyed on December 15, 1964. It was conceptually very simple, consisting merely of four hundred amplifiers operating in parallel, each one driven by a single electrode and displaying the signal as the brightness of a small neon tube. The four hundred neon tubes were then photographed by a high-speed movie camera, originally handmade, but later Wollensak Fastax[T] 8 mm. Since the electrode implant and the recording probe will be described separately, this description will begin with the input to the first stage tube.

The circuit diagram is shown in Figure 8. Note that all circuitry below the broken line is common to all four hundred channels. Note also that no reference or indifferent electrode is used. The only information available at the toposcope input is the four hundred individual signals. These are averaged by the floating power supply of the first stage tube, which is common to all four hundred channels. Each channel thus amplifies the difference between its individual signal and the instantaneous mean of the four hundred signals. Common-mode signals are rejected, whether they are of biological origin or extraneous artifact. The 12AX7 is a relatively low noise tube as well as very inexpensive. The power supply for the four hundred first stage tubes is a single dry cell.

The midsection of the amplifier, stages two and three, is very straightforward. The 12BZ7 is used in stage three because it is less likely to draw grid current under the somewhat heavier load. For convenience, these stages were powered in groups of sixteen

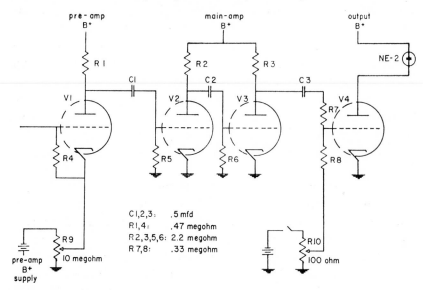

FIGURE 8. Schematic of amplifiers: V1 (pre-amp), 1/2 12AX7; V2 (main amp stage 1), 1/2 12AX7; V3, 1/2 12BZ7; V4 (output), 1/2 12AT7. Note that V1 and V2 are not one tube. The two triodes in each tube are used by adjacent channels, not by two stages within the same channel. R9 adjusts in-phase noise rejection, R10 adjusts zero-signal brightness of the NE-2 display tubes. Both potentiometers are common to all channels.

channels, each group supplied by a separate 150 V line-operated power supply. These power supplies consisted of a half-wave rectifier with a capacitor input, brute force filter. Since the sixteen channels in parallel draw only a fraction of a milliampere, sophistication is not required.

These first three stages were mounted on 12-inch by 12-inch printed circuit boards, sixteen channels per board. The two sides of each twin triode were used by adjacent channels, so the tubes were arranged in three rows of eight tubes each. A grounded brass shielding strip ran between the first and second rows to minimize capacitative coupling between stage one and later stages.

The filaments of each row of eight tubes were connected in series, the three series strings then connected in parallel, so that each board required 96 V, .45A for filament power. The entire toposcope contained twenty-five of these boards, connected in two groups of twelve and thirteen boards. Each group thus required slightly more than 5 A at 96 V. This filament power was obtained from two series strings of lead-acid storage batteries. When fully charged, these batteries would operate the filaments for about fifteen minutes. The batteries could be recharged through a massive bridge rectifier in about fifteen minutes.

The circuit boards carrying these first three stages were mounted in individually shielded compartments inside a large, shielded booth. This booth, six by seven feet in area and eight feet high, also contained the subject's cage, all behavioral apparatus, and a small desk facing a control panel, from which the experimenter could operate the toposcope, camera, and learning apparatus.

The fourth stage tubes were mounted outside the shielded booth. The tubes were mounted on printed circuit boards, sixteen channels per board, as in the preceding stages. Again, each board of sixteen channels had its own power supply. For this display stage, 500 V at 50 mA was needed, which was obtained from a voltage quadrupler, half-wave rectifier with a brute force filter. About a .3 V ripple remained after filtering, but it did not degrade the signal at this point in the circuit.

Filaments of the eight tubes per board were connected in series and operated from line through a half-wave rectifier and 150-ohm resistor.

The zero-signal brightness of the neon tube display could be adjusted by varying the bias voltage on the grids of the fourth stage tubes. The range of this adjustment was limited by the tendency of the grid to draw current if biased too near ground potential. In order to avoid this error, an oscilloscope was always connected to the output of one channel (fourth stage anode) for monitoring of the signal. This oscilloscope trace could also be used to record the standard EEG waveform of a selected channel.

The frequency spectrum of this toposcope was deliberately limited at the low frequency end in the erroneous belief that this would eliminate activity of little interest, thus improving the signal-noise ratio of the higher frequency activity. The original frequency spectrum is shown in Figure 9. When this calibration was made, input to the first stage grids was through a .25 mF capacitor. Use of the toposcope soon showed that the low frequency activity was more significant than the higher frequencies, so the capacitor was

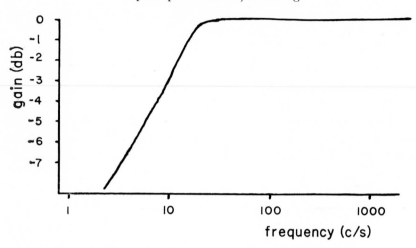

FIGURE 9. Frequency response of original vacuum tube Kinetak. The low frequency cutoff was high enough to attentuate alpha frequencies.

eliminated, making the input stage direct coupled. This lowered the low frequency cutoff to about 4 cycles per second, which was barely adequate.

The neon tubes which displayed the output current of the four hundred channels were arranged in a pattern which approximated the outline of the left hemisphere of the Cebus brain yet permitted the sixteen channels from a single circuit board to be grouped in a standard, irregular hexagon. The neon tubes were mounted in a

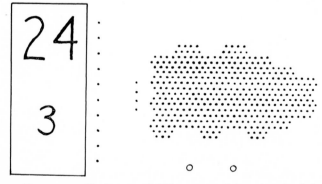

FIGURE 10. Toposcope display panel. The array of four hundred dots represents four hundred neon tubes, each displaying the signal from one electrode. The panel to the left carries film identification. The other dots represent calibration lights and stimulus indicators.

plywood panel, spaced one-half inch apart, as shown in Figure 10. The hexagonal lattice was chosen because it gives a more uniform coverage than the square lattice more commonly used and permits an unequivocal statement of electrode spacing.

The display panel carrying the four hundred neon tubes also carried a time calibration light operated at 60 cycles through a half-wave rectifier, and several lights to indicate stimulus onset and offset, subject's response, and so forth. A transilluminated screen held opaque numerals indicating date and film number for data identification.

When this toposcope was first placed in operation, the output was recorded by means of a 16 mm high-speed motion picture camera which I built myself from junk parts. It could be operated at any speed up to 520 frames per second. I used DuPont 928(a) "Superior" 4 negative motion picture film, which is particularly sensitive to the red light of neon. Since this handmade camera had a tendency to shred film into tiny pieces at unpredictable intervals, I eventually acquired a Wollensak Fastax 8 mm camera, which is capable of much higher recording rates. The available brightness of the neon tubes, however, limits recording to about 1000 frames per second. Almost all recording is actually done at about 250 frames per second, which is fast enough to resolve all normal activity. The use of 8 mm, rather than 16 mm film, which is made possible by the better optics of the Fastax camera, reduces the cost of recording and the space requirements for data storage by 75 percent.

The major drawbacks of this toposcope were the following:
1. Fixed gain.
2. Limited operating time, due to storage battery capacity and tendency to overheat.
3. Maintenance problems created by eight hundred vacuum tubes, fifty-two separate power supplies, and several thousand feet of wiring.

400-CHANNEL A.C. TOPOSCOPE: SOLID STATE

A transistorized version of the Kinetak toposcope was designed to overcome the above limitations as well as to extend the low frequency response to around 2 cps. It was intended to be usable for either a.c. or d.c. recording. However, the development of a workable chopper or pulse-sampling circuit (see Fig. 20) made it possible to measure d.c. potential through a standard a.c. amplifier. The use of solid state circuitry automatically cured most of the maintenance problems of the old vacuum tube Kinetak and greatly reduced the power requirements. At the same time, however, it made the attainment of high input impedance more difficult.

The two problems which proved most difficult to solve were input impedance and gain adjustment. The input impedance must be several megohms to avoid attenuating the signal from the microprobe, which has a generator resistance of nearly 100 kohms on each channel. At the same time, of course, noise must be held to a few microvolts. The difficulty with controlling gain is the impracticability of four hundred individual adjustments. Variations in gain must be accomplished by applying a signal to all channels, and the resulting change in gain must be equal for all channels.

The circuit finally adopted is shown in Figure 11. All wiring below the level of the emitter ground symbols is common to all four hundred channels. The broken lines indicate connecting cables between physically separate stages. These cables may be changed so as to bypass one or more stages completely.

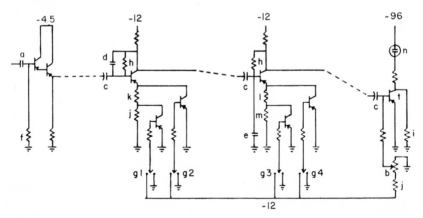

FIGURE 11. Toposcopic amplifier presently in use. *a*, 6.8 mF; *b*, 10 ohms; *c*, 20 mF; *d*, .01 mF; *e*, .1 mF; *f*, 8.2 meg; *g*, gain controls; *h*, 150 k; *i*, 1.0 meg; *j*, 100 ohms; *k*, 47 ohms; *l*, 15 ohms; *m*, 39 ohms; *n*, NE-2; *t*, 2N398. All unlabeled resistors 2.2 k, all unlabeled transistors 2N1305.

The input stages, consisting of two $2N1305$'s form a Darlington circuit, used for a maximum input impedance. When operated at -4.5 V, this gives an impedance of 3 Mohms. As much as 5 Mohms may be achieved by raising the supply voltage to about 6 or 8 V, but the noise level increases faster than the input impedance, so that signal-noise ratio is not generally improved. By carefully choosing the transistor for the first stage, input noise may be held to less than 5μVEq input.

The next two amplifier stages incorporate the adjustable gain feature. The gain of each stage is determined largely by the ratio between collector and emitter resistors. One of three values of emitter resistance may be selected by applying a signal to the base of one of the two transistors in parallel with the fixed emitter resistors. That is, if a signal (-12 V) is applied to the base of the upper control transistor of the first variable gain stage (the transistor shown directly above the symbol g_2 in Figure 11), then the emitter of the amplifier transistor (just below the symbol h in the figure) will be shorted directly to ground through that control transistor, and the stage will be operating at its maximum gain. If a signal is applied instead to the lower control transistor of that stage, then the emitter of the amplifier transistor will be connected to ground through the 47 ohm resistor (k), which reduces its voltage gain by half. If neither control transistor is on, the emitter of the amplifier transistor is connected to ground through 147 ohms resistance (k plus j), reducing its gain by three-fourths. Similarly, signals may be applied to the control transistors of the second variable gain stage to achieve reductions of one-half or three-fourths. (These resistors are of different values from the preceding stage because of the different output loads.) If both variable gain stages are set for minimum gain, the overall amplifier gain is one-sixteenth of maximum. Since the full voltage gain of each variable gain stage is thirty-two, a further reduction of one-half may be obtained by bypassing the first variable gain stage, and so forth. The total usable signal range may thus be varied from about 10μV to 5mV.

The output stage is similar to that used in the old Kinetak, except that a transistor has been substituted for the $12AT7$, requiring some added stabilization. Control b varies the bias on the $2N398$, thus changing the zero-signal brightness of the neon tubes. The 2.2

K resistor in the collector circuit is necessary to prevent thermal runaway, the 1.0 meg resistor in parallel with the 2N398 is needed to keep the neon tube ionized at extreme signal levels.

The size of the coupling capacitors was chosen to give a low frequency response down to 1.5 cps (voltage gain down ½).

The averaged reference system and the spatial configuration of the output display tubes were kept the same as those of the old vacuum tube toposcope. Since the new toposcope is completely battery powered, the entire circuit is divorced from ground, thus making it almost interference-proof. We found that little shielding was required.

All the circuits are mounted on etched circuit modules for rapid servicing. Circuits, power supplies, and controls are contained in a standard relay rack.

A new feature of this toposcope which greatly facilitates interpreting records of evoked potentials is a clock, accurate to the nearest millisecond, with a binary decimal display on the front panel. The clock may be reset externally, so that it is a fairly simple matter to take a reset signal from the circuit which controls the stimuli being used. The clock thus displays time since stimulus onset, to the nearest millisecond, recorded on the same film as the primary data.

Credit for much of the development and all of the construction of this transistorized toposcope goes to John Duda, a graduate student of unusual ability and perseverance. He devoted two busy years to its design, construction, and calibration. Anyone interested in duplicating or modifying this toposcope is referred to Duda's doctoral dissertation entitled "Electrotoposcopy of auditory cortex responses to acoustic stimulation in the lightly anesthetized squirrel monkey," obtainable from the University of Rochester library.

CHRONIC ELECTRODE IMPLANTS: 400-CHANNEL

For recording from an unanesthetized, chronically prepared animal, the toposcope is connected to the preparation through a 400-connector recording probe (described below) and a permanently implanted electrode array which I refer to as a "stainless steel cortex." The construction of such an array is a lengthy and complicated process, each step of which is critical, but no simpler technique has been found that is satisfactory.

The process begins with the construction of an electrode frame from a 2- by 3- by ¾-inch block of acrylic plastic (see Fig. 12A). Four holes are drilled and tapped in locations matching screw holes on the recording probe to be used, and a hole is cut with a coping saw to the outline of the electrode array needed. The screw holes and the sides of the electrode frame must be perpendicular to the surface of the plastic block.

The electrodes are cut from .032-inch, heavy Formvar insulated stainless steel wire. The wire is straightened by stretching, then cut into 1½-inch lengths. About two thousand are required for each implant. Five strands of wire may be cut simultaneously with sharp metal shears, but care must be used to avoid bending the wire, as it is important that the electrodes be straight. A simple guide clamped to the shears helps to keep the electrodes of uniform length.

The electrode frame is stood on one end and filled with electrodes (Fig. 12B), taking care to keep the electrodes parallel. The frame should be filled completely but not tightly. Machine screws are inserted into the tapped holes from the upper side until the ends are just flush with the lower surface of the frame. These are to prevent these holes from filling with liquid plastic at a later stage in the process. These screws should be greased lightly with petroleum jelly, but care must be exercised to keep any grease from the under surface of the frame.

The animal is anesthetized, shaved, and disinfected. The scalp is incised and reflected from the area to be used. I prefer a cross-shaped incision, since the four flaps aid in holding the mold edge at a later step. For most preparations, the skull is removed over the area to receive electrodes. The dura is nearly always left intact.

A strip of soft aluminum, about 1½-inch wide by 8 to 12 inches long is now curved by hand to fit around the area of exposure. This area must be somewhat larger than the craniotomy, since a margin of bone is needed for mounting the electrode array. It is also important that the exposed skull subtend a total arc of more than 90 degrees so that the bone screws to be placed around the margins will have a large angle between their axes. Ideally, this angle between bone screws should be 180 degrees,

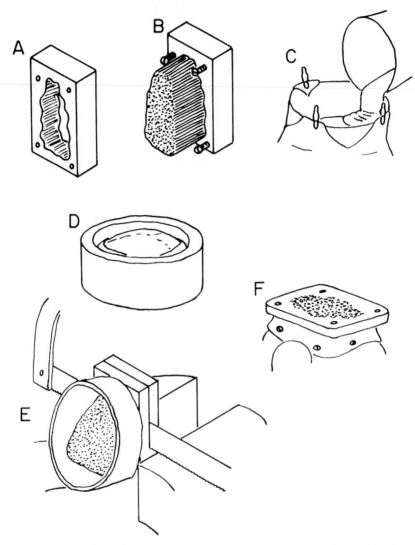

Figure 12. Construction of chronic electrode implant. *A*, Frame cut from ¾-inch acrylic plastic. *B*, Frame filled with about two thousand varnished stainless steel electrodes. *C*, Pouring impression of craniotomy, using a quick-setting silicone rubber. *D*, Positive model of craniotomy. The electrode array shown in *B* is settled into place on this model, then saturated with a thermosetting plastic. *E*, After curing, the implant is trimmed by cutting lengthwise through the acrylic frame with a hacksaw. *F*, Completed implant, installed with bone screws. The four tapped holes in the upper surface are for mounting the recording probe.

which is achieved by placing the screws around the equator of the skull. If this angle can be approximated, the implant is almost impossible to pull loose. (This aspect of constructing a durable implant was first pointed out to me by Dr. E. R. John, then at the University of Rochester.) The four scalp flaps may now be clipped to the aluminum strip, thus forming a pocket surrounding the area of exposure.

A medical grade RTV (room temperature vulcanizing) silicone rubber is catalyzed and poured into the pocket formed by the aluminum strip and scalp flaps (Fig. 12C). I use Dow Corning Silastic 382, which sets firm in about fifteen minutes. As soon as it is reasonably hard, it is removed, together with the aluminum strip, rinsed gently, and placed in an oven at 200 to 300 degrees F to complete its cure. The preparation's scalp is closed with wound clips, and he is placed in an incubator. When a craniotomy has been performed, it is important to keep the animal sufficiently sedated during the next few hours to prevent his staggering around the incubator, banging his soft head against the walls.

The silicone rubber impression is removed from the oven and separated from the aluminum strip. Some trimming may be desirable at this stage. The impression should be approximately the shape of the intended implant. It is greased with a thin coat of petroleum jelly, and placed upside down in the bottom of a mold which is at least ¼-inch larger than the impression on all sides. I use a mold formed by bending a 2-inch wide aluminum strip into a circle and placing it on a small aluminum plate. The mold is then filled with catalyzed silicone rubber and placed in the oven.

When the rubber is again hard, it is separated from the mold and from the original impression. This second impression should now be an accurate model of the exposed brain and skull with a vertical edge, as in Figure 12D. This edge should be trimmed down to the level of the highest point of the "brain."

The filled electrode frame and silicone rubber model are now brought together, holding them on edge, of course, so as not to spill electrodes. They are aligned so that the electrode array covers the desired area, then, holding the electrode frame snugly against the vertical rim of the model, they are rotated into normal orientation. The electrodes should drop into place on the rubber model.

It is important that all electrodes make contact with the silicone rubber. Usually a few taps on the frame will settle any sticking electrodes, but sometimes it is necessary to remove a few electrodes with small forceps in order to loosen the array.

The next step requires patience. The mold must be filled with a liquid plastic (Castolite; The Castolite Co., Woodstock, Ill.) which must saturate the array of electrodes. If the plastic is simply poured in at the edge of the mold, the center of the electrode array will not be saturated. The liquid plastic must be poured *through* the array of electrodes by dribbling a few drops on the upper ends of the electrodes, waiting for it to soak in, and repeating the process until the liquid can be seen oozing from the entire edge of the electrode array. The rest of the mold can then be filled from one edge until the plastic makes good contact with the under side of the electrode frame. The Castolite is then jelled and cured according to the manufacturer's instructions, a process which takes about ninety minutes. Meanwhile, the operating room is prepared for the second stage of the operation.

The cured head plate is removed from the mold, clamped in a vise, and cut with a sharp hacksaw parallel to the large face of the electrode frame, about midway of the thickness of the frame (Fig. 12C). This cut surface must then be filed smooth and flat, with no short circuits between electrodes. The head plate should be cooled with water at frequent intervals during the cutting and filing.

I place the file flat on the work bench, in a jig, and rub the head plate over it. I file a few strokes in one direction, then turn it 90 degrees and file a few more, and so on. With a very sharp file, a strong arm, and a straight hacksaw cut, the filing can be finished in fifteen minutes. With only the sharp file, it may take two hours. Without a sharp file, it cannot be done at all, because the file produces short circuits between electrodes. A new, good quality mill file can be used for about three head plates, then it must be retired to less exacting service.

When the upper surface of the electrode array has passed inspection, including sampling with an ohmmeter for short circuits, the film of plastic covering the lower ends of the electrodes must be removed with a carving tool such as the Mototool and a spherical bit. Just enough plastic should be removed to expose small areas of metal from each electrode. If the bit cuts too deep, it will create short circuits which cannot be removed. Next the holes for the bone screws are drilled around the outside edge of the plate. In order to avoid shattering the edges of the plastic, I drill the holes from the under surface, and stop just short of breaking through. The upper end of the hole can then be opened with the carving tool, and countersunk until about 2mm of bone screw projects through the under side.

For bone screws, I use 4-40 by ¼-inch flat head stainless steel machine screws. They are far cheaper than surgical bone screws, and the flat end of the machine screw is less likely to irritate the dura than is the sharper end of a bone screw.

Finally, any excess plastic is carved away with the carving tool, and the probe mounting holes are retapped with a sharp tap. A good deal of artistic freedom is allowed here. Since the Castolite tends to shrink, the fit of the head plate is checked against the silicone rubber model, and the under surface shaved as necessary to achieve the best possible fit. The finished head plate is then washed and placed in ethyl alcohol while the animal is prepared for the second stage of surgery.

The animal is reanesthetized as necessary and the scalp reopened. The head plate is placed in position (if there is any question about fit at this point, close up the scalp and go back to the rubber model) and screw holes drilled in the skull. I use an ordinary high-speed drill bit, with the shank broken off, and the cutting end held in a needle clamp with the desired length protruding. It helps to install the bone screws as the holes are drilled. When the last hole has been drilled, the screws are removed and the head plate and skull cleaned carefully with gauze sponges. "Grip" dental cement (L.D. Caulk, Co.) is mixed and applied to the bone margins, and the head plate is quickly pressed into place and the bone screws reinserted and tightened. This is always a panic procedure, because the cement sets very quickly. Finally, the scalp is trimmed and sutured as necessary to fit around the edges of the head plate (Fig. 12F; also Fig. 26).

While the animal still sleeps peacefully, a harness and leash are tied on him, and his identification tatooed. He is then placed in an incubator overnight.

I have not found it necessary to use antibiotics if some care is exercised in aseptic procedure. The resistance to infection of the electrode implant depends largely on the tightness of the seal between the plastic and the skull. The monkeys tolerate it well, showing no tendency to attempt to pull it loose, and do not seriously object to having the recording probe attached.

If the technique is used with a squirrel monkey, it is important to make every effort to cut away excess stainless steel and plastic, as the weight of such a head plate is rather cumbersome for a squirrel monkey.

The most unique aspect of this electrode implant is that the electrodes themselves are randomly arranged by simply stacking them in a frame. In use, the four hundred recording sites are determined by the location of the four hundred spring contacts in the recording probe, which make electrical contact with the upper surface of the stainless steel cortex. As long as the electrodes are parallel with each other, the pattern of recording sites on the cortex is identical with the pattern of spring contacts in the probe.

CHRONIC RECORDING PROBE: 400-CHANNEL

Electrical connection between the electrode implant and Kinetak is through a 400-conductor probe, designed to mount quickly and firmly to the animal's head plate. Requirements of a recording probe are that it be light and flexible so as not to hamper the animal's movements, produce a minimum of movement artifact, and be tough enough to resist frequent gnawing by frustrated monkeys. The probe has undergone considerable evolution during the course of this research. Two stages in that evolution are illustrated in Figure 13. The third stage (see Fig. 5B) has not actually been used as of this writing. The majority of existing Kinetak data have been recorded through the probe illustrated in Figure 13B.

The evolution of the probe has been primarily in two characteristics: the source of spring tension for making contact with the electrode array, and various techniques for the reduction of movement artifact.

A

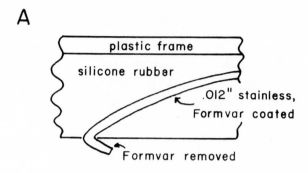

B

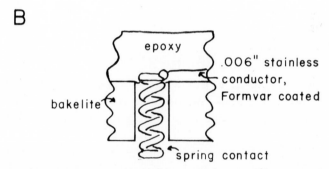

FIGURE 13. Magnified view of individual contacts in two styles of recording probe. *A*, Original 160-channel model. *B*, 400-channel model used with vacuum tube toposcope. See also FIGURE 5.

The earliest successful probe (Fig. 13A) used the natural spring tension of the .012-inch stainless steel conductor, bent at an acute angle where it protruded from the face of the probe. Movement artifact was controlled (not too successfully) by saturating the cable with a mixture of liquid latex and powdered aluminum. Some of the movement artifact with this probe undoubtedly stemmed from the fact that it mounted to the head plate with two screws, which probably allowed some rocking motion. It was usable, however, with the 160 channels then completed.

When the 400-channel toposcope was finished, it was very obvious that the same principle could not be extended to that number of contacts, since the .012-inch wire was too stiff for a 400-

conductor cable, and anything smaller was inadequate for the spring contacts. Attempts to splice two different diameter wires resulted in a hopeless snarl. Eventually, I was forced to have small compression springs custom-made which fit into holes of a Bakelite™ wafer as in Figure 13B. In this model movement artifact was controlled by saturating the cable with powdered graphite, which actually increased the flexibility while reducing artifact. The probe mounted to the head plate with four screws, thus eliminating any contact motion. This probe was very satisfactory, except that adjacent springs tended to tangle and required some maintenance work with watchmakers' tools. The newest model in this phylogenetic sequence (see Fig. 5B) is designed to eliminate this possibility.

It seems probable that the technique recently published by Straw, *et al.* (1967) might further reduce movement artifact. I have not yet tried it.

MICROPROBE

A critical dimension in the design and use of a toposcope is the interelectrode spacing. If this distance is too large, significant details may be missed, and organized patterns may break down into apparently unrelated activity. However, the number of channels needed to record from a given area is inversely related to the square of the interelectrode distance. It is most important, therefore, to estimate this dimension accurately.

When the first Kinetak was still in design, I estimated this spacing by recording EEG with bipolar electrodes, varying the tip separation. The figure of 1.5 mm which I derived from this experiment seemed to work well with the cat and the Cebus monkey. It is a little bit coarse for a squirrel monkey. One can check the adequacy of the electrode spacing in toposcopic data by examining adjacent regions of positive and negative potential and noting whether or not points of intermediate voltage intervene between the extremes.

As an additional demonstration of the adequacy of the 1.5 mm spacing, I constructed a probe with slightly less than .25 mm electrode spacing, which I refer to as the microprobe. It was constructed of .006-inch stainless steel wire with heavy Formvar insulation, which brings the outside diameter to about .009 inch. The wires are simply glued together into the desired array, then

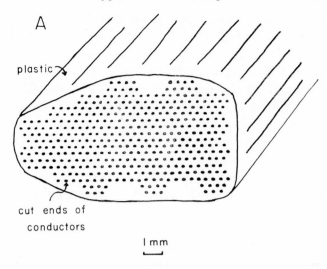

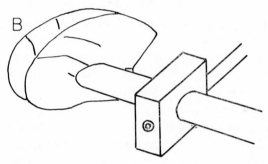

FIGURE 14. Microprobe. *A*, Magnified view of the recording surface, which was placed flat against the surface of the cortex. Each dot represents a stainless steel conductor. *B*, Microprobe in position on right auditory cortex of a squirrel monkey.

cut through and filed to form a flat surface. It can be used only with acute preparations.

When the microprobe is placed against the cortical surface, it usually records only very broad, shallow gradients, as expected. If, however, the microprobe is placed in primary sensory cortex, and the preparation stimulated through the appropriate modality, a sequence of finely detailed patterns is recorded. This type of recording has been termed *microtoposcopy* (DeMott, 1966). The patterns are of such spatial dimensions that they can only be detected by an array of electrodes spaced .5 mm or less apart.

The microprobe presently in use was constructed from the same .006-inch Formvar-coated stainless steel wire, but the array was assembled with the aid of a template. The desired array of four hundred holes at .4 mm spacing was drilled into .002-inch steel shim stock, using a No. 80 drill bit. Each conductor was threaded through the proper hole in the template, then the entire array was saturated with a liquid plastic (see chronic electrode implants, above). When the plastic was cured, the array was cut through with a jeweler's saw adjacent to the template and filed smooth (Fig. 14).

The display panel of the old vacuum tube Kinetak had 12 mm spacing between neon tubes. With the original microprobe, this gave a magnification of approximately ×50. The new, transistorized Kinetak has a display panel with 9 mm spacing between neon tubes. With the present microprobe, this gives a magnification of about ×23. When the toposcope is being used exclusively for microtoposcopy, however, it is moved closer to the recording camera, thus compensating for the display panel spacing. The equivalent magnification is then ×30, and the resolving power, which is dependent only on electrode spacing, is three-fifths as good as the old toposcope.

This loss in resolving power from the old apparatus to the new is accompanied, of course, by an increase in area covered. It was made possible by the reduced noise level of the new apparatus, which permits less redundancy in the data.

COMPUTER

Toposcopic data may be completely specified by four dimensions: two of space, one of time, and one of voltage. The spatial and temporal dimensions are easily and directly quantifiable to the limits imposed by electrode spacing and camera speed. The voltage dimension, however, is represented by the density of the film emulsion and may be quantified only by densitometric methods. A computerlike device was built to perform this densitometry automatically.

A block diagram of the computer is shown in Figure 15. The

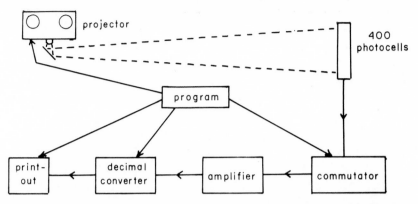

Figure 15. Block diagram of computer used for quantification of toposcopic data. It consists essentially of four hundred densitometers, with logic circuitry to convert the output of each densitometer into a digit from 0 to 9 and to print these digits in an array corresponding to the array of display tubes on the toposcope.

film to be quantified is projected by a Vanguard M-8 projector head onto a Bakelite panel carrying four hundred CdS photocells (RCA 4402) in positions corresponding to the projected images of the Kinetak display tubes. A 400-pole stepping switch reads the output of each photocell in turn, and connects it to a signal correction circuit which permits the operator to correct for variation in overall density and contrast of the film records, and thence to a decimal converter, which produces a 12-V pulse on one of ten output lines, depending on the voltage of the incoming signal.

These ten output lines drive small solenoids poised over the keys of an IBM Selectric typewriter to print numerals 0 through 9 on a roll of teletype paper. The space and return keys of the typewriter, as well as the other functions of the computer, are controlled by a punched tape program. The data are printed out in a spatial format conforming to the arrangement of the Kinetak display panel. A typical computer output is shown in Figure 16A.

To prepare data for publication, a sheet of tracing paper is laid over the computer printout, and contour lines are drawn as desired. In the illustration shown in Figure 16B, contours have been drawn between *1* and *2*, between *3* and *4*, between *5* and *6*, and between *7* and *8*. The areas bounded by these contour lines are then shaded according to a standard code: *0* and *1* is left blank,

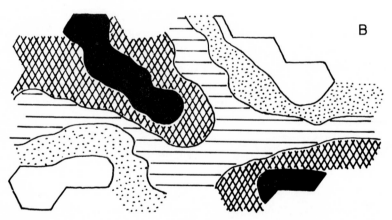

```
        9 9 8 7              5 3 2 1                              A
      9 9 8 8 7            5 4 3 2 1
  6 6 7 7 8 9 8 7 7 7 6 6 5 4 4 2 1 1 0 0
6 7 7 7 7 7 9 8 7 7 6 6 6 5 4 3 2 2 1 1 0
  7 7 7 7 7 8 9 9 8 7 6 6 5 5 4 3 3 2 1 1 0 0 0 0
  6 7 7 7 7 8 9 9 8 8 7 6 5 4 4 4 3 2 2 1 1 1 0 0
  6 6 6 6 7 7 7 8 9 9 7 7 6 6 5 4 3 3 2 2 1 1 1 1 2 2 2 2
6 5 5 6 6 6 7 7 7 8 9 9 8 7 6 5 4 3 3 2 2 1 1 1 2 2 2 2 2
5 5 5 5 5 6 6 6 7 8 9 9 8 7 6 5 5 4 3 3 2 2 2 2 2 3 3 3
  4 4 4 4 4 4 4 5 6 7 9 8 7 7 6 5 5 5 4 4 4 4 3 4 4 4 4
  4 4 4 4 3 3 3 3 4 5 6 7 7 7 6 5 4 4 4 4 4 4 4 4 4 4 4 4
  4 4 3 3 3 3 2 3 3 3 4 5 6 6 6 5 4 4 4 4 5 5 5 5 6 6 6 6
  3 3 3 2 2 2 2 3 3 4 4 5 5 5 5 4 4 4 5 5 6 6 6 6 7 7 7
    2 2 2 1 1 1 1 2 2 3 4 4 4 5 5 5 5 6 6 6 6 7 7 7 7 7
  1 1 1 1 1 0 1 1 2 3 4 4 4 5 5 5 6 6 7 8 8 8 8 8
1 1 1 1 1 0 0 1 2 2 3 4 4 4 4 5 6 7 7 8 8 9 9 9
  1 0 0 0              2 3 3 3            6 7 7 8
    1 0 0              2 3 3            6 7 7
```

Figure 16. Sample computer printout of a single data frame together with the stylized representation of the same frame prepared for publication.

2 and *3* is stippled, *4* and *5* is horizontally lined, *6* and *7* is cross-hatched, and *8* and *9* is blackened. This scale of shading corresponds to the scale of densities on the original film so that the final schematic representation of a frame of film bears some resemblance to the original.

By applying known signals to the Kinetak input, and by photographing and quantifying the results with the computer, it was possible to assign numerical voltages to the computer output

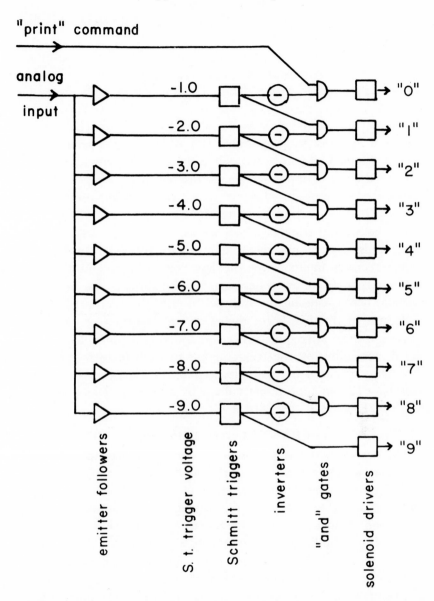

Figure 17. Block diagram of the logic circuitry used to convert the analog densitometer output into decimal form. The solenoid drivers operated typewriter keys. The "print" command was a −12 V pulse from the programmer.

without making any assumptions about linearity, et cetera, of either Kinetak or the computer.

Since the decimal converter is the only portion of the computer circuitry whose details are not intuitively obvious, it will be described in somewhat greater detail. The block diagram is shown in Figure 17.

The decimal converter was assembled from Digibit (Behavioral Research Systems, Inc.) modules. If I were doing it again, however, I would build my own, since the Digibit Schmitt triggers tend to drift. The input signal is a discrete pulse, shaped by the punched tape program, going negative from ground to some voltage which is proportional to the film density.

All the Schmitt triggers which are set for a voltage less than the signal pulse switch on, the others remain off. The "and" gate which receives inputs from the last "on" trigger and the first "off" trigger responds, generating a pulse through its associated solenoid driver, causing the solenoid to print the appropriate digit.

Because of the drifting of these Schmitt triggers, it is necessary to realign them at frequent intervals, applying a controlled analog signal, and adjusting the trigger point of each in turn. I believe this could be cured by a simple network of high gain amplifiers, each biased to an appropriate voltage by a voltage divider of fixed resistors. I have not yet tried it.

48-CHANNEL D.C. TOPOSCOPE

The design of this d.c. toposcope is based on a concept of d.c. recording which may be termed the *pulse-sampling technique*. The critical circuit consists of only three elements: the electrode, the input capacitor to a toposcope channel, and a photocell whose other end connects to some reference voltage (Fig. 18). The photocell is periodically illuminated by a stroboscope.

To understand the constraints upon this circuit, it is necessary to keep in mind the voltages across the three elements, and their d.c. resistances. The electrode and the photocell will never carry a potential difference greater than the signal to be recorded. The input capacitor, on the other hand, may have a potential across it of several volts. In order to accurately display the d.c. potential under the electrode, the potential across the electrode tip must

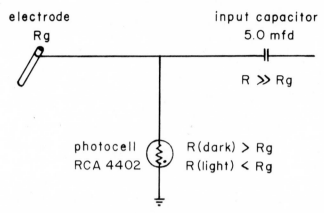

electrode
Rg

input capacitor
5.0 mfd

R ≫ Rg

photocell
RCA 4402

R(dark) > Rg
R(light) < Rg

FIGURE 18. Input circuit used to permit d.c. recording through a.c. amplifiers. The photocell is illuminated by strobe light about once every two seconds. For a discussion of component requirements, see text.

be essentially zero between sampling pulses. This means that the dark resistance of the photocell must be large compared to the electrode resistance and that the leakage current through the capacitor must produce a negligible voltage drop across the electrode resistance. If we consider the case of a 1 Mohm electrode resistance, with actual d.c. signal level about 1 mV, it is clear that an input capacitor leakage current of 1 nA would produce an artifact of magnitude equal to the signal, or a signal-noise ratio of one, which is quite unacceptable. This artifact may be reduced by (1) reducing electrode resistance, (2) increasing the d.c. resistance of the input capacitor, or (3) reducing the voltage across the input capacitor.

When the photocell is illuminated, the input is momentarily connected to the reference voltage through the (light) resistance of the photocell. To avoid losing signal, this resistance should be small compared to the electrode resistance. In the case of very low resistance electrodes, it may be necessary to use a fixed resistor in series with them.

Some of the charge on the input capacitor is bled off during this sampling pulse and must be replaced through the electrode before the next sampling pulse arrives. The time constant of the electrode-input capacitor combination thus fixes a maximum sampling rate. This is not a limitation, except with very high resistance

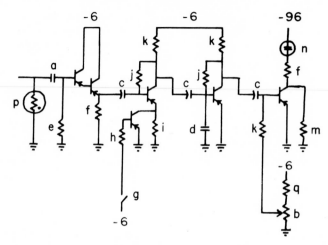

FIGURE 19. Toposcope amplifier for a.c. or d.c. recording: *a*, 6.0 mF metallized paper; *b*, 10 ohms; *c*, 20 mF; *d*, .1 mF; *e*, 8.2 meg; *f*, 2.2 k; *g*, gain control; *h*, 3.9 k; *i*, 330 ohms; *j*, 150 k; *k*, 2.2 k; *m*, 1.0 meg; *n*, NE-2; *p*, RCA 4402; transistors 2N1305 except last stage 2N398.

electrodes, where the leakage artifact mentioned above becomes prohibitive anyway. With any likely combination of values, it is possible to sample at least once per second. Any activity too fast for this sampling rate may be recorded by standard a.c. techniques.

Illumination of the photocell thus produces a voltage excursion from the signal level to the reference level, and then back, more or less slowly, to signal level at the termination of the illumination. The voltage pulse entering the toposcope amplifier, therefore, is of equal voltage but opposite polarity to the desired d.c. signal. This pulse could be displayed by an oscilloscope or other recording instrument, but for toposcopic purposes it is best displayed as the brightness of a neon tube. The array of tubes needs only be photographed once for each sampling pulse, but it is simpler to record with an ordinary 8 mm movie camera at 30 to 40 frames per second. The cost of the wasted film is insignificant compared to the cost and complication of trying to maintain synchrony between camera and strobe light.

The amplifier circuit used in this toposcope is shown in Figure 19. This was actually a prototype for the solid state a.c. topo-

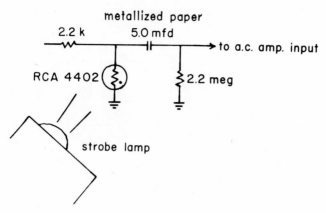

FIGURE 20. Circuit for converting any a.c. amplifier for d.c. "pulse sampling" recording.

scope amplifier described above and is somewhat inferior to it. Actually, any a.c. amplifier may be used to amplify the sampling pulse produced by the photocell sampling circuit. The only critical aspect of the circuit is the input capacitor, which must have a near infinite d.c. impedance and a capacitance large enough to keep low frequency noise to a few microvolts. I used the Sprague 118P60502S2, a metallized paper capacitor that is very well insulated and constructed in such a way that it is difficult to get fingerprints on the critical insulation.

Since the a.c. amplifier is not unique, except in the quality of its input capacitor, the same toposcope may, if desired, be used for a.c. toposcopy simply by raising the gain and turning off the stroboscope. The only real drawback to this arrangement is that the metallized paper capacitors are so bulky as compared with the other components in the solid state a.c. amplifier that the total volume of the toposcope would be nearly doubled by using these rather than the tantalum capacitors actually used. I prefer to use a conversion unit, consisting of circuits such as shown in Figure 20, which plugs into the a.c. toposcope input. The low frequency noise of the combined circuits is a bit higher than if only a single input capacitor is used, but not enough to affect the high voltage d.c. signals. The 2 meg. leak to reference between the two input capacitors reduces the voltage drop across the metallized paper capacitor, thus further reducing its already low leak-

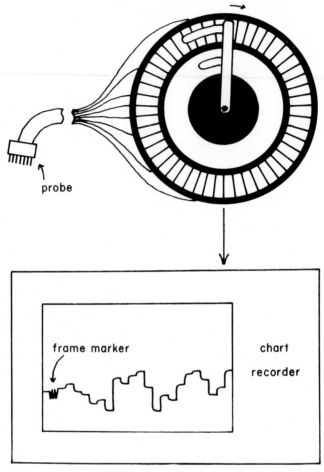

FIGURE 21. Commutator used for 48-channel d.c. recording. The commutator segments were etched from circuit board laminate. It operated at 1 to 4 rpm. A typical record is shown below. The record is essentially a histogram of the voltages under the forty-eight electrodes.

age current. Also, the stroboscope can be built into the housing for the d.c. sampling circuit, so that once the optimal alignment with the photocells is found, it may be left undisturbed.

48-CHANNEL COMMUTATOR

None of the significant data reported in later chapters were actually collected with the d.c. toposcope described above. Instead the d.c. toposcopy used a much simpler apparatus consisting of a 48-channel commutator and a Bausch and Lomb V.O.M. 5 chart recorder. The commutator (Fig. 21) was constructed by etching the desired segments and annulus into an etched circuit board, which was then mounted to an acrylic backing plate for rigidity. A brass wiper arm, driven by a synchronous motor, connects each segment in turn to the annulus. For low noise level, it is necessary to polish the commutator with steel wool or a very fine emery paper about once a week more or less depending on the humidity.

Actually, the commutator has forty-nine segments. The extra segment is connected to a square wave generator which produces a distinctive waveform on the chart record. Something of this sort is necessary for identifying the beginning and end of each sweep.

Reference may be to an indifferent electrode, but is usually to an average of the forty-eight input voltages obtained by connecting a 2.2 meg resistor from each input to a common reference point. This matrix of resistors is mounted in such a way that it can be quickly inserted between the recording probe and commutator input. It is thus possible to change from an indifferent electrode reference to an average reference in a few seconds for comparison of the two techniques.

The output of this system is a strip chart containing a rectangular waveform. The height of each horizontal segment in this waveform represents the d.c. voltage of a particular electrode. This record is converted to toposcopic form by laying it over a transilluminated template and aligning the "frame marks" made by the square wave generator with the indicator marks at each end of the template. The voltage of each electrode may then be read in turn and recorded on a data sheet which has spaces for the voltages, arranged in spatial correspondence to the electrode array.

The disadvantage of this system, as compared with a toposcope, is the hand work needed to convert the strip chart record into a spatially correct format. For d.c. recording, where only one record is normally taken each day, this is not a serious drawback and is outweighed by the two major advantages of the system: unlimited gain control, and complete freedom of electrode ar-

Cebus 27 (Satan)   Date 5/30/67

Extra-cranial nickel, 4/25/67

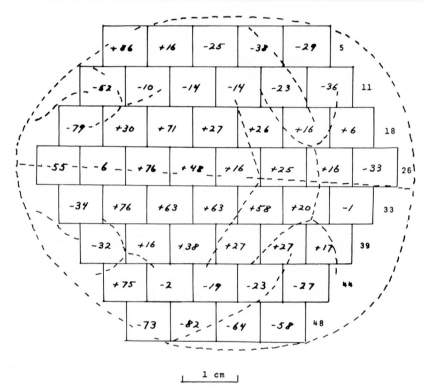

| 1 cm |

FIGURE 22. Actual data sheet as recorded from Cebus 27. The recorded voltages are in millivolts. The date 4/25/67 refers to the date of survey. See also FIGURE 23.

rangement. The latter stems from the fact that the output is placed in spatial format only at the stage of writing the voltages onto a record sheet. By making a different record sheet for each preparation, the usual toposcopic constraints on electrode arrangement are eliminated.

A typical record sheet is shown in Figure 22. Since it is an individual sheet, used only with one preparation, it can contain a good deal of specific information, such as the location of prin-

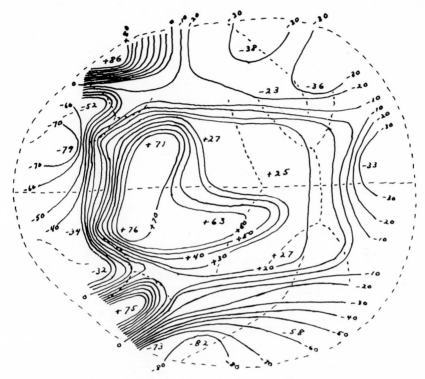

FIGURE 23. Actual voltage contour map recorded from Cebus 27. The raw data from which these contours were drawn is shown in FIGURE 22.

cipal sulci relative to the electrode array, type of electrode implant and date of surgery, and, of course, marginal comments on experimental status.

For most analyses, a contour map is drawn from the record sheet, as in Figure 23. The spacing of contours depends on the type of electrodes used. In the case of nickel electrodes, as in this example, a contour line is drawn at every 10 mV. With silver electrodes, a contour is drawn at every 1.0 mV.

The chart recorder used with this system is not critical, as long as it can be read accurately to the nearest .5 mV and has a reliable chart speed. I have found the Bausch and Lomb V.O.M. 5 to be very satisfactory, and the flexible input of this instrument makes it generally useful around the laboratory. I also have three Heath EUW-20A recorders, which are less pleasant to use than the Bausch and Lomb, because of their noisiness and the tendency of the paper to jam, but might be preferable for student use because of their low cost and the easily replaced pens.

The commutation rate depends on the expected rate of change of potentials and on the frequency response of the chart recorder. Initially, I used a 4 rpm rotor speed, in order to estimate the occurrence of the infra slow potential oscillation as described by Aladjalova (1964). Since oscillations of about this frequency (2 per min) proved to be infrequent and not very interesting, I changed to a 1 rpm rate in order to permit the chart recorder to follow more accurately.

For monopolar d.c. recording, either the Heath or the Bausch and Lomb, and undoubtedly other makes as well, may be connected directly to a silver, gold, or nickel electrode. Infra slow potential oscillations may be seen as well as d.c. shifts upon falling asleep or awakening. With nickel electrodes, particularly in the region of the arcuate sulcus of monkeys, very dramatic shifts of well over 100 mV in two or three minutes may be found. Such a simple arrangement is a foolproof means of introducing students to the wonderland of electrophysiology.

A very simple version of the same commutator arrangement was built for undergraduate student use. It uses an ordinary eleven-position selector switch as the commutator. (A larger version has also been built, using a 23-position selector switch, but the electrode implantation is a bit beyond most students.) The circuit is shown in Figure 24. The 2.2 meg leak resistors from each input form an averaging network to provide a reference voltage. The zero calibration push button permits the student to mark the reference voltage on the chart record at the beginning and end of each sweep. In use, the chart recorder is started and the zero calibration button depressed. The operator then watches the chart recorder and releases the zero button as the pen crosses a vertical chart line, thus producing a trace of the voltage on channel 1. As the recorder pen crosses the next line, the switch is moved to position 2, and so on through the eleven positions. Finally, the calibration button is again depressed to provide a final zero value. Data analysis is exactly as with the 48-channel model described above.

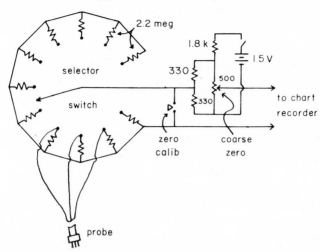

FIGURE 24. 11-channel d.c. toposcope for student use. The selector switch functions as a hand-operated commutator.

This toposcope also has a built-in coarse zero control, which permits high-gain recording of the waveform from a channel, even though the absolute voltage of that electrode may be as much as 100 mV from the reference level.

The implantation technique has also been simplified for use by undergraduate students on rats or other small mammals. The skull is exposed, a drilled electrode guide positioned over it, and the eleven electrodes dropped through the desired guide holes onto the skull. Nu-Weld dental cement (L. D. Caulk Co.) is then dusted around the electrodes and allowed to set. The dental cement with its embedded electrodes is then lifted off the skull, the electrodes trimmed, a plug connected to them and cemented in place, and so on, very much as in the more complex procedure by which I prepare the plastic implant with forty-eight electrodes, described in the immediately following pages. When the array is ready for insertion, the temporal muscles are scraped down far enough to place a stainless steel jeweler's screw on each side of the skull, the electrode array placed on the skull and bonded to the screws with more dental cement (see Fig. 25).

Eleven electrodes are adequate to cover one hemisphere of the rat brain. Some data collected by undergraduates using this device are included in later chapters.

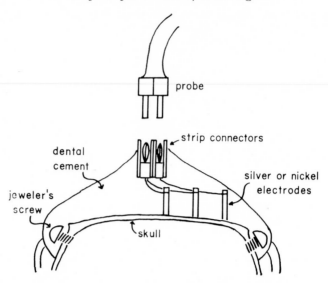

FIGURE 25. A simple method of chronically implanting up to twenty-five cranial electrodes. Intended primarily for student use.

CHRONIC ELECTRODE IMPLANTS: 48-CHANNEL

Only the technique for the implantation of silver or nickel electrodes will be described. Gold electrodes necessitate some differences in procedure, but since no data from gold electrodes are presented in later chapters, I will not further confuse this description with those particular details. If any reader wants to try making sense of the rather mysterious potentials emanating from gold electrodes, he is welcome to write me for details of the implantation procedure as I have worked it out.

Before surgery is begun, the electrodes and the connecting plug are prepared. The electrodes consist of reasonably straight lengths of pure silver or nickel wire, about 1 mm diameter and 30 to 40 mm long. For a connecting plug, I cut lengths of Amphenol™ strip connector (221-2153), four lengths of ten holes each, and one of nine holes. The appropriate wire-form contacts (220-P01) are crimped to 40 mm lengths of No. 28 stranded hook-up wire, the other ends are stripped back about 6 mm. The contacts are snapped into place in the strip connectors. For most preparations one empty hole is left at one end of the nine-hole strip. If, however, an indifferent electrode is to be used, all forty-nine contacts will be needed.

Also needed before surgery is an electrode placement guide. This may be a block of acrylic plastic about 50 by 75 mm by 6 mm thick, with an array of holes in the locations desired for the electrode array. I use a block with several hundred holes, spaced 2 mm apart, from which I can choose the locations I want as I construct the array. The guide holes should be a sliding fit for the electrode wire and must be parallel to each other.

The surgical procedure begins with the construction of a silicone rubber model of the exposed skull and brain, exactly as in the previously described technique for implantation of four hundred electrodes. The only difference is that in d.c. recording I nearly always leave the skull intact. The broad gradients of d.c. potential are not blurred by the intervening skull, and the mildly toxic electrode materials are best kept away from the meninges. In trimming the vertical edge of the rubber model, however, it should extend about 10 to 15 mm above the highest point of the "skull."

The electrode guide is now laid across the top of the rubber model, and the electrodes dropped through the guide holes onto the desired locations on the "skull." This electrode array and spacing should be recorded. The mold is filled with liquid plastic to within 2 or 3 mm of the top, taking care not to let the liquid make contact with the electrode guide. The plastic may then be jelled and cured, and the electrode guide lifted off.

At this stage the location of the electrodes relative to the skull sutures may be fairly accurately determined by examining the underside of the plastic. This information should be recorded.

The electrodes are trimmed down to within a few millimeters of the plastic, and the connecting wires are soldered to them in proper sequence. The five short lengths of strip connector are then assembled into a plug by impaling them either on the recording probe to be used or on another plug previously made to exactly duplicate the probe. The strip connectors are then cemented in place with a dental cement such as Nu-Weld. The connecting wires are also covered with cement for protection.

The implant is completed in the same way as the head plate

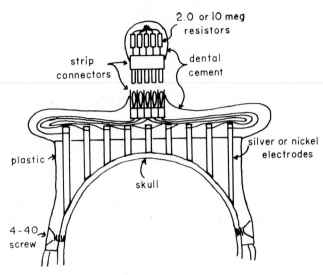

FIGURE 26. Cross-sectional view of the 48-electrode implant used in the present research. The process of forming the plastic implant is similar to that shown in FIGURE 12. The load plug of 2.0 or 10 meg. resistors is connected between recording sessions to minimize d.c. artifacts.

for four hundred channels. The under side of the electrodes is shaved with a carving tool, holes are drilled for bone screws, and excess plastic is carved away. It is sterilized and implanted in the preparation just as described above (Fig. 26).

For the recording of absolute d.c. potentials, it is necessary to keep an electrical load on the electrodes at all times to prevent the development of differential offset potentials. I use a "load plug," assembled from Amphenol strip connectors (221-2253) to match the plug in the electrode implant. A ⅛W resistor is crimped into each contact (220-S01), and the upper ends are brought together into a common connection and soldered. The matrix of resistors is saturated with dental cement for mechanical protection.

At first I used 10 meg load resistors on silver electrodes almost exclusively. I note, however, that the recorded potentials drift toward the reference value for the first few minutes after the animal is connected to the recording apparatus. More recently I have used a 2 meg load plug, to match the 2 meg load of the average reference system which constitutes the input impedance of the recording apparatus. In this case, of course, there is no drift when the electrodes are connected, as the load does not change. The patterns recorded under these conditions, however, are of somewhat lower voltage then those recorded when a 10 meg load is used between sessions. I do not yet know whether this means that the electrodes tend to polarize under the 2 meg load or whether they tend to develop an artifact under the 10 meg. I suspect the former.

MONKEYS: HOUSING AND HANDLING

Before going on to describe the behavioral techniques used in this research, I would like to mention some of the methods and hardware developed for storing and manipulating the South American monkeys used, partly because the methods of housing and handling affect the animals' behavior, and partly because some of the ideas might prove useful to others working with these interesting but often frustrating primates.

The cage that I have evolved for housing Cebus and Saimiri is shown in Figure 27. It is built of 1-inch by 2-inch mesh welded wire fencing material without a frame. The lack of frame makes it less expensive, much lighter, and eliminates the surfaces and corners which collect dirt and feces. The cage stays remarkably clean. The entire cage is folded from a single piece of fencing material. The seams are fastened by leaving projecting pieces of wire along one edge of the seam, then, after folding, wrapping these around the opposite edge wire. With a little practice, this "stitching" can be done rapidly, leaving no sharp ends protruding, and is quite monkey-proof.

The tall, narrow shape of the cage is designed to maximize climbing behavior, which helps to keep monkeys healthy. The perch, consisting of two ½-inch aluminum rods spaced two inches apart, is at the top rear of the cage, the water bottle at the bottom front, and the food hopper at the center front, so that the monkey has to do a fair amount of climbing just to eat, drink, and sleep.

The cages are suspended from a pipe rack about 16 inches above the drop pans. It is important that this distance from cage floor to drop pan be longer than the longest monkey's arm, or there will be sawdust, feces and used monkey chow in every corner of the animal room. It is also helpful, if space permits, to leave

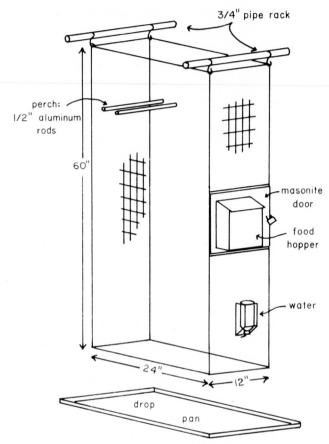

FIGURE 27. Cage used for Cebus or squirrel monkeys. It is formed of a single piece of welded wire fencing material, 1- by 2-inch mesh without frame.

an unreachable distance between cages, lest a playful monkey torment the one next to it into a state of neurosis. If space is limited, it is possible to arrange the cages so that bullies find themselves next to monkeys somewhat larger than themselves. As a last resort, one side of each cage may be covered with a sheet of metal, designed for easy removal for cleaning purposes. This is an undesirable solution, however, as it cuts down on air circulation and normal social intercourse, both of which are important to the animals' health.

The cage is designed so that the animal may be kept on a leash, the end of which is brought through a notch in the edge of the door. A knot in the end of the leash keeps it from slipping back, yet permits it to swivel. The end of the leash cannot be tied or clamped, as the animal's acrobatics will soon have it twisted up short. It is vital that the perch be located near enough to the rear of the cage that the leashed monkey cannot slip down behind it.

I have also used a group version of this cage, identical in every dimension except width, which should be at least 8 inches per Cebus, or 6 inches per Saimiri. The group cage is particularly important if squirrel monkeys are to be held for any length of time, since they seldom survive more than a few months in isolation, but thrive in groups of four of five. Naturally, animals cannot be kept leashed in a group cage.

Some monkeys make a career of smashing water bottles. Once an animal has embarked on such a criminal course, it is almost impossible to thwart him. The use of plastic bottles is merely an admission of defeat, does not eliminate a great deal of mopping, nor prevent gnawing of the rubber stoppers beyond use or recognition. The only mechanical device I have found that Cebus monkeys cannot undo more easily than their keepers is a padlock. I therefore make a wire basket to contain the water bottle, deep enough so that the bottle does not extend above the top edge. A hinged cover is made from the same 1-inch by 2-inch mesh wire, two extending wires looped around the top wire of the basket to form the hinge. The cover can then be padlocked in place, thus frustrating the most persistent monkey.

They will still, however, pull the stopper from the bottle, thus inundating the room, and gnaw at it through the mesh. This trick can be prevented with the aid of standard ketchup bottles. First, buy your ketchup in "family size" bottles (about 1 pint). Save the empty bottles and screw caps. Insert a stainless steel drinking tube into No. 3 one-hole rubber stopper, drive it snugly into the mouth of the bottle, and mark the stopper at the edge of the bottle rim. Cut the stopper as marked, so that when it is inserted tightly into the mouth of the bottle, it will be exactly flush with the rim. Then drill a $\frac{3}{8}$-inch hole through the center of the screw cap, slip it over the drinking tube and screw it tightly to the bottle. Thus far, my most ingenious monkey has failed to solve the problem of removing such a stopper.

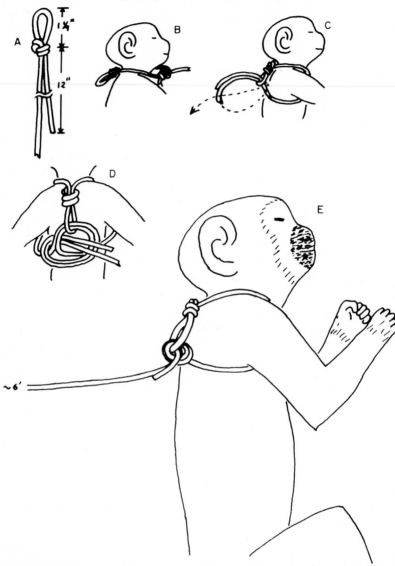

Figure 28. Tieing the harness and leash on a squirrel monkey. *A*, Advance preparation. If intended for a Cebus, the free end of the rope should be 14 inches, rather than 12 inches. *B*, A square knot is tied under the chin, forming a loose collar. *C*, The ends are brought under the arms and passed through the preformed loop, then tied around themselves in an overhand knot as shown in *D*. The long end of the rope then forms a leash, as in *E*. It is strongly recommended that the monkey be anesthetized the first few times you try this.

The monkeys are maintained on a diet of Purina Monkey Chow 25 and water. I usually supplement this with fresh fruits and sweet potatoes, not for nutritional purposes, but to project an image of myself as the benevolent father figure. It helps if the monkeys are glad to see you.

The harness and leash arrangement has gone through more versions over the years than has the toposcope. The present model seems fairly satisfactory. Figure 28 attempts to depict the manner in which the harness and leash are created from a single length of ⅛-inch polypropylene rope. I have found that different brands of rope vary greatly in stiffness. It should be as limp as possible. A nine-foot length of rope is turned back on itself 18 inches from an end, and an overhand knot tied close to the end of this bight. The small loop thus formed is placed at the back of the monkey's neck and the two ends of the rope brought around either side and tied loosely in front, using a square knot. The two ends are now passed under the monkey's arms and brought together in back. Keeping the two ends together, as if they were a single rope, pass them through the small loop originally formed, then back in an overhand knot around themselves so that the original loop is caught within this knot. This final knot should be reasonably snug against the monkey's back. The long end of the rope is used as the leash. The cut ends of the polypropylene rope can be kept from fraying by melting them slightly in a flame.

After a few years' practice, it is possible to tie this harness with one hand while restraining a wild Cebus monkey with the other, put it is much less trying to tie the harness on the monkey after surgery while he is still relaxed.

The harness and leash are used to restrain the monkeys in the experimental apparatus. The "chair" is actually just a vertical panel of acrylic plastic with a hole about 8 inches above the floor. The end of the leash is slipped through this hole, and the monkey drawn back against the panel. The leash is then clamped in a clothesline clamp well out of the animal's reach (see Fig. 31).

The monkeys adapt rather quickly to this minimal restraint, except for a few human haters who cannot be adapted to anything. After two or three months of training, the monkey usually climbs

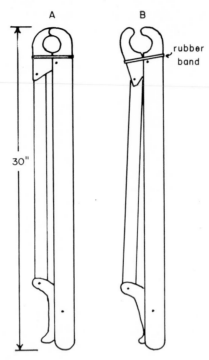

FIGURE 29. Handling stick used for manipulating leashed monkeys without loss of fingers. *A*, Closed. *B*, Open.

into the apparatus by himself and backs up to the chair. I have to move quickly to get the leash through the hole before he gets in my way.

For the first few days, however, when the animals are still wild and frightened, a handling stick is very helpful in placing them in the chair without loss of fingers. The present stick is shown in Figure 29. It is simply a rigid, 30-inch stick with a hole in one end. The leash is slipped through the hole (while the monkey is still in his cage, for really wild ones) and drawn up so that he cannot reach the handle end of the stick. The handle and leash may be held together in one hand, thus keeping the monkey under safe, positive control.

When the monkey is to be placed in the restraining chair, it is necessary to construct the stick so that it may be slipped off the leash after the leash has been drawn through the hole in the chair. As may be seen from Figure 29, rocking the trigger grip backward opens the jaws of the stick so that it may be slipped off. When removing the monkey from the chair, it may be slipped over the leash before the leash is unclamped.

BEHAVIORAL TECHNIQUES: PROGRAMMING

The earliest learning problems were individually constructed, with all contingencies permanently built into the apparatus. As the need for greater flexibility became clear, I examined various programming systems that were commercially available, and settled on the Behavioral Research Systems. I used their modules directly in the construction of the computer described above, then copied the circuits in a smaller physical size, with minor modifications, for programming learning problems. I found that it was possible to reduce all the important modules to a 2-inch by 3-inch etched circuit format.*

The cards mount on paired rails by means of banana plugs (Fig. 30), which supply power. All other inputs and outputs are connected to an Amphenol strip connector riveted to the outer edge of the card. Connections are made with jumper wires which have the appropriate contacts crimped to each end.

Interfacing relies heavily on a photo-relay consisting of a small incandescent lamp securely taped to an RCA 4402 photocell with plastic electrical tape. Placing such a relay between an input switch and the logic modules eliminates the problem of switch contact bounce. By also using photo-relays on the output side, the logic modules are electrically isolated from all other wiring, which eliminates many potential problems of voltage matching and stray signals. The disadvantage of the photo-relay is the few milliseconds delay it introduces, but this is seldom a problem in behavioral programming.

The details of the circuit diagrams are of no interest here, partly because a flip-flop is a flip-flop regardless of the particular transistors and resistors used, but more significantly because the recent rapid development of integrated circuits has made this new form of logic module less expensive than even homemade assembled

---

*The Behavioral Research Systems modules from which ours were copied are called Digibits by the manufacturer. We promptly dubbed our miniaturized versions "Bitty-bits." The integrated circuits with which we are now working are naturally referred to as "Itty-bitty-bits."

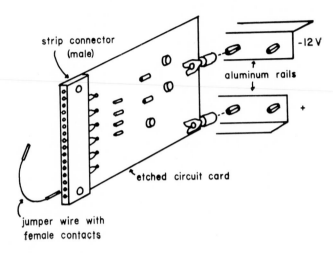

strip connector
(male)

-12 V

aluminum rails

etched circuit card

jumper wire with
female contacts

FIGURE 30. Details of mounting and interconnection used with "bitty-bits" logic modules.

circuits. There is no longer any point in building flip-flops and gates when they can be purchased in rugged, reliable, and exquisitely small integrated form for less than the cost of the transistors needed.

ONE-STRING PROBLEMS

The behavioral measure I have used most intensively is an operant conditioning paradigm which I refer to as a one-string problem. From the monkey's viewpoint, it is extremely simple. The animal faces a panel containing a cup and a string (Fig. 31). If the string is pulled at the proper time a grape drops into the cup. The proper time is indicated by one of a variety of visual or auditory stimuli. The problem may also be complicated by the addition of neutral or meaningless stimuli, from which the significant stimulus must be discriminated.

A naive animal is introduced to the apparatus in gradual stages. First, he is simply placed in the restraining chair and fed grapes. When he has accepted the restraint with some grace, the panel is placed in front of him and the grapes delivered through the cup. Next, he is required to pull the string in order to get a grape, then this string-pulling response is trained to about 25 percent partial reinforcement schedule. The animal thus begins the

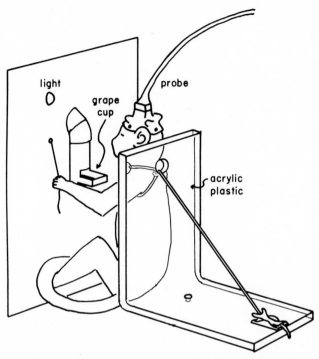

FIGURE 31. The one-string problem. If the string is pulled during the cue stimulus, a grape drops into the cup. The cue stimulus is normally either the light shown on panel, or a 2000-cycle tone.

learning problem with a well-established motor response which must be attached to the correct stimulus. There is no punishment for incorrect responses. The monkeys are always fed and watered ad libitum in their home cages, the only restriction being that monkeys currently working on learning problems are never given any fresh fruits before the training period, although they may be given bananas and apples when they are returned to their cages after training. Purina Monkey Chow 25 is always available. In fact, if a monkey's food hopper is found to be empty immediately before a training session, it is filled, and the monkey permitted to eat before he is taken to the laboratory. The monkeys are never fed grapes (their favorite food) except in the apparatus. The reinforcement during the learning problem is therefore not drive reduction. The grapes serve as a hedonistic reward, and, probably more importantly, as a signal that a correct response has been made. The monkeys learn for the pleasure of eating grapes and/or for the pleasure of solving problems. The general behavior of the Cebus monkeys suggests that both of these rewards are important factors. Saimiri seems to be motivated largely by the grapes.

The temporal spacing of stimuli is fixed by the rate at which a typical monkey consumes a typical grape. The usual cycle is stimulus on for ten seconds, unless a response occurs, in which case the stimulus is turned off coincident with delivery of the grape. If no response occurred, the stimulus is left off for twenty seconds, then back on for ten seconds, and so on. When a reinforced response occurs, the stimulus is left off for forty-five seconds, which is a bit longer than most monkeys need to eat an average grape.

The number of reinforcements which constitutes a daily session is fixed by the number of grapes an animal can eat before he loses interest. For the sake of uniformity, I have settled on six reinforcements per session, which approaches satiety for Saimiri. Cebus can easily consume twice this many grapes at a sitting and will continue to work on the problem even when filled to capacity, leaving the grapes in the cup. I have found, however, that learning requires about two to three daily sessions, regardless of whether the sessions consist of six, seven, or ten trials.

The significant stimulus is usually either a small incandescent light on the panel facing the monkey or a 2000-cycle tone. If the situation is not complicated by further contingencies or irrelevant stimuli, the former problem is termed the "one-light, one-string problem," the latter is called the "one-tone, one-string problem." The tone problem has been varied by adding a neutral tone, generally of 5000 cycles, thus becoming the "two-tone, one-string problem." Variations of the light problem that have been used include leaving the light on dimly between trials, so that the critical stimulus is an increase in luminance (the "bright-light, one-string problem") or reversing the contingency to either of these stimuli (thus, the "light off, one-string" or the "dim-light, one-string" problems). A particularly interesting situation was the "simultaneous light-tone problem," in which the critical stimulus was the simultaneous presentation of light and tone, either one alone being neutral.

In all these problems, the monkey must learn that string-pulling is rewarded only in the presence of a particular stimulus. The significant learning appears to be perceptual. In order to be observable, of course, this perceptual learning must become attached to some motor components.

During the years that I have been using this learning paradigm, I have tried various criteria of state of learning. The first criterion used was number of incorrect responses, or responses in the absence of the stimulus, during a session. A few animals show the expected pattern of a decrease in this statistic with learning. Others, however, who are obviously learning by other criteria, may show no change or an actual increase in errors. Some animals seem to use the string to signal the experimenter that they are ready for another trial. When they finish the last grape, they give one tug on the string and then wait for the stimulus. If the stimulus is not rather promptly forthcoming, they may give a rapid sequence of responses, probably out of frustration. If such an animal has a low threshold for frustration, as most Cebus do, he may produce more "error" responses than he did when he was naive.

The second criterion adopted was the latency of correct responses. It would appear that a response which was elicited by the stimulus should occur nearer to the stimulus onset, on the average, than one of a random series of responses that occurs by chance during the stimulus. This criterion proved even worse than the first. A naive monkey usually responds fairly rapidly in the absence of the stimulus, so that the latency of the correct response will be quite short before any learning has occurred. As the animal begins to learn the significance of the stimulus, his first reaction may be to stop responding when the stimulus comes on and attend to the stimulus. In such a case, of course, latency increases abruptly. A few monkeys show the expected decrease in latency, and others show no change, even though other criteria show them to be learning. One particularly intelligent monkey, at a stage in learning where there was no question as to his sophistication on the problem being used, showed very short latency responses during some sessions and eight- or nine-second latencies during other sessions. Careful observation through the experimenter's spy mirror made it quite apparent that, on his long latency days, he was playing a game whose object was to respond as near as possible to the end of the ten-second stimulus duration.

Failure to respond to a stimulus also bears little relationship to state of learning. A naive animal will usually respond during about 90 percent of the stimuli simply because he normally makes at least one response during any ten-second period. A well-trained animal also responds to about 90 percent of the stimuli because he will be busy about some activity of his own invention on about one-tenth of the trials. One very sociable monkey, who apparently recognized the fact that a session lasted until he had received the specified number of grapes (under the paradigm then in use), would respond to the first four or five trials, then stop responding for several minutes while he carried on a long and expressive monologue, apparently directed toward me. When he had everything he wanted to say off his chest, he would go back to work, making quick, decisive responses, until the session was completed. The number of missed stimuli, of course, could not adequately describe his state of learning.

No single criterion of learning has been found which is satisfactory for all monkeys, or even for a single monkey at all times. It is necessary to observe the animal closely, noting orienting responses toward the stimulus, interruption of other activities to respond, and, in particular, symptoms that the delivery of a grape is expected following a correct response, but not following incorrect responses. This is most often shown by the monkey's reaching for the grape cup with one hand while he grasps the string with the other. Many monkeys use the same hand for pulling the string as for picking up the grape. In such an animal, the first sign of learning most often consists of the monkey's reaching for the grape cup at the stimulus onset, then correcting himself, pulling the string, and then taking the grape.

These criteria are unfortunately subjective. It would obviously be preferable to use an objective criterion, provided it accurately measured the monkey's psychological state. Because of the wide personality differences among Cebus monkeys, no such objective criterion exists. Fortunately, the great majority of experiments reported in this book do not use rate of learning as a variable. Only in the ablation experiment (Chap. VIII) does the criterion of completion of learning become crucial. This experiment used squirrel monkeys almost exclusively. The less imaginative behavior of Saimiri eases the problem of finding workable, objective criteria of learning. A combination of the three criteria discussed above gives a reasonable index of learning in the squirrel monkey, provided it is combined with observation in order to disclose those few cases of idiosyncratic behavior in which the objective indices are highly misleading.

TWO-STRING PROBLEMS

This paradigm was developed in an attempt to devise a situation which would permit an accurate, objective measure of the state of learning. It demonstrated only that the subjects are smarter than the experimenter.

The monkey faces a panel containing two strings, to right and left of the grape cup in the center. The critical stimulus, which is either a light or a tone, is on 50 percent of the time in a complex cycle which is controlled by the logic module program. While the stimulus is on, the right-hand string controls the grape dispenser; while it is off, the left-hand string produces grapes. The monkey therefore always has a correct response available to him, and can obtain grapes as rapidly as he desires. My expectation was that incorrect responses would start at at least 50 percent and drop toward zero as learning progressed. This was the only pattern that was not found.

Some animals use only one string, thus converting the apparatus into a one-string problem. Some use one string for part of a session, then switch to the other for a time, thus presenting themselves with a one-string problem in which the contingencies are frequently reversed. They learn nothing. Other monkeys grasp both strings and pull them simultaneously. They are therefore always correct, have nothing to learn, and the recording equipment shows a remarkably constant 50 percent correct. The most frequent pattern, however, is to grasp both strings and pull them alternately. This gives a 50 percent chance of being rewarded on the first response, and, failing that, a certainty of reward on the second. This pattern of response is efficient enough that the monkeys never try to improve on it but devote their attention to eating grapes and playing more interesting games that they invent themselves. The percentage of incorrect responses starts at 33 percent and does not change.

HYPOTHESIS PROBLEM

This problem was intended to present more of a challenge to the intelligence of the Cebus monkey and to permit me to explore a longer and more complex learning process than that provided by the string problems. The monkey is presented with a row of four upright levers, spaced 4.5 cm apart, mounted on a sliding block that may be withdrawn beyond his reach (see Fig. 32). The four levers are of four different shapes (cylinder, T, triangle, sphere) and four different colors (black, white, yellow, and blue), chosen from a complete set of sixteen. The positions of the four shapes and the four colors are randomly determined for each trial before the session begins.

The monkey is permitted to watch the setup of the levers, but the setting of the switch that determines the correct lever is shielded from his view. The block is then moved forward within his reach, and he is permitted to move the levers until he finds the correct one. Moving the correct lever by about 10 degrees in any direction makes the electrical contact which rings a door chime. The block is then withdrawn, uncovering a grape in a cup at the front of the shelf.

Each trial is scored according to the first lever moved. This lever may be described by position, color, or shape. For analysis of the data, they are plotted on a chart containing twelve rows, one for each position, each color, and each shape. Every trial is thus scored by marking an X in three rows, indicating the characteristics of the lever first moved. If the animal responds consistently to some dimension for a few trials, a row of X's appears on the chart (see Fig. 33).

Only the most intelligent and well-adapted monkeys are able to solve this problem. Most Cebus find it too frustrating and either try to move all four levers simultaneously or refuse to re-

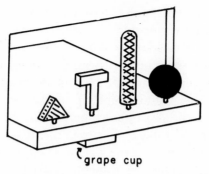

grape cup

FIGURE 32. Hypothesis problem. When the correct handle is moved, the board is withdrawn, leaving a grape in the cup. The four handles are of four distinctive colors. Any shape may appear in any color and in any position.

	51	52	53	54	55	56	57	58	59	60	61	62	63	64	65	66	67	68	69	70
1 (right)																				
2	X	X					X								X				X	X
3				X	X	X		X	X					X		X		X		
4 (left)			X							X	X	X	X				X			
black			X					X		X			X	X		X			X	X
white	X				X		X				X							X		
blue				X		X						X			X					
yellow		X							X								X			
cylinder	X	X	X			X		X	X		X			X	X		X			X
sphere				X	X		X													
triangle																				
"T"										X		X	X			X		X	X	

3/6/63   3/7/63

FIGURE 33. Hypothesis problem record sheet. Each trial is scored according to the first handle moved. Notice that on 3/7/63 all responses were either cylinder or "T."

spond at all. The most intelligent animals, however, soon learn to move the levers one at a time, and appear to become interested in solving the problem for its own sake.

They normally begin with a position tendency, usually the end of the array nearest the preferred hand. After a few sessions, they adopt hypotheses of shape or color, usually trying one hypothesis for ten to fifteen trials before switching to another. Occasional intervals of apparently random responding may represent rapid changes of hypothesis. This point, of course can never be known.

This paradigm can also indicate perceptual differences between the experimenter and subject. For example, in a problem in which the correct response was to the cylinder, a very intelligent Cebus reached a partial solution in something over one hundred trials, consisting of responses to either T or cylinder. He obviously saw the shapes as either tall or short, and responded to which-ever of the tall shapes was nearer his preferred hand. The discrimination between T and the cylinder, which appeared so obvious to the experimenter, was made very gradually over the next two hundred trials.

If, when the monkey has solved the first problem, the definition of correct is changed, the animal usually becomes frustrated and refuses to respond. The problem is apparently very near the intellectual limit of the Cebus. It has never been used with Saimiri.

CAT DISCRIMINATION APPARATUS: DELAYED CHOICE

A very simple apparatus was constructed for use with cats. It consisted of a board approximately 29 cm wide with two shallow wells drilled into the front edge, each well 4 cm in diameter, 1.5 cm deep, and the two wells centered about 23 cm apart. Each well was covered with a wood disk from which a flat panel, 5 cm square, projected upward. This panel was oriented normal to the cat's line of sight. It provided a large surface area for visual discrimination, as well as a lever which made it very easy to knock the cover off the well (Fig. 34).

One of the wells was baited with a small piece of tuna fish or raw liver, then the board moved within reach of the cat. In some cases a correction procedure was used, in other cases the board was withdrawn after one well had been uncovered. Occasionally a cat was able to knock off both covers with one sweep, but none developed this skill to the point where it became a problem.

When I first tried this apparatus, I was concerned with equalizing

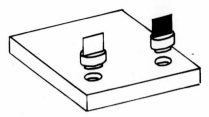

FIGURE 34. Black-white discrimination, cats. One food well was baited with tuna fish, covered with the white cap, and the board moved within reach of the animal.

olfactory cues. I quickly discovered, however, that the scent of tuna fish rapidly becomes all-pervasive, and the cat shows no indication of attempting to sniff out the correct food well. I also found that tuna fish is better than liver, as the latter makes the cats too eager, thus actually delaying learning.

As with the monkeys, the cats were fed Purina Chow and water ad lib. between sessions.

References

ALADJALOVA, N.A.: *Slow Electrical Processes in the Brain. Progress in Brain Research*, Amsterdam: Elsevier, 1964, Vol. 7.

DeMott, D.W.: Cortical micro-toposcopy. *Med. Res. Engin.*, 5(4):23-29, 1966.

STRAW, R.N., McAdam, D., Berry, C.A., and Mitchell, C.L.: A simple cable for reduction of movement artifact in electroencephalographic recordings. *Electroenceph. Clin. Neurophysiol.*, 22:90-92, 1967.

Chapter IV

A. C. TOPOSCOPY: RESULTS

ALTHOUGH data reported in this chapter were collected during the years 1961 through 1964, none of them have previously been published. These data comprise the main body of this report; those data described in the following chapters serve to confirm and extend the basic conclusions derived from the use of the a.c. toposcope with chronically prepared monkeys and cats.

The technique used in this research is laborious and slow; however, it is the best that I have been able to devise. If all goes well, an animal can be implanted and adapted to the experimental situation in about one month. Only about one-fourth of the animals used, however, actually yield significant amounts of trustworthy data. The others are wasted because of postoperative infection, disease, failure to adapt to the apparatus, unsuccessful new techniques, apparatus failures, and so on and so forth. One of the most serious handicaps in this research is that an animal can be taught a particular problem only once. The critical data may appear on only two or three days during the course of learning. In several instances an animal that had been implanted, adapted, and brought to the critical stage of learning was wasted because some apparatus failure or artifact ruined the data on one or two critical learning sessions. Because of the time requirements of data processing and analysis, apparatus maintenance, and the inevitable administrative procedures required under any funding system, only about four animals may be handled during any period. The total time required to obtain the desired learning data from a successful preparation varies from three to twelve months. In a good year, therefore, my total N might be increased by four or five animals. In a bad year. . ., fortunately, there were not many of those.

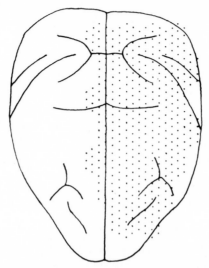

Figure 35. Array of four hundred recording sites as typically installed on the left hemisphere of a Cebus monkey. Interelectrode spacing was 1.5 mm.

All the data described in this chapter were recorded by means of the vacuum tube toposcope described at the beginning of Chapter III. This toposcope had a low frequency limit around 5 cps. The gain was fixed at a level which gave a usable range of signals from about $\pm 50\mu V$ to about $\pm 200\mu V$. The recording probes used had electrode spacing of 1.5 mm. A typical probe placement on the left hemisphere of a Cebus is shown in Figure 35. The electrode array was shaped to give most efficient coverage of the left hemisphere of a Cebus monkey. Because of the geometry of the recording booth, the left hemisphere was more accessible than the right. I assumed the two hemispheres were equivalent, since the Cebus does not show any strong manual preference. Several attempts to obtain comparison data from the right hemisphere of a Cebus failed because of miscellaneous difficulties, such as postoperative infection, or failure to adapt. In the squirrel monkey (*Saimiri sciureus*) the same recording array covered the entire left hemisphere and most of the right, with some electrodes at each end of the array being wasted. The 1.5 mm spacing, however, was rather coarse for the squirrel monkey, so that it was possible for significant activity to be missed.

The limitations of these data are therefore as follows:

1. Activity of less than 50μV is not visible.
2. Waveforms of less than 5 cps are greatly attenuated.
3. There are no data from the right hemisphere of the Cebus.
4. In the squirrel monkey, spatially small patterns may be invisible.

The Cebus monkeys used were almost exclusively *Cebus albifrons,* and most of these were female. Enough males and other species of Cebus (*capucinus* and *apella*) were used to be confident that the only sex and species difference is in ease of handling. The *Saimiri sciureus* were of both sexes but, again because of ease of handling, were mostly female.

The primary means of data analysis was simply viewing the motion pictures produced as primary data. Since the camera was usually operated at 250 to 300 frames per second, the projected films were about one-tenth to one-fifteenth original speed. For more detailed examination of portions of the data, a hand-operated movie editor was used. This allowed the film to be run at any speed in either direction or stopped for examination of individual frames.

Time is quantified on the films by the appearance of a 60-cycle flashing light. Space is quantified by the electrode spacing. The location of the array relative to the cortical convolutions was determined at autopsy by passing a direct current through the stainless steel electrodes at two standard reference points, and then removing the electrode array and rinsing the exposed tissue with potassium ferrocyanide to develop the Prussian blue stains. These reference points were then punctured with a sharp instrument, the dura and any scar tissue that had formed over it were removed, and the exposed cortex was photographed. The puncture marks that showed the location of the two reference points were marked on the photograph. The outline of the entire array could then be superimposed on the photograph with the aid of a template which showed the location of the reference points relative to the array.

ONE-TONE, ONE-STRING PROBLEM

This problem used the string-pulling apparatus described in Chapter III. Pulling the string produced a grape only when the tone was on. The tone was 2000 cycles at moderate intensity, delivered through a loudspeaker. The actual tone generator, amplifier, speaker location, and so forth, varied from one replication to another, but this had no effect on the toposcopic data.

Each daily session consisted of ten presentations of the tone, each presentation lasting ten seconds or until a response occurred. If the animal did not respond, the tone remained off for from ten to sixty seconds before the next presentation. In some replications this interval was fixed, in others it was randomly varied. If the animal did respond during the tone, and thus received a grape, the tone remained off for a period of from thirty to ninety seconds. This interval also was fixed in some replications and varied in others.

A total of nine animals have completed this problem, five Cebus and four Saimiri. The first indications of learning occurred sometime during the first four sessions, depending on the level of preadaptation. An animal that had already completed other learning paradigms, and was thus thoroughly adapted to the experimental situation and apparatus, usually showed clear indication of learning before the end of the first session. A naive animal, poorly adapted to the experimental situation, might show no indication of learning until about the fourth session. Most well-adapted but naive animals showed the first indication of learning during session three. All animals reached a fairly stable level of performance by the tenth session. The term stable, of course, is relative to the basic personality of the animals. A Cebus monkey tends to be moody, so that even a well-trained animal will sometimes refuse to have anything to do with the apparatus. The squirrel monkey's behavior is much more predictable.

The first indication of learning varied from one animal to another. If a monkey had a low rate of "spontaneous emission" of string pulling, the first sign of learning was usually a response immediately following tone onset. This could occur by chance, of course, and had to be confirmed by repetition or by other indications of learning. Animals with an initially high rate of responding might show learning by a pause in responding at tone onset or by reaching for the grape cup at tone onset. Rate of responding between tone presentations (errors) was a very poor

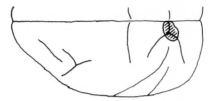

<small>Figure 36. Location of the learning focus during operant conditioning to an auditory cue.</small>

indicator of learning. In some animals it might increase during the early stages of learning, apparently correlating with general enthusiasm for the situation. It never decreased until late in learning and sometimes remained high for twenty sessions, when I generally gave up.

Toposcopic patterns were recorded on one or more trials during each session. The camera was started about ten seconds before tone onset, and remained on for a total of thirty seconds, which is one roll of film. Camera speed was about 250 frames per second.

In the Cebus monkey, the normal appearance of toposcopic records is a moderately fine-grained flickering. Spatial synchrony seldom extends beyond 2 or 3 mm. Frequencies are normally from the alpha range (10 cycles) upward to around 50 cps. When the data are viewed as motion pictures, there is an appearance of lateral movement of activity. Examination of successive frames shows this appearance of movement to be illusory.

Of the nine animals who have completed the one-tone problem, all have displayed a toposcopically distinctive type of electrical activity straddling the parieto-occipital sulcus coincident with or immediately preceding the first observable signs of learning. This activity has not been seen in these or in other animals spontaneously or during visual learning problems.

Figure 36 shows the location of this activity, which will be referred to with deliberate ambiguity as a "focus." It is distinguished from normal activity primarily by a broader spatial synchrony, usually extending across 4 or 5 mm in the Cebus. The frequency of activity within the focus is somewhat slower than normal, extending down to the frequency limit of the amplifiers (5 cps). Voltage is over $\pm 200 \mu$V, but because of the fixed gain of the toposcope, it is impossible to state whether the voltage of the focal activity is beyond the normal range.

The apparent lateral movement of activity in the region of the focus seems to be sharply limited, as if by an invisible fence around the critical area. This illusion is presumably due to the different spatial and temporal parameters of activity within the focus, which creates a discontinuity of apparent movement at the boundary of the focal region. The boundary appears to be quite sharp on the scale of the electrode array.

The presence of a focus over the parieto-occipital sulcus is not correlated with the onset of the tone or with the emission of a response on the recorded trial. If two or more records are taken during a single session, they tend to look very similar. The appearance of the toposcopic records changes from day to day but not from trial to trial.

In the squirrel monkeys the smaller dimensions of the brain were reflected in the toposcopic activity, which appeared to be on a finer scale. Spatial synchrony normally could not be seen at all, presumably being of smaller dimensions than the 1.5 mm electrode spacing. During the initial phases of learning the one-tone problem, a focus could generally be seen over the parieto-occipital sulcus. It was usually more difficult to distinguish than that in the Cebus.

In those squirrel monkeys having bilateral electrode arrays, I was never able clearly to distinguish homotopic foci in the two hemispheres. In some animals the focal activity appeared on the right hemisphere, in others, on the left. I assumed at the time that the corresponding focus on the other hemisphere was invisible because of its small dimensions, or poor probe contact, noisy channels, et cetera. Later data (see Chap. V) make it appear likely that this unilaterality was genuine.

When the focus first appeared, it tended to be small, weak, and intermittent. During the next one to three sessions, it became larger (Fig. 35 shows the maximum size) and more constant. As the monkey became more proficient at the instrumental response, the focus tended to decrease in area, then become intermittent again, and finally, as the monkey's performance approached its asymptote it disappeared.

TWO-TONE, ONE-STRING PROBLEM

This learning problem was identical to the one-tone problem described above, except that a neutral tone was added to the paradigm to complicate the discrimination. Tones of 2000 cycles and 500 cycles were used. Subjects in the first replication were three squirrel monkeys.

For one monkey, the 2000-cycle tone was positive, the 500-cycle tone negative. For the second monkey, the significance of the two tones was reversed. The third monkey served as a control; both tones were actually irrelevant, but the string-pulling response was reinforced at random intervals which were made similar, at each stage of the problem, to the frequency of reinforcement of the other two animals. This monkey quickly reached a stable rate of responding. His toposcopic records showed no focal activity at any time.

The two other subjects both showed focal activity identical to that found in the one-tone problem, beginning with the first indication of response to a tone. The focal activity persisted somewhat longer in this case than it had in the one-tone problem. It did not disappear until the discrimination between the two tones appeared complete. There was no apparent difference in toposcopic activity between the animal for which the high tone was positive and the one for which the low tone was positive.

When the discrimination was well established, reversing the significance of the two tones caused an immediate reappearance of the focal activity.

In addition to the focus over the parieto-occipital sulcus, a new pattern of focal activity appeared in frontal cortex during this learning problem. This activity consisted of three foci as shown in Figure 37. The spatial and temporal characteristics of the toposcopic activity within these foci appeared identical to that of the parieto-occipital focus. The frontal foci, however, appeared later in the learning process, apparently correlating with the development of the discrimination between the two tones. The frontal foci were bilaterally symmetrical in those animals having bilateral electrode arrays.

Similar auditory discrimination problems were learned at other times by two Cebus monkeys with identical results, except that

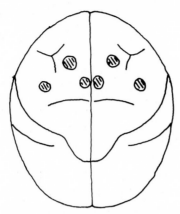

FIGURE 37. Location of focal activity found on the frontal lobe during discrimination reversal and during simultaneous light-tone problem.

the bilaterality of the frontal foci could not be confirmed, as the Cebus electrode arrays are unilateral.

ONE-LIGHT, ONE-STRING PROBLEM

In this version of the basic one-string problem, the cue was an incandescent bulb mounted in the panel facing the monkey. The bulb was usually mounted 1 or 2 inches above the hole from which the string hung, but the location of the bulb proved unimportant as long as it was prominent. A 6 to 12 V indicator style lamp was used, sometimes mounted directly into the panel, sometimes in a commercial indicator lamp housing with a clear envelope. In these experiments, the relationship between cue light and reinforcement was positive, that is, string pulling was reinforced when the light was on.

The monkeys learned this visual problem almost as well as the one-tone problem. The only essential difference was that the animal would sometimes fail to see a stimulus if it occurred while he was twisted around in the chair, studying some of the apparatus behind him.

The earliest indications of learning in this situation were similar to those in the auditory problems. Another indication which sometimes appeared was a pawing of the light bulb in between trials. This seemed to correlate well with other indices of learning, such

FIGURE 38. Location of the learning focus during operant conditioning to a visual cue.

as orienting toward the light, short latency responses, and reaching for a grape at light onset.

Three Cebus and two squirrel monkeys have completed this simple visual problem. Each one displayed focal activity in a portion of the parietal lobe adjacent to the sylvian fissure (see Fig. 38). The distinguishing characteristics of this activity are exactly the same as those of the focal activity over the parieto-occipital sulcus found with the one-tone problem. It appears during or immediately preceding the experimental session in which the first signs of learning are observed. The focal activity strengthens for one or two sessions and then fades as the instrumental response becomes well established.

TWO-LIGHT, TWO-LEVER PROBLEM

This particular paradigm was used with only one Cebus monkey. The situation is similar to the one-light problem described above, except that two lights are used, about 8 cm to each side of center. A plastic knob, about 1 cm diameter, protrudes from the panel directly beneath each light. These levers can be withdrawn between trials.

On each trial the levers are presented to the monkey, and one of the two lights is turned on. If the monkey moves the lever under that light, he receives a grape. The other lever is inactive. A trial lasts for ten seconds, or until a correct response is made. Incorrect responses are not punished. On each trial, the first lever moved is noted. Two toposcopic records were taken during each session of ten trials.

The animal learned this problem in four sessions. His toposcopic data showed focal activity identical to that found in the one-light, one-string problem. No frontal foci were found.

In comparing this paradigm with the two-tone problem described above, it must be borne in mind that both lights in this problem were positive stimuli, whereas in the two-tone problem, one of the tones was a neutral stimulus. Both problems require discrimination of two stimuli, but the two-tone problem, for efficient solution, requires suppression of the response to one of the stimuli, while the two-light problem does not require that a response be suppressed.

SIMULTANEOUS LIGHT-TONE PROBLEM

This paradigm proved particularly interesting. For efficient solution, it requires that auditory and visual information be correlated. Data have been obtained from three Cebus and one squirrel monkey.

The apparatus used is the basic one-string apparatus, exactly as in the one-light, one-string problem. In this paradigm, however, tone is also used, the contingencies being that string pulling is reinforced when both tone and light are on simultaneously, but not during either tone or light alone.

A daily session consisted of ten trials with simultaneous light and tone, each such trial lasting ten seconds or until a response was made. Interspersed with these were five trials with light alone, and five with tone alone, each of these trials lasting five seconds. The intertrial interval was varied between thirty and sixty seconds. The sequence of stimuli was randomized within the stated restrictions.

Each of the monkeys used in this experiment had previously completed either the one-light problem, the one-tone problem, or both. Every animal thus started the problem by responding consistently to either the light or the tone, depending on his most recent previous experience. The learning in this case consisted largely of suppressing the response to his preferred stimulus whenever it was not paired with the other.

Every animal displayed focal activity in the frontal lobe prior to or coincident with the first signs of learning. In addition, every animal showed focal activity either near the parieto-occipital cortex or on the anterior lip of the sylvian fissure, depending on whether his most recent previous experience had been with the light or the tone. Specifically, Cebus 5, who had previously completed only auditory problems, developed focal activity adjacent to the sylvian fissure ("visual" focus) during the first session on the simultaneous light-tone problem. Cebus 13, who had completed the one-tone problem immediately prior to the simultaneous light-tone problem, and who had finished the one-light problem seventeen days previously, similarly showed "visual" focal activity during the first session of the simultaneous problem.

Cebus 9, on the other hand, had completed the one-light problem immediately prior to this problem, and had finished the one-tone problem seventy-one days previously. He displayed focal activity over the parieto-occipital sulcus ("auditory" focus) in session three of the simultaneous light-tone problem. Similarly, squirrel monkey 10 had completed the one-light problem immediately prior to this, and the one-tone problem twenty-five days previously. He showed an "auditory" focus in session one.

The focal activity recorded in the region of the parieto-occipital sulcus and on the anterior lip of the sylvian fissure in this experiment appeared to be identical with that found previously in the simple auditory and visual problems. The frontal foci were somewhat more variable. In the two-tone, one-string problem described above, three foci were found in the frontal lobe, as shown in Figure 37. In this experiment the focus just medial to the arcuate sulcus was always seen, but the two foci in architectonic area 6 were found only in Cebus 5 and squirrel monkey 10. These facts do not suggest any correlation with genus or with sensory modality.

SUMMARY: OPERANT CONDITIONING

The results of these simple auditory and visual problems seem to form a coherent picture. They are summarized in Table I.

It may be seen that in every case where the cue, or the novel aspect of the cue is auditory, focal activity appears over the parieto-occipital sulcus. In every case where the cue, or the novel aspect of the cue is visual, focal activity appears on the anterior lip of the sylvian fissure. In every case requiring suppression of an inefficient response, focal activity appears in the frontal lobe

TABLE I

Learning Paradigm	Recent Previous Experience	Location of Focal Activity
One-tone	none	parieto-occipital
Two-tone (one neutral)	one-tone	parieto-occipital and frontal
One-light	none	anterior lip of sylvian fissure
Two-light (both positive)	one-light	anterior lip of sylvian fissure
Light-tone	light	parieto-occipital and frontal
Light-tone	tone	anterior lip of sylvian fissure and frontal

just medial to the arcuate sulcus, and sometimes in architectonic area 6 as well.

This focal activity always appears coincident with or immediately preceding the earliest observable signs of the corresponding learning.

HYPOTHESIS PROBLEM

The hypothesis problem is much more complex than the simple operant problems described above. It is close to the upper level of ability for the Cebus monkey.

The apparatus and technique are described in some detail in Chapter III. Briefly, the monkey is presented with four handles differing in position, color, and shape. When the correct handle is moved, he is rewarded with a grape. His main task is to determine the definition of correct, whether it is a particular position, color, or shape.

The solution to this problem normally requires several weeks. Only two Cebus monkeys in this series successfully completed hypothesis problems. One of these was given a second hypothesis problem, with a different definition of correct. He was unable to solve it, and it was discontinued after 440 trials.

The toposcopic data from these animals was consistent with the tendencies found in the simpler operant conditioning problems, as summarized in Table I. Cebus 5 in his first problem, for which the correct response was a cylinder, showed many foci of short duration and shifting locations. Focal activity was prominent in the frontal lobe, medial to the arcuate sulcus, until the correct response was quite well established. After completing this first problem, Cebus 5 was given another hypothesis problem, in which the correct response was yellow. A particularly strong focus appeared medial to the arcuate sulcus and in the lateral portion of area 6 in the first session of this problem, fading out by session three.

Cebus 13 was trained on the hypothesis problem with cylinder as the correct response. Presumably by chance, the first hypothesis he adopted was cylinder, so that he solved the problem in twenty trials. For him, therefore, the complexities of the problem were irrelevant, and it was essentially a simple, visual, operant conditioning problem. His toposcopic data showed only a focus on the anterior lip of the sylvian fissure in session one.

BLACK-WHITE DISCRIMINATION: CATS

In order to acquire comparative data on the toposcopic appearance of cortical activity during learning, two cats (cats 6 and 7) were prepared for chronic toposcopic recording. In deference to their relatively simple mentality, a black-white discrimination problem was chosen. It was described in Chapter III. Briefly, the cat had to learn to knock the cover from one of two food cups in order to obtain two or three grams of tuna fish. The reward was always under the white cover.

The cats' performance remained at chance level for ten sessions (100 trials), then climbed slowly toward an asymptote of 90 percent correct. Both cats learned at the same rate. In the toposcopic records, both cats displayed focal activity straddling the anterior leg of the suprasylvian sulcus and in the anterior portion of striate cortex on the session just preceding the upturn in the learning curve and for three or four sessions thereafter (see Fig. 39).

Another cat (cat 2) also completed the black-white discrimination problem. Unfortunately, the electrode array in this cat stopped on the edge of the area showing focal activity in cats 6 and 7. On the session during which the discrimination appeared, cat 2 displayed what is probably the edge of a focus on the anterior limb of the suprasylvian sulcus, but the pattern is too fragmentary to interpret with confidence.

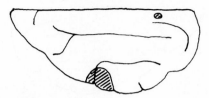

FIGURE 39. Location of learning foci in cats during black-white discrimination.

Cat 2 is interesting for another reason, however. On sessions nine through thirteen, she showed a strong position preference. Her toposcopic data show weak focal activity over the genu of the suprasylvian gyrus during the first seven sessions. Toward the end of session eight, this focal activity strengthened and broadened to straddle the suprasylvian sulcus. This area is adjacent to that showing focal activity in cats 6 and 7.

DELAYED RESPONSE: CATS

The primary purpose of investigating a delayed response problem was to examine the activity of the brain during an interval in which the animal was required to remember a particular relationship. The only data thus far have been obtained from cats. Although similar paradigms have been attempted with monkeys, the New World primates I have been using are too easily frustrated to tolerate a delay in responding.

The apparatus used was the same as that for the black-white discrimination problem, except that both food-cup covers were painted white. The cup was baited and covered in clear view of the cat, then moved within reach after a three-second delay. The experimenter operated a foot switch which controlled an indicator light on the toposcope output panel in order to demarcate the three-second delay period on the toposcopic data.

Of six cats completing this experiment, all but one showed focal activity on the anterior limb of the ectosylvian gyrus. The one exception, cat 3, had electrodes on only part of the gyrus. There is a statistical tendency for responses to the right cup to be associated with a more anterior locus of focal activity, and responses to the left cup to be associated with a more posterior locus (Fig. 40).

This tendency does not reach statistical significance. If all trials are analysed, each cat shows about 65 percent of his "right"

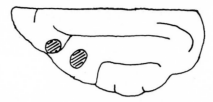

FIGURE 40. Location of focal activity during the delay period of a left-right delayed response. The anterior locus is associated with response to the right cup, the posterior locus with response to the left cup.

responses associated with the anterior locus, and a similar percentage of his "left" responses with the posterior locus. If we confine the analysis to those responses which were correct, the percentage association goes up to about 75 percent.

In all the previous learning paradigms, the association between a particular behavioral index and the cortical location of focal activity has been essentially perfect. The difficulty here seems to be that, whereas there exist reliable, observable indices of the state of learning, there is no certain index of the contents of an animal's immediate memory. We infer from a response to the left-hand cup that the animal was remembering that the food was in that cup. It is also possible, however, that the animal remembered the food as being in the right hand cup until near the end of the delay period when he became confused and made simply a random response.

Although the relationship between cortical location of the focal activity and the content of the cat's memory is not as clear and certain as could be desired, one very significant aspect of these data is certain: the focal activity recorded in this situation does not disappear when learning is complete. In every previous paradigm, the focal activity faded before the learning had reached its asymptote. In this case, the activity is still strong in animals whose behavior is well practiced.

This paradigm is distinguished from all the previous learning situations by the fact that an active recall is required on every trial. In previous situations the response could become automatic, since a particular cue was invariably associated with the correct response. In the delayed-response paradigm there is no distinctive cue to the correct response outside the animal's memory.

Chapter V

D. C. TOPOSCOPY: RESULTS

The results of the d.c. toposcopic recording described in this chapter are central to the main theme of this book. At the conclusion of the a.c. toposcopic recordings described in the last chapter, I was in the position of knowing a good deal about the psychological parameters of the focal activity found but not understanding the activity itself. My original purpose in starting this research program was to understand the brain mechanisms underlying learning. The a.c. toposcope disclosed a symptom of some cortical mechanism which was clearly important to the learning process but gave little clue as to what the mechanism itself really was. It was in hope of learning more about the alteration in cortical activity which I have termed a *focus*, that I decided to try recording the d.c. contours of the cortical surface in a monkey undergoing training. The task proved unusually difficult.

Most of the trials and tribulations of the search for valid d.c. potential recordings from a chronic preparation were described in Chapters II and III. Briefly, it proved necessary to use pure silver electrodes over an intact cranium, left in place for at least thirty days before recording was begun, with all electrodes connected to a common point through a fixed load resistance. Furthermore, it was found essential to keep the animal infection-free during that thirty-day period as well as during the experimental training itself. Because of this extreme sensitivity of the technique to infection, as well as the usual apparatus breakdowns and difficulties in adapting wild monkeys to a learning situation, very few reliable data have been collected. By themselves, these data would not be convincing. Since they confirm in almost every respect the predictions derived from the previous a.c. data, however, and are further supported by the results of nickel electrode recording and selected cortical ablations, these few data form a critical part of a reasonably complete picture. They show that the focal activity found with the a.c. toposcope is accompanied by persistent peaks in the d.c. potential contours, and are thus almost certainly related to the "dominant focus," as described by many scientists, mostly in Russia.

The majority of the data presented in this chapter were collected from three *Cebus albifrons*, numbers 24, 26, and 35. Cebus 24 (Sugar) was a female, about two years old at the time she was used. She was unusually placid for a Cebus, extremely affectionate, and very healthy until her untimely death.* Cebus 26 (Spice) is male, very intelligent, affectionate in a boisterous sort of way, now two and one-half years old and still in use. Both these monkeys were purchased as infants and raised by hand. This is a tedious but effective method of overcoming the problems of adaptation to the experimental situation. Cebus 35 (Missy) is an adolescent female, purchased fully grown, and still moderately hard to handle.

The learning situations used with these preparations consisted of the one-tone, one-string problem, the one-light, one-string problem, the simultaneous light-tone problem, and the hypothesis problem. Because of several experimental difficulties (ordinary mortals make mistakes; scientists have "experimental difficulties"), good data were obtained for the one-tone problem only from Cebus 35. The early death of Cebus 24 and the relatively intractable nature of Cebus 35 made it impossible to obtain data from them on the hypothesis problem. Only the visual problem and the simultaneous light-tone problem, therefore, were studied in more than one animal.

The existence of the postulated d.c. shift over the learning-specific response areas of cortex had already been demonstrated with nickel electrodes in several Cebus and squirrel monkeys before these records from silver electrodes were obtained. The pur-

*Cebus 24 was found dead in her cage the morning of June 19, 1967, with one end of her leash tied firmly to the top of her cage, the other knotted around her throat. This is the only animal that succeeded in choking on its own leash without assistance. No suicide note was found.

pose of this experiment, therefore, was not to determine whether or not the phenomenon existed, but to obtain clean records of such a d.c. shift during learning without the obscuring influence of the nickel potentials. I therefore considered that obtaining one such set of "typical" data for each type of learning situation was adequate, although replication would obviously be desirable.

SURGERY

The technique for the implantation of forty-eight electrodes has already been described (see Chap. III). For d.c. recording, the electrodes are made of pure silver wire, 1 mm in diameter, implanted extracranially in a plastic matrix. It is particularly important in this case to seal the array firmly to the skull in order to minimize the possibility of infection. For this reason, a fairly wide margin of plastic must be left around the outside of the electrode array. This fact makes it essentially impossible to get good, bilateral coverage of the more lateral portions of the cortex.

Since the presence of infection under the implant is disasterous to this recording, I watched the preparations carefully for any such symptoms. The plastic of which the implant is constructed is transparent, so that it is possible to see the surface of the cranium through the array. At the first sign of infection, I administered penicillin in the animal's drinking water.*

The location of the electrodes relative to cortical landmarks was estimated at the time of implantation and then determined more accurately when the implant was removed. After such an array has been removed, very small lesions may be seen in the scar tissue which has formed under it. The animal is placed in a stereotaxic instrument, and the horizontal coordinates of several such lesions determined. These are then used to construct a map of the entire array of forty-eight electrodes, plotted in stereotaxic coordinates. This map is then superimposed on a similarly determined stereotaxic map of the principal sulci.

Since Cebus 26 and 35 were both kept alive at the end of the experiment (we are pleased to announce that they are expecting a baby shortly), it was necessary to use a cortical map constructed from autopsy data on another Cebus monkey, female, of the same

*Lilly: V-Cillin K, Pediatric; 5 cc (200,000 units) per pint of water ad lib.

age and weight. There are strong indications that this caused a significant error in registration in the case of Cebus 35.

The nature of the artifact caused by infection is a rather interesting problem. An active site of infection appears as an electrically negative region, frequently reaching potentials of —50 mV. When such an infection is cured with antibiotics, an area of positive potential may remain as a permanent feature. Cebus 35 had such a permanent artifact under three electrodes on the left temporal region. Fortunately, it was not extensive, nor was it in a particularly critical location. The region remained about 10 mV positive to the average reference value throughout her three months of experimental use. (These electrodes were ignored in drawing the maps shown in figures below.)

The artifact is not due to a chemical change in the electrodes themselves, since an array removed from such an animal and filled with Ringer's solution drops toward zero potential difference in a few hours. The permanent d.c. potential may be related to the erosion of the skull which is invariably found under such an infected site. If so, it is probably closely related to the postmortem "ghost" potentials described in Chapter II, which were found whenever d.c. electrodes were inserted in holes drilled in the skull.

RECORDING

The forty-eight silver electrodes were connected, by means of a very flexible probe cable, to an averaging circuit consisting of forty-eight 2.2 Mohm resistors, one from each input lead to a common point. The average potential thus obtained was used as the reference voltage.

The forty-eight signals were then multiplexed by the commutator shown in Figure 21 into the input of a Bausch and Lomb V.O.M. 5 chart recorder. The recorder was normally set at a full scale sensitivity of 10 mV. Occasionally it was necessary to take a second record on the 100 mV scale in order to include extreme peaks.

The histogram of forty-eight voltages recorded by the chart recorder was then used to construct a numerical record of the potentials arranged in a spatial array corresponding to the electrode array (see Fig. 22). Contour maps were drawn from these data sheets with contour spacing at 1.0 mV intervals.

BEHAVIORAL DATA

The learning situations and apparatus used were described in Chapter III. In the one-string problems, the animal was rewarded with a grape for pulling a string whenever the cue stimulus or stimulus combination was present. The string was always available, false responses were not punished. The auditory cue used in this series of experiments was a 700-cycle tone generated by a homemade oscillator driving a homemade audio amplifier and four-inch speaker. Any resemblance to a pure sine wave tone was accidental. Previous work has shown, however, that the nature of the auditory stimulus does not affect the location of the auditory learning focus. The visual cue was a 6 V incandescent bulb (No. 46) mounted in a standard indicator lamp housing with a clear lens. The light was located 3 cm above the top of the string, about at eye level for a Cebus monkey, 10 cm left of the center of the panel. The grape rewards (usually red Emperor grapes, but other varieties were occasionally used) were delivered into a cup directly in front of the animal.

Restraint was minimal (see Fig. 31). Cebus 24 was always quiet and ladylike in the apparatus, Cebus 35 was quite active, particularly fond of twisting around to examine the parts of the apparatus behind her, and Cebus 26 managed to perform incredible acrobatic feats within the limitations of the harness and recording probe, usually without missing a response. When using the visual cue, it was necessary to watch the monkey through a mirror system, and time the trial so that the animal was facing the panel when the light came on.

A learning session consisted of ten presentations of the positive stimulus. In the case of the simultaneous light-tone problem, five trials of light alone and five trials of tone alone were randomly intermixed with the ten light-tone trials. The intertrial interval was varied according to the speed with which the grapes were consumed. With Cebus 24, the interval was typically around sixty seconds, because she was a very dainty eater. Cebus 26 usually received a trial every twenty-five seconds, Cebus 35 about every forty-five seconds. The cue remained on for ten seconds, or until a response occurred, whichever was shorter.

The frequency of false responses was noted on a semiquantitative scale (many, some, few, or none), the latency of each response from cue onset recorded electronically, and my subjective judgement as to whether or not a response was "intentional" or merely a random yank was noted.

With Cebus 24 the frequency of false responses seemed to be a good index of learning. With Cebus 35, a combination of latencies and subjective judgement seemed better; her false responses remained high throughout. With Cebus 26, only the subjective judgement indicated any learning. He typically pulled the string at a furious rate until he became interested in something else, when he refused to respond even to the cue. When the cue stimulus came on, however, if he felt like responding at all, he would reach for the grape cup at the same time as, or even slightly before, he grasped the string. I took this as an indication that he knew what he was doing.

RESULTS
One-tone, One-string Problem

Data on this problem were obtained only from Cebus 35. Since she is still alive, the location of her electrodes relative to cortical landmarks is not known with certainty. The locations shown in the figures were estimated from a stereotaxic map drawn from another Cebus brain. There is very strong and consistent evidence that her electrodes were actually farther posterior (or the principal sulci farther anterior) than the figures show.

The d.c. contours during the first six sessions of the one-tone, one-string problem are shown in Figure 41. Her behavioral data indicate that she may have started to learn the contingency during session two, and had clearly learned it by session four. The most interesting features of her d.c. potential contours during this period are the 6 mV positive peak in front of the left parieto-occipital sulcus during sessions two and three, the 4 mV positive peak just posterior to the genu of the left arcuate sulcus during the same two sessions, and the striking, 8 mV positive peak anterior to the medial end of the sylvian fissure on the fifth and sixth sessions when

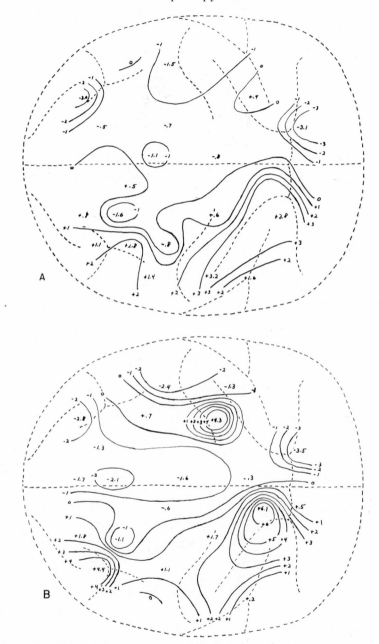

FIGURE 41. D.c. contours recorded from Cebus 35 during operant conditioning to an auditory cue. Records are at 24-hour intervals except for a 72-hour

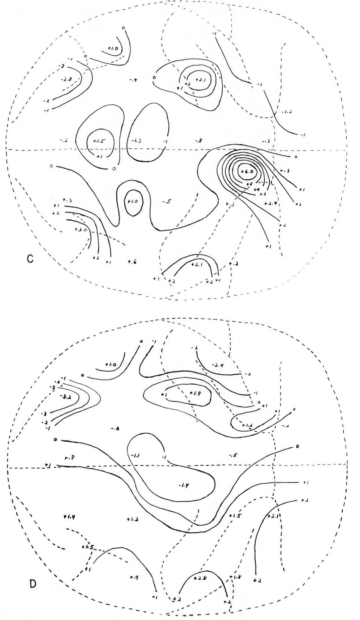

lapse between *D* and *E*. The distinctive auditory learning focus appears over the left posterior parietal lobe in *B* and *C*.

Since this animal is still living, the electrode locations are estimated. I sus-

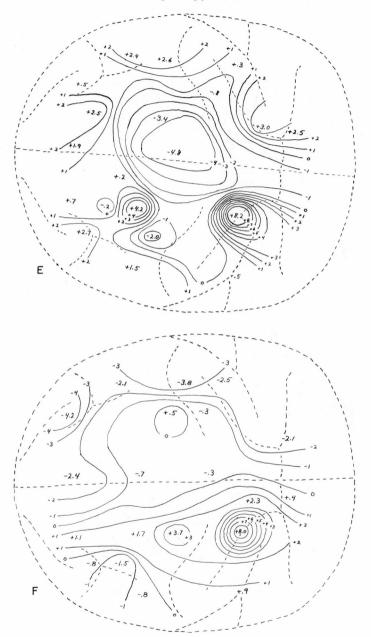

pect the locations shown are a bit too far forward. The auditory learning focus normally straddles the parieto-occipital sulcus.

learning was complete. In addition to these, transitory peaks and valleys may be seen in every portion of the left hemisphere and in parts of the right hemisphere.

One-light, One-string Problem

Good data on this problem are available from Cebus 26 and 35. The electrode array on Cebus 24 did not extend far enough laterally to cover the visual learning area. Contours from Cebus 26 for the first five sessions of this problem are shown in Figure 42. His behavioral data show the first indication of learning on the fourth session and very clear learning by session five. Again we can see dual foci on the left hemisphere, one over the visual learning area with a maximum potential of +11.8 mV, and another peak of about one-half that voltage medial and anterior to the left arcuate sulcus. Although the contours for the sixth session are not shown

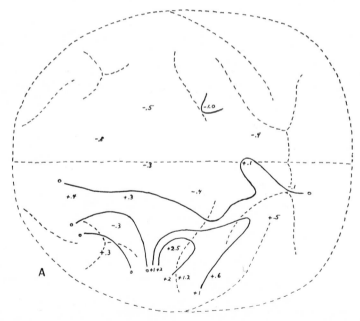

Figure 42. D.c. contours recorded from Cebus 26 during operant conditioning to a visual cue. Records are at 24-hour intervals. The distinctive visual learning focus appears over lateral left parietal lobe in *C*, *D*, and *E*.

Since this animal is still living, the electrode locations are estimated. The location of the focus agrees well with other data, however.

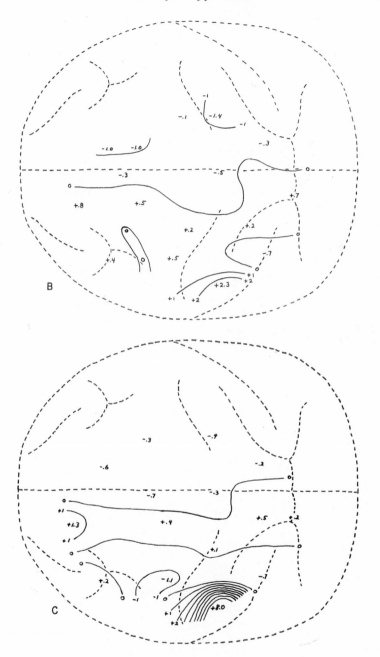

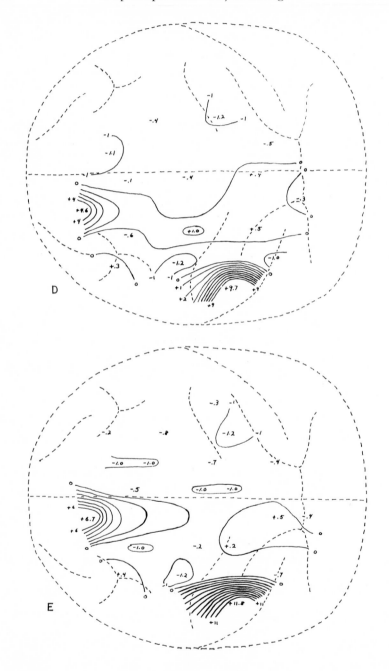

(they had some artifact in them), these two foci were definitely absent, and there was a suggestion of a positive shift over the medial end of the left sylvian fissure. These data are notable for the absence of other features. It is unusual to find contours as "flat" as these.

Cebus 24 completed the negative light, one-string problem (the cue is the offset of the light, which is normally on) and the bright light, one-string problem (light normally on at about ½ brightness, the cue is a change to full brightness). Although her electrodes did not cover the visual learning area, her contours showed a sharp positive peak over the medial end of the sylvian fissure following completion of the learning on each of these problems. Her data also confirm the presence of a positive peak medial to the arcuate sulcus during the early sessions of visual learning.

Cebus 35 also confirmed the positive peak over the visual learning area (maximum about 10 mV) and medial to the arcuate sulcus (maximum 9 mV). The positive shift near the medial end of the sylvian fissure, however, appeared simultaneously with the other two foci, and disappeared at the same rate. In her case, the foci appeared primarily on the right hemisphere, although there were weak positive foci symmetrically opposite them.

Simultaneous Light-tone Problem

The significant feature of the simultaneous light-tone problem is that for efficient performance the animal must learn not to pull the string to either the light or tone cues alone, but only to the simultaneous occurrence of the two. The reader may recall that in the a.c. toposcopic experiments a learning focus was found in the frontal lobe, medial to the arcuate sulcus, during this type of learning. The present d.c. data confirm this finding by showing a positive peak in the same area during the early stages of learning. They also add some interesting details to the picture, which could not be seen in the a.c. data.

The d.c. contours from Cebus 26 on this learning problem were fairly simple. In Figure 43 are shown the patterns from the fourth, tenth and fourteenth sessions. It is not possible to establish precise correlations with the progress of learning because performance in this situation is largely a matter of response inhibition, and Cebus

26 is a very uninhibited monkey. Even after learning was obviously quite complete by subjective indices, he continued to pull the string vigorously throughout the session, during neutral stimuli, positive stimuli, and no stimuli.

On session four, he began to show some differential response to tone, as compared with light or simultaneous light-tone. At this time his d.c. contours showed a weak positive peak in the right prefrontal region, somewhat more medial and posterior than the predicted location. This focus then disappeared, as did all behavioral signs of discrimination among stimuli. On sessions nine and ten, he began to show fairly clear differential responses. He responded vigorously to the combination stimulus, less so to the light, and either weakly or not at all to the tone. At this point his d.c. contours developed a weak positive peak in the left frontal region, just medial and posterior to the arcuate sulcus and extending back onto motor cortex. The anterior end of this positive re-

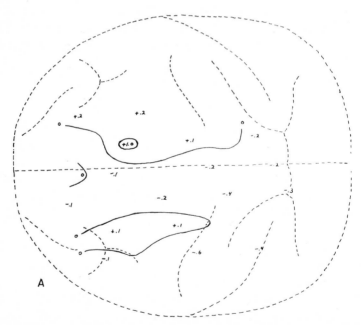

FIGURE 43. D.c. contours recorded from Cebus 26 during the simultaneous light-tone problem. The records shown are from the *(A)* fourth, *(B)* tenth, and *(C)* fourteenth sessions. The frontal focus seen in C is fairly typical of the patterns found in situations requiring response inhibition.

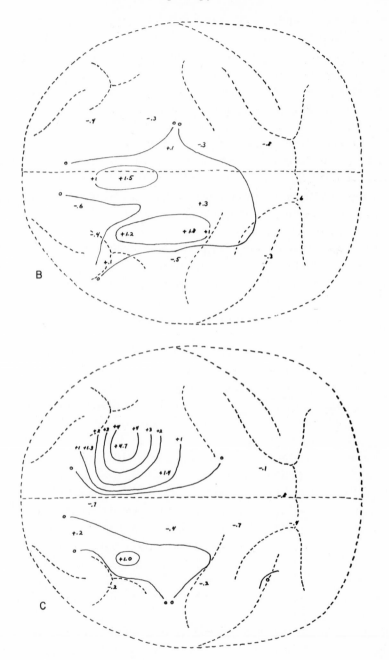

gion was very close to the predicted locus for the learning focus, but the extension onto motor cortex was unexpected. This positive peak was accompanied by a second weak focus over the midsagittal fissure. This may have been fortuitous. Cebus 35 showed a similar peak over the midsagittal fissure, but I have also found the same focus appearing in other, apparently unrelated situations. (More about this midsagittal focus below.)

By session fourteen learning was progressing well, and the d.c. pattern had become almost exactly what was predicted on the basis of the previous a.c. data. The learning focus had shifted to the right hemisphere, increased to 4.7 mV, and was in exactly the predicted location. A weak focus appeared in the corresponding area of the left hemisphere.

Figure 44 presents the d.c. patterns from Cebus 35 during the first six sessions of the simultaneous light-tone problem. The activity is obviously much more complex than that found in Cebus 26. The major features of Cebus 26 data, however, are also found in Cebus 35. In the second session, positive foci may be seen over the midsagittal fissure, and from the left arcuate region back to motor cortex. By session six the pattern has simplified to roughly symmetrical foci just medial to the arcuate sulci.

The most interesting feature of Cebus 35 data, however, is the appearance, in sessions one and two, of an auditory learning focus on the right hemisphere, followed, in sessions two and three, by a visual learning focus on the same side. (I am assuming her sulci anterior to their indicated locations.) It is also interesting to note, in sessions four, five, and six, the appearance of a focus over the medial end of the right sylvian fissure. This appears to be a rather common feature of the late stages of various learning problems. The strong positive peak over the left central sulcus in session five, which grew from the posterior end of the original learning focus, and then, in session six weakened, broadened, and moved back onto parietal cortex, is interesting but not interpretable.

Cebus 35 learned this problem considerably faster than did Cebus 26. This was not due to superior intelligence, which appears about equal for the two animals, but to much greater concentration on the problem. Cebus 26 seldom concentrates on anything, but he was being particularly difficult during this problem.

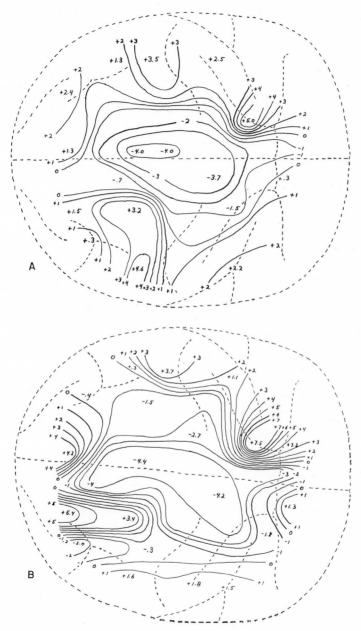

FIGURE 44. D.c. contours recorded from Cebus 35 during the simultaneous light-tone problem. Compare with FIGURE 43 from Cebus 26 on the same problem. Although the early patterns are much more complex, the foci in *F*

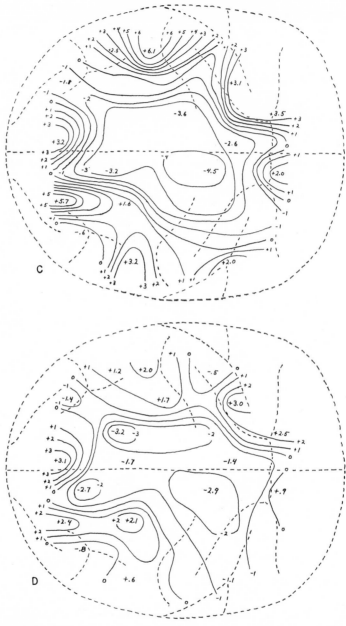

are essentially identical to that seen in 43C, except that they are bilaterally symmetrical.

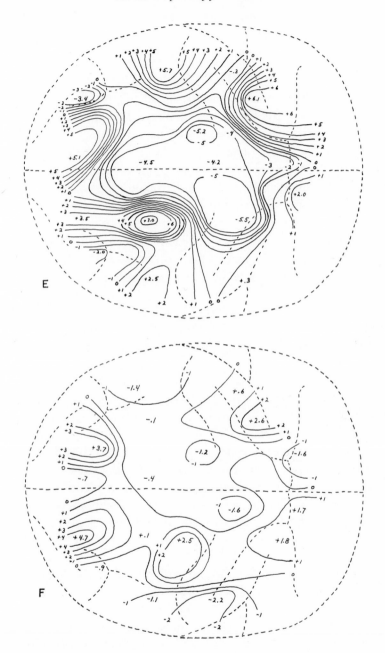

Whether or not this difference in approach to the situation is in any way related to the obvious difference in the steepness of their d.c. gradients is a question for future research.

HYPOTHESIS PROBLEM

The hypothesis problem was designed to provide a more complex learning task for the Cebus monkey. The apparatus and procedure were described in detail in Chapter III.

The monkey faced a panel with a large opening through which the manipulanda could be presented, with a cup for the grape reward. The manipulanda consisted of four upright handles, of four distinctive (to me) shapes and four colors, black, white, blue, and yellow. They were mounted across the front (from the monkey's viewpoint) edge of an 8-inch wide board. The handles were spaced about 1¾ inches apart on centers. When the correct handle was moved slightly in any direction, a chime sounded and the board was withdrawn, leaving a grape in the cup.

The color and shape of the handles were randomized independently, with the restriction that each array include one handle of each of the four colors and of each of the four shapes. The monkey had no clue available to whether the correct handle was defined by its color, shape, or position in the array.

Behavioral data consisted simply of noting, on each trial, which handle was moved first. This initial response was then tallied on a data sheet in three locations, according to its shape, color, and position (see Fig. 45). If the animal responded consistently to a particular dimension for several trials, this was assumed to indicate hypothesis behavior. Naturally, such a series of identical responses could occur by chance, and conversely, an hypothesis could be tested and rejected in a single trial, so that there is no certain way of determining what hypotheses, if any, the monkey was actually using.

Certain facts, however, may be rather confidently deduced. Cebus 26 is the only animal with silver electrodes thus far tested on the hypothesis problem. He completed three such problems, the first with black as the correct stimulus parameter, the second with the T shape correct, the third with position three (second from his left) always correct. His data clearly indicate the formation and

```
               Sess. 1           2              3             4
1 (right)        X    XXX     XXXXX          X      X     XXXX XXXX
2              X X         X       X X       X X       X    X
3                X                         X X   X
4 (left)       X X   X       X         X       X       XX

black            X  X  X    X X     X       X XX       X      X
white              X  X    X    X           X      X      X     XX
blue               X         XXX  XX    XX      XXX     X    XX X
yellow         XX X    X                                   X

cylinder         X  X             X    X   X X  X    X  XX    X
"T"                     X           X      X       X           X X
sphere         XXXX   X         XX           X X X     X         X
triangle         X X      X XXXX  X      X                 XX


                5               6             7             8
1 (right)      XXXXXXXX     X  XX   XXX        XX  X     X X XX X
2                          XX            X XX       X      X   X X
3            X                    XX             XX     X X
4 (left)                          X  X

black            XX X   X   XX      XXXXX    X XXXX XX   XX X     XX
white        X    X XX                           X
blue                  X          X           X X          X  XXX
yellow       X                   XX                       X

cylinder     XX       X X            XX      XXX   XXXX   X XX    X
"T"             X XX        X     X XX        X       X   X  XX  X
sphere       X        XX        X   X                          X  X
triangle       X X         X X                   X           X   X


                9              10            11
1 (right)    X      X X          XX      X  XXX
2              XX     XX      XXX   X     X      X X
3               X X         X      X               X
4 (left)     X               X          X     X  X

black        XXXXX X X     XXX    XXXX   XXXXX   XXX
white                 X
blue                 X       XXX                 XX
yellow              X

cylinder     XX    X X  X    X  XX     X     XX
"T"          X    XX        XX          X  X
sphere                   X    X
triangle       XX   X       X  X     X  XX    XX
```

FIGURE 45. Behavioral data recorded from Cebus 26 during his first hypothesis problem. Correct response was black. Note the sequences of position one
responses in sessions four and five, shifting to black responses in session six.

testing of hypotheses, even though we cannot always know what hypothesis he was using.

In his first hypothesis problem (black correct), the random arrays happened to include a yellow sphere on seven of the ten trials. He chose this handle the first three times it appeared (trials 1, 2, 4) and a black sphere on the intervening trial (3). On trial five he avoided the yellow sphere, choosing a blue triangle instead. The yellow sphere appeared again on trial eight when he chose it, and on trials nine and ten when he avoided it. At this point, I could not be sure whether he had been testing a yellow hypothesis, sphere hypothesis, or simply making random responses. The data show, however (Fig. 45), that he consistently avoided yellow for the next two sessions, and averaged less than one yellow response per session for the remainder of the problem, even though his responses to white or to the sphere were at about a chance level.

During sessions two and three his black responses were apparently at a chance level, but his blue responses were somewhat above chance. From observing his behavior, it appeared quite clear that he was deliberately choosing a handle, not simply responding randomly. It also appeared probable that he did not clearly discriminate blue from black. If so, then he may well have become frustrated by the apparent inconsistency of reinforcement. In session four and five his behavior indicated that he had given up trying to solve the problem, and adopted a fairly stereotyped response pattern, from position one to four. He solved the problem rather abruptly on session six. He continued to make errors, sometimes because of confusing blue with black, sometimes because of a preference for either the cylindrical or T-shaped handles, which were taller than the other two and therefore easier to grasp and move, and sometimes, especially from session nine onward, out of boredom: he would reach for a handle without looking.

This description of his behavior, of course, is quite anthropomorphic. When the monkey looks at all four handles carefully, starts to reach for one, then stops, looks at them all again, and then finally grasps a handle and pulls it firmly, I conclude that he is doing something which is most accurately described as "thinking." If anthropomorphic terms are the best in which to describe a monkey's behavior, it may be because monkeys are, indeed, "anthropomorphic."

During this learning problem his d.c. contours underwent rather complex changes (Fig. 46). During session one the contours were remarkably flat, with a total range of less than 1 mV. At the beginning of the second session, however, a weak focus had appeared medial to the right arcuate sulcus, with an interesting negative trough over the left visual learning area. By the end of this session, however (a time period of about 15 minutes), both of these features had disappeared, to be replaced by a single weak focus on the left frontal lobe, medial and anterior to the arcuate sulcus. This great a change during an experimental session is very unusual.

On the following day, session three, the pattern was again quite different, although this one remained fairly stable throughout the recording session. The pattern consisted only of a broad, shallow positivity over the anterior portion of the midsagittal fissure.

I have come to call this midline focus the "what the ——" response. It seems to appear in situations where the animal is confused or surprised by the contingencies. I think it is probably important, but I do not really understand it yet. No doubt my own d.c. contours would show a similar peak as I consider this phenomenon.

On session four, the central peak had disappeared, and a negative focus or trough could be seen just anterior to its former location. In addition, a moderately strong positive focus had appeared just medial to the left arcuate sulcus. This pattern remained fairly constant throughout the session. On this day, in order to find out what this brain was doing when I was not watching, I moved my recording apparatus to the animal room and made another recording two and one-half hours after the learning session. The basic pattern was still present, which is what I primarily wanted to know, but two features, probably unrelated to the learning situation, had appeared: a small positive focus on the right prefrontal region, and a negative trough over the right motor cortex. These may have been related to some learning problem which the monkey had undertaken on his own. A more detailed all-day recording session is described separately below.

Cebus 26 final assault on this problem, is sessions six, seven and

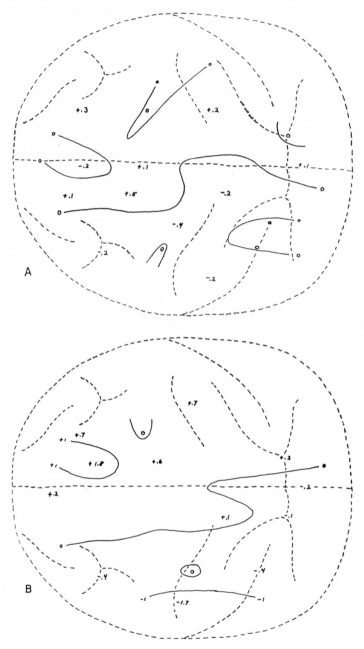

FIGURE 46. Contours recorded from Cebus 26 during the first hypothesis problem. Note the "suppressor" focus over left frontal lobe in *E* and *F*.

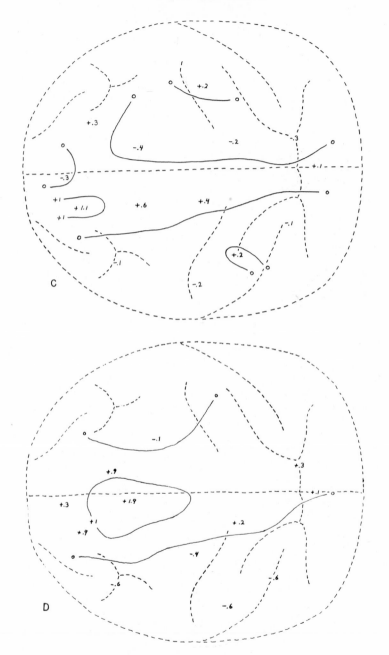

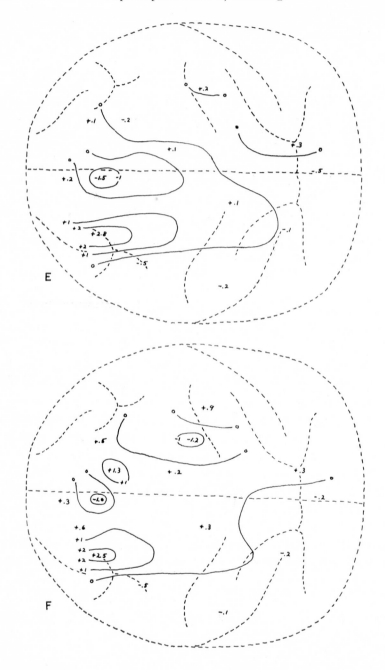

eight, yielded d.c. contours basically similar, although of lower voltage, to those found during the one-light, one-string problem. During sessions nine, ten, and eleven the pattern shifted toward a midsagittal focus, in this case apparently correlated with boredom.

Second Hypothesis Problem

After eleven sessions on the first hypothesis problem, in which black was the correct response, the criterion was changed, so that the T-shaped handle was always correct. This second problem was begun following a six-day rest interval, during which Cebus 26 was not brought to the laboratory. As expected, he started in responding quite consistently to black.

He solved this second problem very abruptly, insofar as his behavioral data were concerned. During the first thirteen trials (see Fig. 47) he responded first to the black handle eleven times. On trial fourteen he started responding to the T and continued to do so very consistently thereafter. In the remainder of that second session, and in each of the two succeeding sessions, he made only two errors, and in each case only one of these two errors was black.

This sudden change in his initial response, of course, does not mean that he was not forming and testing hypotheses during the first thirteen trials. On every trial the manipulanda are left in front of the animal until he moves the correct handle. If his learning process were maximally efficient, the problem could theoretically be solved in two or three trials, regardless of which handle he might happen to move first.

His d.c. contours during this second hypothesis problem tend to confirm most of the phenomena noted during the first problem. On session one, he started the session with only a long, narrow positive focus on the right frontal lobe (see Fig. 48). By the end of the session that focus had almost completely disappeared, and a midsagittal focus ("what the ——") appeared. By the next day, a fairly weak focus had appeared medial to the left arcuate. The remainder of the problem showed only the addition of a roughly symmetrical focus on the right frontal lobe and some fluctuation of the midsagittal focus.

```
                Sess. 1              2              3              4
1 (right)          X            X     X      X XX X      X   XXX
2               XX    XXX   X X    X X        X           X       X
3               X             X X X       XX           X   X     X
4 (left)        X   XX        X            X        X X  X

black           XXXX X XXX   XXX    XX     X   X   X              X
white              X            X         X     X      X X  X   X
blue                  X          X          X           X       X
yellow                        X   XX    X   XX   X   X   XX

cylinder        X  X X X      X       X X       XX
"T"                XX                 XXXX X   XXX  XXXXX   XXXXXX  XX
sphere             X          X
triangle        X     X    X   X                              XX


                Sess. 1              2              3
1 (right)          XX X      X XX   X XX      X   XXX
2               X         X   X  X  X  X    XX   X
3               XXX             X         X      XX
4 (left)           X   X

black              X         X X   X         X X   X
white           XX X            XX         X      XX
blue                          X      X
yellow          X     XXXXX     X        XX   XX X X

cylinder                     X      X X            X
"T"             XXXXXXX X    X X    X     XXXX XX X
sphere                       X XX            X
triangle              X             X      X


                   4              5
1 (right)       X XX           XXX   X
2                  X   XXXXX    X    XX X
3               X              X
4 (left)                       X

black              XX          X X  X
white           X   X               X
blue                  XX      X X  X
yellow          X   XX   X   X    X   X

cylinder           X          X    X
"T"             XXXX     XX   XX XX   X
sphere             X               X
triangle        X   X          X    X
```

FIGURE 47. Behavioral data from Cebus 26 during his second and third hypothesis problems. During the first four sessions shown, the correct response was "*T*." Note the initial responses to black, which was previously correct, and the abrupt shift to "*T*" on trial fourteen.

For the third problem, correct response was position two. He appeared to have solved it during the last half of session four, but his behavior became random and moderately violent during session five.

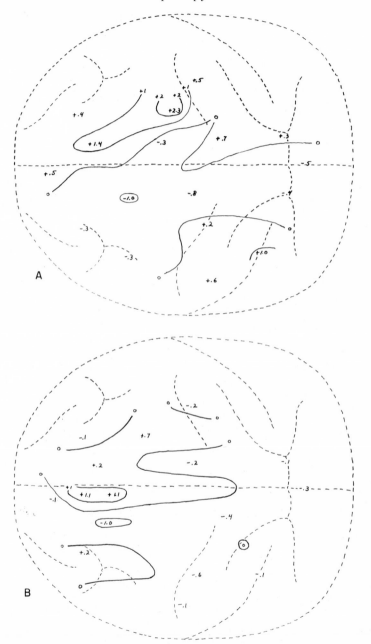

FIGURE 48. D.c. contours from Cebus 26, during the second hypothesis problem.

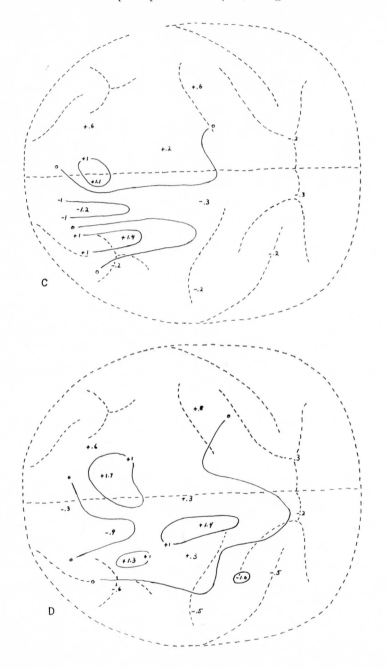

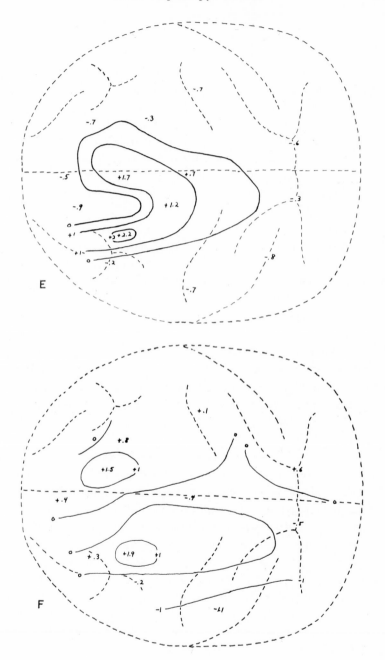

Third Hypothesis Problem

After a two-day (weekend) interval, the criterion was again changed, this time to the third position. That is, the correct handle was always the one in position three (second from the left end), regardless of shape or color. I soon realized that this was a mistake. Color and shape are about equally prepotent stimulus dimensions, but position in the array is perceptually quite different. After having been trained to respond to color and to shape, Cebus 26 was only confused by this third problem. He started in, of course, responding consistently to the T. On each trial, he seemed to be responding carefully, and was apparently searching for a new hypothesis. Failing to find anything consistent about the color or shape of the correct handle, he gave up trying by the third session. His responses became random and apparently careless, and he spent more time entertaining himself with acrobatics and attempts to dismantle the apparatus. The problem was discontinued after five sessions.

His d.c. contours during this problem showed the appearance of a rather strong ($+3.4$ mV) focus medial to the left arcuate sulcus on session two, when he was apparently trying to solve the problem, which was replaced by the familiar midsagittal focus on session three. This midsagittal focus remained fairly constant during the remainder of the problem, fluctuating around a peak voltage of 2.0 mV, and was accompanied on sessions four and five by a focus of similar voltage posterior to the left arcuate sulcus.

The most interesting activity seen during these hypothesis problems is consistently in the frontal lobe. Since this is near the intellectual limit of the Cebus monkey, it is not surprising that the activity correlated with its solution should appear in the phylogenetically youngest part of the brain. In fact, in all of these data I have been impressed by the fact that most of the "action" is in prefrontal cortex. This seems to be true any time I permit them to use their intelligence to any significant extent. The one-light and one-tone problems, which present no challenge to the Cebus monkey, appear to use the older parietal and occipital portions of the cortex. The simultaneous light-tone problem and the hypothesis problem seem to use primarily premotor frontal cortex. I suspect that this is not accidental.

SOME NEGATIVE RESULTS

Some months ago when I was presenting some of these data to a graduate seminar in physiological psychology, a graduate student asked me what happened to the d.c. contours when a response was extinguished by nonreinforcement. I admitted that I had not done the experiment, but added that I knew what would happen: the original learning focus would recur, accompanied by a focus medial to the arcuate sulcus, such as always appears during suppression of a response. A few weeks later, feeling a bit less confident, I decided to try it with Cebus 26.

I first retrained him on the one-tone, one-string problem, which he had originally learned about seven months previously. He relearned the problem quickly, producing a rather weak auditory learning focus. After six retraining sessions, when the response to the tone was prompt and reliable, I discontinued the grape reward. On the first two extinction sessions, the only behavioral change was a freely expressed sense of frustration. He was obviously angry at me, the apparatus and the whole world. His d.c. contours remained quite constant. The pattern was dominated by a $+2.0$ mV focus medial and anterior to the left arcuate sulcus. The only change seemed to be an extension of this focus posterolaterally to include the area of the usual "suppressor" focus. At the beginning of the third extinction session, the pattern had changed to the usual positive focus just medial to the left arcuate sulcus plus the not-unexpected "what the ——" midsagittal focus. His behavior during this session showed definite extinction of the response. There was not even the smallest positive shift in the auditory learning area of either hemisphere.

I repeated this extinction experiment with Cebus 35, except that this time I took additional records one and two hours after the critical extinction sessions, hoping to catch a transient appearance of the learning focus. Again the results were completely negative. I am forced to conclude that extinction of a response does not require the appearance of a positive focus in the modality-specific learning areas.

ALL-DAY RECORDING

During the retraining of Cebus 26 on the one-tone, one-string problem, I spent one day recording his d.c. contours at fairly frequent intervals in order to get some idea of how rapidly they may change and how this time course is related to the experimental session. He was brought to the laboratory at 9:00 A.M. and kept there until 4:00 P.M. Records were taken at about fifteen-minute intervals. A few records were lost because of artifacts, but enough good data were obtained to show in considerable detail the course of changes in his contours.

It must be remembered that this was not a normal day for the monkey. He was placed in the apparatus, which would normally indicate that a training session was about to begin, then handed a grape without having to work for it (this was necessary to keep him from destroying the apparatus), and then, very shortly, removed and placed in a "resting" cage.

His concept of resting is rather strenuous. His first occupation was tearing the newspapers into tiny pieces and then lying on his back hurling confetti in five directions simultaneously. His antics became progressively more complicated throughout the day, until by midafternoon he had worked out quite a repertoire. One of his more complicated games consisted of taking two "fistfuls" of torn newspaper in his hind paws, then walking on his forepaws the length of the cage while scrubbing the ceiling with the paper. Since the newspapers by this time were in a deplorable state, this added nothing to the already dubious cleanliness of his surroundings. It helped, however, to insure that the changes noted in his d.c. contours could not be attributed to boredom.

Neither could any changes be attributed to chemical changes in his electrodes because of the increased frequency of recording. Every preparation, when not connected to the recording apparatus, has inserted in his connector plug a "load plug" which exactly reproduces the electrical load of the recording circuit. Taking a record, therefore, has no electrochemical effect on the electrodes.

The regularly scheduled training session (one-tone, one-string retraining session three) was conducted in early afternoon. By this time, changes due to the novelty of the day's procedures had probably stabilized, but there was still time enough remaining to follow postsession changes.

The results of this experiment are shown in Figure 49. The frontal focus seen at the beginning of the day shifted posterolaterally during the first hour and then returned to its original location. Little change in pattern occurred during the training session, but during the hour immediately following the session, the entire pattern changed markedly. The frontal focus disappeared, being replaced by the familiar midsagittal focus and the usual focus just medial to the arcuate sulcus, and a weak auditory learning focus appeared on the opposite hemisphere. During the remainder of the afternoon, the frontal focus again shifted anteromedially toward its original location, but the midsagittal focus and the auditory learning focus remained.

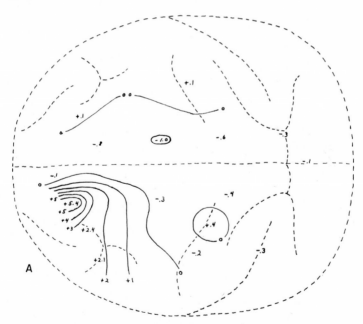

FIGURE 49. Changes in d.c. contours during a 27 hour period. Recorded from Cebus 26 during operant conditioning to an auditory cue. Records shown were taken at approximately 45 minute intervals. A through K were recorded on December 21; the training session occurred between G and H. Records L through O were recorded the following morning, after a 17 hour interval. Another training session occurred between L and M.

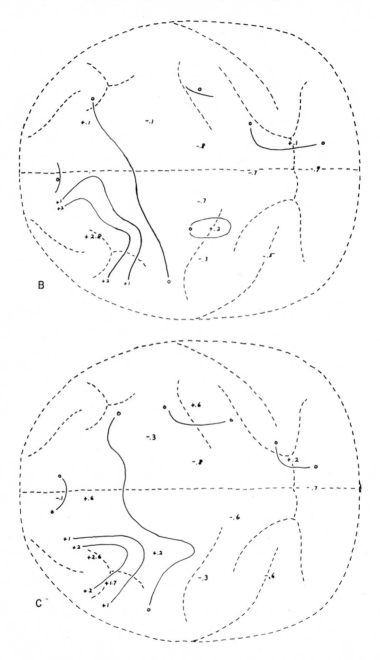

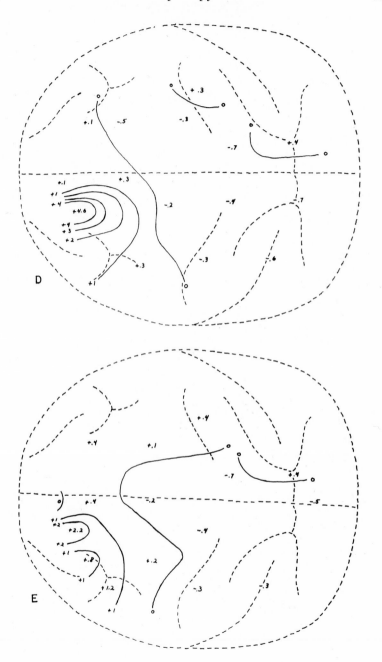

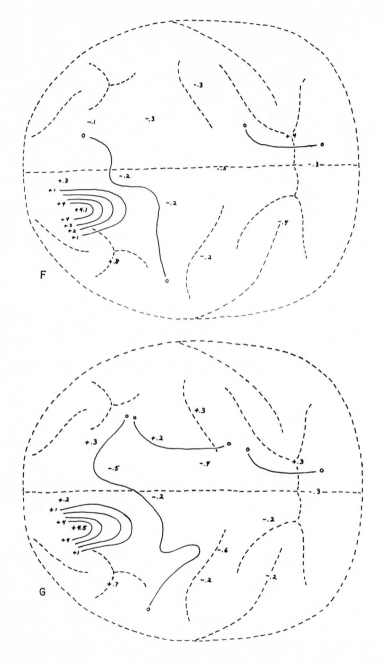

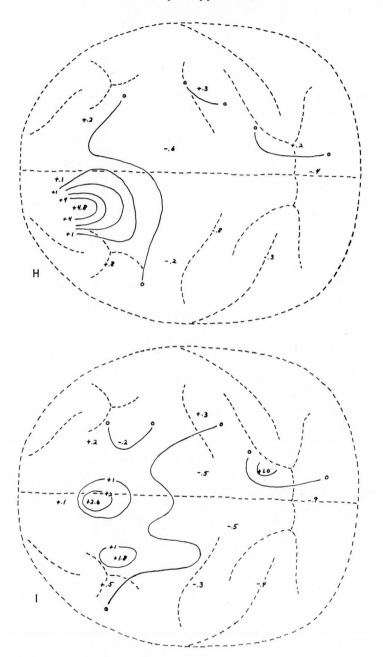

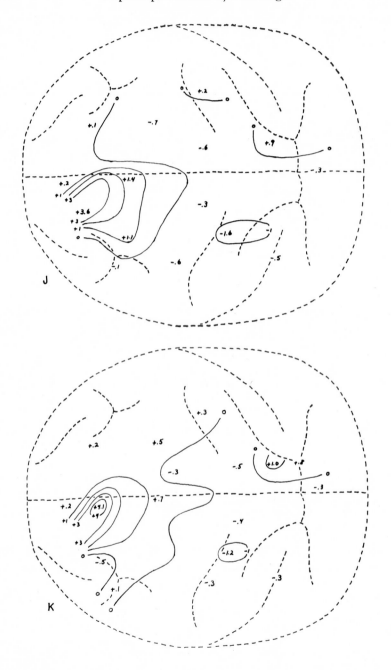

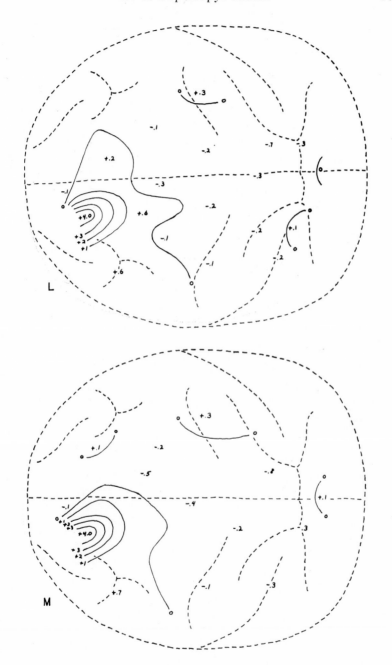

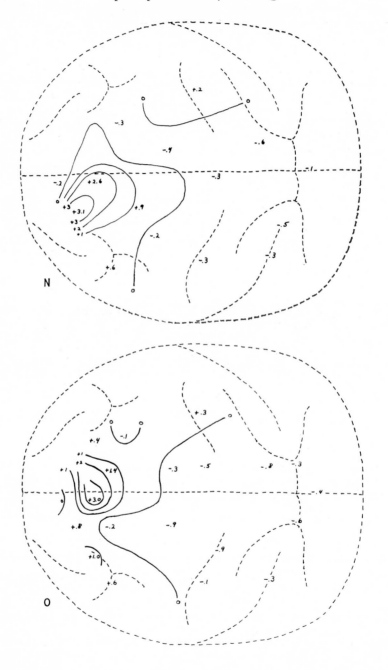

The following morning the d.c. contours had returned essentially to the pattern of twenty-four hours earlier. I again followed the changes during and after the next training session (session four), but this time only the midsagittal focus appeared, replacing the left frontal focus. Since his auditory learning was essentially complete by this time, the absence of an auditory learning focus is not surprising.

A more detailed presentation of the temporal course of the d.c. potential from selected electrodes is shown in Figure 50. It is quite evident from these "EEG's" that the increase in positivity over the midsagittal fissure began before the training session, whereas that over the auditory learning area (right, parieto-occipital) began immediately after the session. Electrode 26, (left, anterior to arcuate), which was the most positive electrode at the beginning of the day, showed a dramatic negative shift following the training session, but it had been so variable throughout most of the morning that this could well be coincidental. Electrode 35, just medial to the left arcuate sulcus, apparently started to shift positive before the beginning of the training session, but this, too is inconclusive. From the shape of the rising portion of the curve, it would be possible to conclude that the initial positive shift was accident and that the major positive shift actually began fifteen minutes after the training session, the same time that electrode 26 started its spectacular 4.5 mV plunge.

Perhaps the most interesting aspect of these data is the finding that the d.c. potential may change by as much as 4 mV in fifteen minutes. Other data from Cebus 26 suggest that even more rapid changes may sometimes occur. About two months before this all-day recording session, I had tried running the commutator continually throughout a training session. The commutator was then operating at 4 rpm, so that I obtained a complete record every fifteen seconds.

These data were taken during session thirteen of the simultaneous light-tone problem (on Friday, October 13, which may help explain the results), when his learning was quite complete. About midway through the session, electrode 37, over motor cortex, left hemisphere, shifted 3.2 mV negative between two commutator sweeps, remained at about this potential through the next sweep,

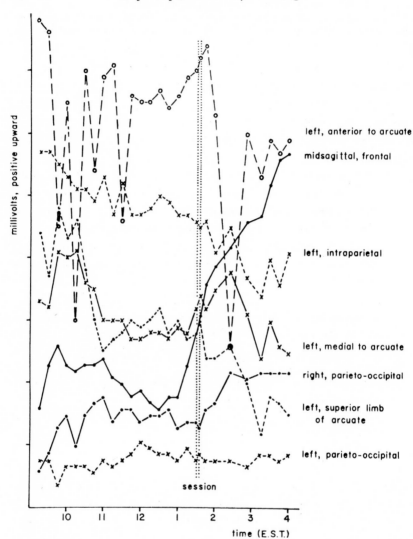

FIGURE 50. D.c. changes from selected points over a 7-hour period. These very low frequency EEG's are plotted from the same data presented in toposcopic form in Figure 49.

then returned to its former potential and behaved itself properly throughout the rest of the session. I will have to see this sort of thing happen a few more times before I really believe it, but it provides food for thought. It was probably just a loose connection somewhere, although this electrode had never shown any indication of psychotic behavior at any other time, and the remainder of the array were reasonably stable throughout this session.

Analysis of the reams of data produced by such continuous recording is so time-consuming that it cannot be adequately attacked without an on-line computer. For now, the subject must be left in a rather unsatisfactory state. Conclusions that appear fairly certain are the following:

1. The greatest lability of potential is found in the frontal lobes. This is supported by the data collected from several preparations using nickel electrodes (see Chap. VI). Although the nickel electrodes are measuring something different from d.c. potential, they also indicate a much greater lability of function in the frontal cortex, particularly around the arcuate sulcus.

2. The only d.c. shift which is clearly time-locked to the training session is that in the learning-specific response area.

3. I still do not understand the midsagittal focus.

"SPREADING" DEPRESSION EXPERIMENT

In two animals, Cebus 25 and squirrel monkey 46, I tried creating a cortical depression by the application of crystalline potassium chloride to exposed cortex. In the primate, of course, this reaction does not spread as it does in the rodent.

This experiment was done with animals whose data appeared useless for the learning studies, due largely to fixed artifacts, presumably caused by bone damage. In the potassium chloride experiment, however, I was looking for changes occurring over the course of a few minutes, so that these artifacts could simply be subtracted out.

The best cortical coverage was in squirrel monkey 46. A few milligrams of potassium chloride were applied to exposed pia mater anterior to the electrode array on the left hemisphere. A clear shift was seen within five minutes, reaching a maximum in about eleven minutes. Figure 51 shows the pattern of change during the first eleven minutes. The small positive shift over most of the cortex is caused by the use of an average reference. The significant changes are two areas of negativity on the left hemisphere; -22.1 mV

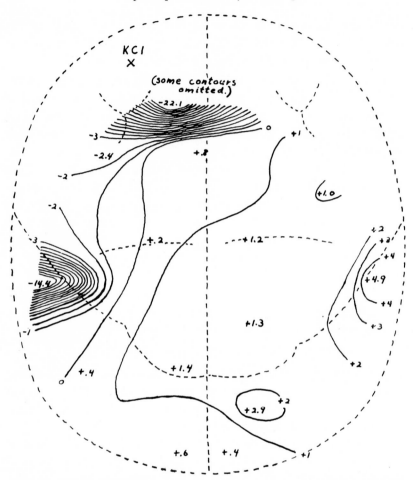

FIGURE 51. D.c. changes produced by the application of dry potassium chloride to exposed cortex near left frontal pole. Voltage contours are voltage at eleven minutes postapplication minus voltages preapplication. The site of potassium chloride application is shown by X.

near the frontal pole, —14.4 mV on the temporal lobe, and a much smaller positive shift on the right temporal lobe. About forty-five minutes after this record was taken, the monkey entered a grand mal convulsion. At this time, the d.c. shifts had returned to within 1 or 2 mV of baseline.

Cebus 25 had a much more limited coverage of the frontal lobes, his electrodes extending only slightly in front of the motor area. Potassium chloride was applied to the frontal lobe in a location corresponding to that used in squirrel monkey 46. In this case, only a 2.3 mV negative shift occurred in the frontal lobe, and a +5.8 shift on the temporal lobe.

Since the application of potassium chloride is known to cause shifts in d.c. potential of about this magnitude and time course (Leão, 1951), this experiment serves as a calibration of the apparatus. Essentially, I put in a "known signal" and obtained the expected output. The areas of positive potential change were unexpected, but the data are too fragmentary to attempt to draw conclusions. They do demonstrate, however, that these d.c. potentials, ordinarily fairly static, can change rapidly under appropriate conditions.

Reference

Leão, A.A.P.: Further observations on the spreading depression of activity in the cerebral cortex. *J. Neurophysiol.*, *10*:409-414, 1947.

Chapter VI

NICKEL ELECTRODES

THE fact that this chapter is titled according to the electrodes used in this aspect of the research, rather than the phenomenon being examined, emphasizes the fact that I do not know what I am recording. To a certain extent, of course, this is always true. We still are not certain what cerebral elements or structures generate the classical EEG, but we study it because it shows interesting correlations with physiological and psychological states. This state of ignorance is considerably more profound for the electrical potentials recorded from nickel electrodes over the brain.

The phenomenon will be referred to as *nickel potentials*. The physiological and psychological correlates that have thus far been explored will be described in detail below. First, however, I will describe the little that has thus far been established about the chemistry of nickel in contact with body fluids.

When nickel remains in contact with body fluids for a few days, a black deposit forms on the surface. This is not true of nickel in Ringer's solution or in other saline solutions tried. The only likely inorganic nickel salts which are insoluble under normal conditions are NiO (or possibly a higher oxide) and NiS. We have been unable to produce any similar deposit with mild oxidizing agents, such as H_2O_2, but can produce a similar looking deposit with H_2SO_4, H_2S, or dilute H_2SO_4 in contact with air.

The oxide can be dissolved by dilute acids, the sulphide cannot. When an array of nickel electrodes from a preparation is treated with dilute acid, some of the electrodes lose part of their black coating, and others do not. I conclude from this that the deposit formed in the body is a mixture of nickel salts, probably partly NiO, but also containing higher oxides, sulphide, or complex com-

150

pounds, possibly including organic ions.

Since the deposit is not produced by dissolved oxygen or by mild oxidizing agents, it appears likely that some enzyme system is responsible for its production in the body. Whatever the reaction may be, it is apparently reversible, for the deposit does not show a monotonic increase in thickness with time *in situ* but reaches an asymptote in two or three days. The formation of any nickel salt in combination with ions already present in solution would produce an excess of electrons, thus driving the electrode negative. The reverse reaction would presumably use electrons, thus driving the electrode positive.

The picture is complicated still further by the fact that these electrodes are quite sensitive to the presence of infection. Every preparation that has shown symptoms of a localized, bacterial infection under the electrode array has simultaneously displayed very steep (150 mV/cm or more) potential gradients in the area of the infection. However, similar gradients may also appear in healthy preparations.

In order to be certain that the potentials were not due to some minute difference in electrode materials, and also to prove that the potential gradients were not due only to pathology, a simple experiment was performed on a Cebus monkey at the time she was undergoing surgery to replace one electrode array with another. Two nickel electrodes were autoclaved. The monkey was anesthetized with pentobarbital, 30 mg/kg. When the old electrode array had been removed, and a craniotomy performed over the left hemisphere, one nickel electrode was positioned in contact with dura at the vertex of the brain over the midsagittal fissure. The other electrode was placed on prefrontal area, then occipital area, then back to prefrontal, and so forth. It was left undisturbed in each position for about thirty seconds for the recorder to reach a stable reading.

Recording was by direct connection to a Bausch and Lomb V.O.M. 5 strip chart recorder, set for full scale deflection at 100 mV. The input impedance of this recorder is approximately 17 Mohms. Control recordings with the electrodes in air or saline solution showed no measurable drift over ten minutes.

When the active electrode was over the occipital region, it consistently indicated a potential about 50 mV positive to the reference. When the active electrode was placed on premotor cortex, it indicated a potential of from 25 mV positive to as much as 50 mV negative to reference. The variability was presumably due to very steep voltage gradients across the prefrontal region, which made the reading vary significantly with slight differences in electrode placement. The records also showed indications of rapid changes in potential while the electrode remained stationary on prefrontal dura. Such rapid changes were not seen when the active electrode was over occipital region.

This experiment therefore demonstrated, in the absence of any visible pathology, the existence of potential differences up to 75 mV which cannot be attributed to any differences in electrode material.

In order to test the assumption that these nickel potentials had something to do with oxidative metabolism, a terminal experiment was performed on Cebus 28, who had extracranial nickel electrodes

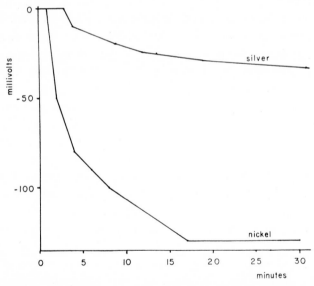

FIGURE 52. Change in nickel potential caused by anoxia and death. Voltage is average of forty-eight cranial electrodes referred to silver-silver chloride rectal electrode. At time O, trachea of anesthetized animal was clamped. Compare with identical experiment (upper curve) using silver cranial electrodes.

and was apparently free of infection. At the time of sacrifice, the animal was deeply anesthetized with pentobarbital. A chlorided silver reference electrode was inserted in the rectum, and the averaged potential of the forty-eight cranial nickel electrodes was monitored on the Bausch and Lomb V.O.M. 5 recorder. When the anesthesia had reached a stable state, her trachea was exposed and clamped.

It is possible, of course, that the d.c. potential in the rectum could change as a result of anoxia, so the results of this experiment are best interpreted in comparison with an identical procedure performed on Cebus 25, who had silver electrodes in his cranium. The two curves are shown in Figure 52. It is obvious that the average potential of the nickel electrodes in Cebus 28 shifted rapidly negative during the first seventeen minutes after the trachea was clamped and then showed no further change during the (3-hour) duration of the experiment. Postmortem examination confirmed the absence of infection under the implant.

Although this certainly suggests a correlation between oxidative metabolism and the nickel electrode potentials, the direction of the shift is opposite to that expected. It indicates that the normal metabolic process is somehow maintaining the nickel at a potential positive to that which is assumes in a metabolically inert system. Additional evidence in the same direction was obtained from an *in vitro* experiment using fresh brain tissue from rats.

Two beakers, each containing 60 cc of Ringer's solution, were connected by a capillary bridge. A new nickel electrode was immersed in each beaker, and a sensitive electrometer was connected between them. I allowed a few minutes for the system to settle down and assured myself that adding a bit more Ringer's solution and stirring it with a glass rod had no effect on the potential. A rat was anesthetized with sodium pentobarbital, and his brain was exposed. A section of brain was removed, largely neocortex, but including some basal ganglia, and trimmed down until it weighed .5 gm. The tissue was quickly macerated (all stainless steel instruments) and stirred into one of the beakers. The time from excision to measurement was about ninety seconds. This procedure was repeated several times with fresh solutions and consistently yielded a positive shift of approximately 5 mV from the beaker to which the brain tissue was added. Next, I tried the same procedure, but adding .5 cc of fresh blood. This consistently caused a negative shift of 22 mV. Finally, I repeated the procedure with .5 gm of liver and .5 gm of kidney. These were not as fresh, as the rat had expired by this time. Each caused a small positive shift, 3.5 and 2.0 mV, respectively.

I checked the pH of these various mixtures and found them to be, as expected, identical to within .01 unit.

All these findings were confirmed in a second replication.

One of the most interesting aspects of this phenomenon is that the positive shift is rather transitory. When the tissue is first stirred into the solution, the potential shifts promptly to about $+5$ mV, then starts drifting back. Within ten minutes or so, it will usually be from 5 to 10 mV negative. Since the negative shift caused by blood is fairly stable over a few minutes, this residual negativity is very probably due to the blood that was added with the brain tissue. It would thus appear that the chemical in brain and other tissues which causes the initial positive shift is unstable outside the body.

The final curious fact about the chemistry of these nickel potentials is that they may equally well be recorded by electrodes on dura or on skull. The first preparations used had craniotomies over the area from which potentials were to be recorded, so that the electrodes were in direct contact with the dura mater. Since the nickel causes a very localized toxic response, I tried leaving the skull intact and found that it made no difference in the recording. This indicates that the chemical system reacting with the nickel can diffuse through skull rapidly enough to cause potential fluctuations, sometimes within a period of only ten or twenty seconds.

To summarize, the data indicate that nickel electrodes in the vicinity of the brain are acted on by an enzyme system, or some chemical not present in Ringer's solution, which reversibly forms a gray precipitate on the surface of the nickel, driving the electrode electrically positive by some 150 mV. The chemical can diffuse rapidly through pia mater, dura, and skull. The electrical potentials, as will be shown below, fluctuate over periods ranging from seconds to weeks, in bilaterally symmetrical, anatomically organized patterns which are related to physiological manipulations, to the general psychological state of the animal, and to short-term psychological states related to the intertrial interval of an operant learning situation. I am thus in the rather uncomfortable position of possessing an instrument for performing a highly localized quantitative analysis for a chemical intimately involved in the normal functioning of the brain, but having no idea as to what the chemical may be.

TYPICAL PATTERNS

One example of a pattern of nickel potentials has already been shown in Figure 23. Another record taken one week earlier from this same animal is shown in Figure 53. Although many features of the patterns are different, it is obvious that the steep voltage gradients lateral to the arcuate sulci remained fairly constant. In fact, these fronto-lateral regions showed little change in pattern

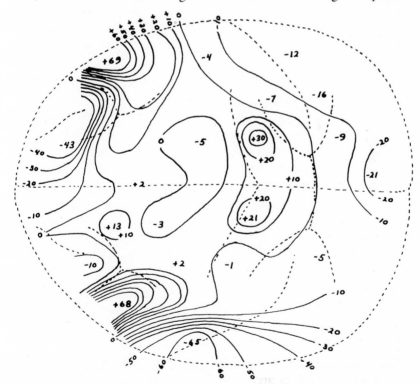

FIGURE 53. Nickel contours recorded from Cebus 27. Compare with FIGURE 23, which was recorded one week later from the same animal.

throughout his six-week experimental lifetime.

This particular monkey was named Satan in reference to his major personality traits. He was clearly terrified of me, the apparatus, and every other aspect of the experimental situation. His behavior alternated between violent attack on anything within reach and a catatonic immobility. He showed no signs of adaptation during the six weeks and was finally used in a terminal, acute experiment.

Another monkey, Cebus 32, who had nickel electrodes over this fronto-lateral region, showed a similar, but lower voltage (about 70 mV) positive peak in this area during the first five sessions of her one-tone, one-string problem. Her behavioral data show that she appeared timid, responded seldom and hesitantly, and seemed generally apprehensive of the experimental situation during these sessions. On the sixth day, she showed a considerable lessening of apprehension, and a marked increase in responses, together with a 50 mV reduction in the positive peak. Although the potentials in this region continued to show considerable change from day to day, nothing more than +40 mV was ever again recorded. Her behavior became much more relaxed and cooperative. Although these data are somewhat complicated by the fact that this monkey had bilateral ablations of the cortex surrounding the parieto-occipital sulcus, it seems very unlikely that those lesions would affect the activity of fronto-lateral cortex.

Other than Cebus 27 and 32, I have no examples of animals showing this highly inhibited behavior, with electrodes in the proper location. There are monkeys with electrodes in this region which do not show the positive peak and do not display timid, inhibited behavior. Such doubly negative results are reassuring, but add little to the weight of evidence. The association between a sharp, positive, nickel potential peak lateral to the arcuate sulcus and timid, highly inhibited behavior with episodes resembling catatonia remains only an interesting possibility. Unless means can be found for producing such a behavior pattern at will, the investigation of this relationship must remain a matter of chance.

Some other examples of nickel potential patterns are shown in Figure 54. These data are taken from Cebus 23, female, who was about average in all respects except health, which was unusually good. Her electrode array was unilateral. The examples shown illustrate the range of voltages and pattern detail to be expected in a typical preparation. The two patterns from 1/30/67 and 1/31/67 show a normal amount of change for a twenty-four-hour period. This animal was operated on 1/9/67. My notes show that she was becoming fairly well adapted to the experimental situation by 2/13/67. The long adaptation period was not because she was particularly difficult to handle, but because I was involved with other matters and only ran her two or three times each week. The first four patterns shown in Figure 54, therefore, were recorded during the adaptation period, when she was still somewhat frightened of the situation. The pattern recorded on 3/10/67 was from the last session (session 9) of her first learning problem. On 5/12/67, she was well into her fourth learning problem, and knew the routine as well as I did. Obviously, there is no correlation between overall voltages and the degree of adaptation.

Every animal that had a bilateral electrode array showed a high degree of bilateral symmetry in the nickel potential patterns. This symmetry was more precise when the patterns were of high voltage than when they showed a range of only 10 to 15 mV. The decrease in symmetry at lower voltages is very probably due to

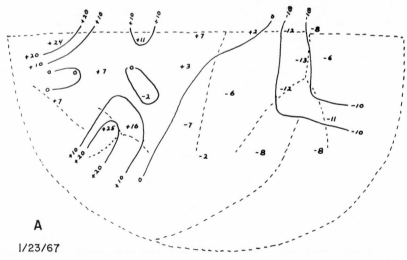

A

1/23/67

FIGURE 54. Nickel potential contours recorded from Cebus 23 over a period of almost five months.

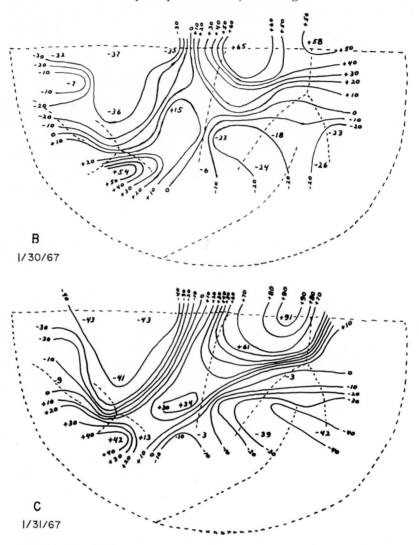

B
1/30/67

C
1/31/67

contamination of the nickel potentials with d.c. potentials. The inherent d.c. potentials of the cortex, as measured with silver-silver chloride electrodes, have a normal range of about 4 mV and are not symmetrical (see Chap. V). These constitute a noise factor in the nickel potentials which is only significant when the nickel potentials are of unusually low voltage.

When recording was begun from a new preparation, adapted

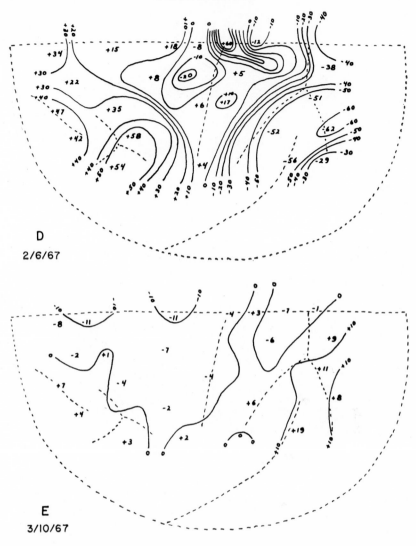

D
2/6/67

E
3/10/67

just well enough to permit the attaching of the recording probe, it was found that the pattern of nickel potential contours changed relatively little over a period of twenty-four hours, but usually changed completely in from four to seven days. After the animal had been working for a few weeks, however, the patterns almost invariably stabilized, so that a particular pattern of gradients would remain recognizable for several weeks. Figure 54 shows patterns

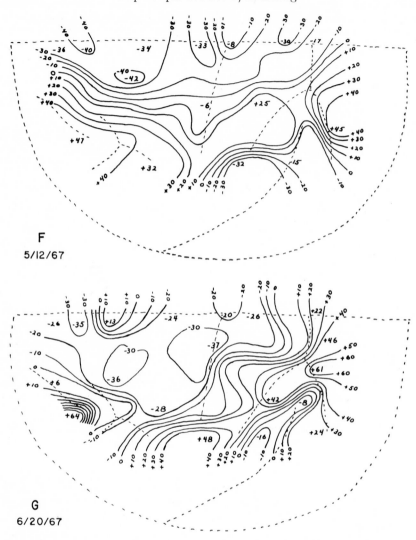

F
5/12/67

G
6/20/67

recorded over a period of five months from Cebus 23. During this time she learned several different operant problems. Her behavior in general, however, remained quite constant. This same sequence from rapidly changing patterns (that is, changing every few days) to relatively static patterns was seen in every successful nickel preparation from which data were collected over a period of months. It appears probable that the pattern of nickel potentials is correlated with some fairly general aspect of brain function, probably something to do with emotional state of the animal.

In those animals that successfully learned the operant problems used, a positive potential shift was typically found over the predicted cortical region at the predicted stage of learning. The magnitude of these potentials, however, and the fact that they were only found over the left hemisphere make it virtually certain that they represent only the inherent d.c. shift as described in the last chapter, which can be much more cleanly measured with silver electrodes. When recording from nickel electrodes, such a potential shift represents only noise. No aspect of the nickel potentials which could reasonably be attributed to the electrochemical reaction of interest appeared to be correlated with the particular problem being learned.

Whenever an animal was sacrificed, the effect of pentobarbital sodium on the contours was recorded. In every animal save one (Cebus 27, see below) the effect of an anesthetic dose was to flatten the nickel potential contours. A typical example is shown in Figure 55. It may be seen that the preexisting pattern disappeared and was replaced with a broad, shallow gradient from positive potentials medially to negative potentials laterally, with a narrow positive strip on the extreme lateral edge of the array. When additional pentobarbital was given to sacrifice the animal, the potential contours consistently dropped to near zero within three to five hours post mortem.

The clearly abnormal behavior of Cebus 27 suggested testing the effect of chlorpromazine on his nickel potential contours and on his behavior. The results are shown in Figure 56. A rather massive dose of chlorpromazine, 50 mg/kg, was administered intraperitoneally. Within a few minutes he became quite drowsy but could be easily aroused by voice or touch. When awake, he appeared as frightened and inhibited as ever but too lethargic to attack. The major effect of the drug on his potential contours was a considerable reduction in the positivity near the vertex, with a shift in the location of this positive plateau from frontal cortex to the parieto-occipital cortex. The apparent increase in voltage of the positive peaks lateral to the arcuate sulcus is probably caused by the average reference used. The reduction in central positivity would

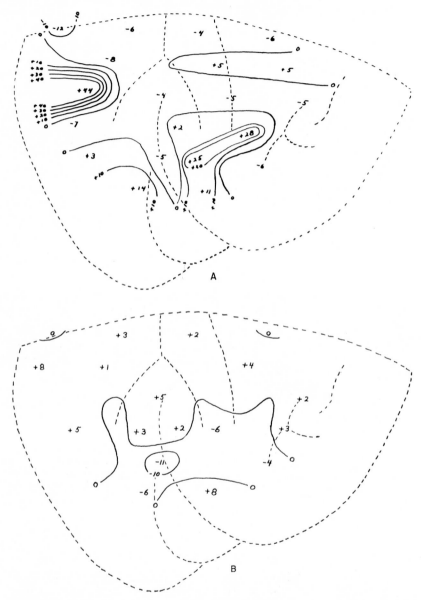

FIGURE 55. Effect of 30 mg/kg pentobarbital sodium on the nickel potential contours of Cebus 28. A: before administration; B: 53 min. after administration.

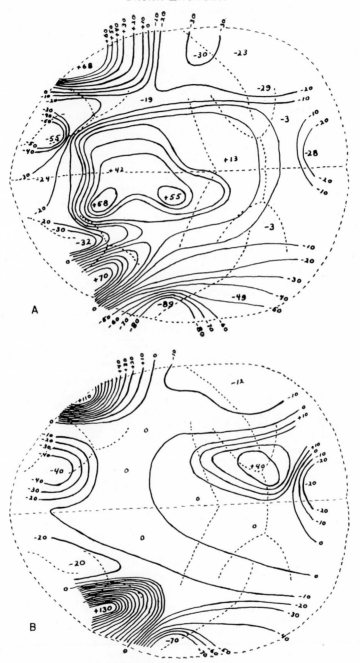

FIGURE 56. Effect of 50 mg/kg chlorpromazine on the nickel potential contours of Cebus 27. A: before administration; B: 2 hrs. after administration.

cause the average reference to become more negative. I would conclude that the positivity lateral to the arcuate sulcus, which dominated the patterns from this animal throughout his experimental lifetime, was unaffected by the chlorpromazine. His basic emotional reaction to the experimental situation also appeared to be unaffected. Whether the marked changes in nickel potential over the motor area of the frontal lobe were associated with the marked lethargy produced by the drug could only be confirmed by replication of the experiment. However, the same treatment in the case of Cebus 28 produced only drowsiness, with no obvious lethargy when aroused and no apparent emotional change. The nickel contours in this animal showed no significant effect from the drug. It appears likely that only a "neurotic" monkey will yield positive effects from chlorpromazine.

Cebus 27 also differed from all the other monkeys used in this series of experiments in that pentobarbital sodium in anesthetic dose (30 mg/kg) did not flatten the nickel potential contours. The effect was rather similar to that of chlorpromazine in this animal. As may be seen from Figure 57, the extreme positive plateau over the frontal lobes shifted posteriorly until it was centered over the parietal region, leaving the familiar positive peaks lateral to the arcuate sulci. At this point the animal could not be aroused, so that the effect on his emotional state could not be assessed.

A third physiological manipulation which produces a dramatic change in these nickel potential contours is the application of potassium chloride to exposed cortex. This was actually one of the first experiments performed, and it provided the data which first convinced me that I was not dealing with some form of electrical artifact.

Squirrel monkey 33 was prepared with a standard nickel array on the dura of the left hemisphere. Anterior to the electrode array, a hole was cut through the plastic implant, skull, and dura to expose the pia mater over the left prefrontal cortex. The exposed cortex was about 6 mm in front of the most anterior electrodes. This hole was then filled with a fast-setting silicone rubber, and the animal was permitted to recover from surgery. Two days later the monkey was placed in the apparatus used for the learning studies, restrained by a light rope harness. After recording her nickel po-

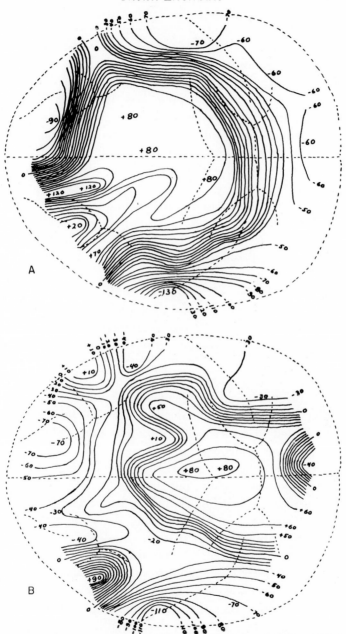

FIGURE 57. Effect of 30 mg/kg pentobarbital sodium on the nickel potential contours of Cebus 27. Compare with FIGURE 55, which is representative of all animals tested except for Cebus 27. A: before administration; B: 18 min. after administration.

tential contours, the silicone rubber plug was removed, and a few crystals of potassium chloride dropped onto the exposed pia mater. The nickel electrode potentials were then recorded every fifteen seconds until a reaction was seen.

In Figure 58 the first reaction may be seen at two minutes following the potassium chloride application. It consists of a positive shift over the medial parietal area. At nine minutes this has steepened to a sharp, positive ridge extending about 10 mm from the midline. I then applied more potassium chloride, about four or five times as much as the first gentle application, and continued recording. Within nine minutes of this second treatment, the entire parietal and temporal lobes had become strongly positive while the frontal lobe was broadly negative. A sharp voltage gradient existed just posterior to the central sulcus. The maximum voltages were achieved at time forty-four minutes from the first application, when the maximum voltage difference between two cortical points was 198 mV. After this, the voltages gradually declined until, about six hours after the beginning of the experiment, the contours were very similar to those existing before the experiment began.

Since this experiment was then crucial to my own faith in the reality of the nickel potentials, I performed two control experiments. A row of nickel electrodes in a dish of Ringer's solution in which a potassium chloride gradient was established from one side to the other showed no potential differences, so the response cannot be attributed to a direct effect of potassium chloride on the nickel. Actually, it is inconceivable that any significant concentration of potassium chloride reached the parietal area by direct diffusion in the squirrel monkey, but the negative effects of the control experiment are reassuring. Secondly, I repeated the procedure with squirrel monkey 33 the following day, going through the identical manipulations, except that no potassium chloride was actually used. Her nickel potential contours remained essentially static over a period of thirty-four minutes, so the reaction could not be attributed to the psychological effects of restraint and handling.

Since all this unplugging of the implant eventually started an infection under the electrode array, the animal had to be sacrificed a week later. Her postmortem data showed the usual reduction to zero gradients within a few hours postmortem.

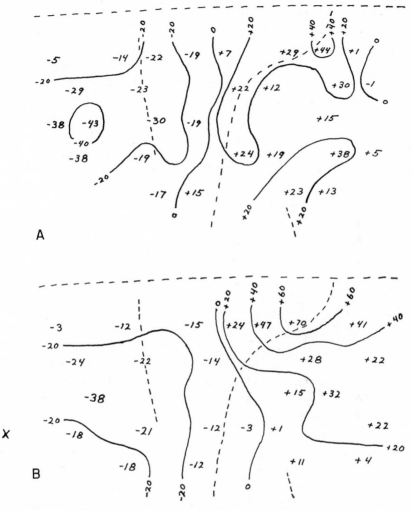

FIGURE 58. Nickel potential contours recorded from squirrel monkey 33 following the application of potassium chloride to frontal lobe. *A*, Contours before the application. *B*, Two minutes following application of crystalline potassium chloride at X. *C*, Nine minutes post application. *D*, Nineteen minutes post application. *E*, Forty-four minutes post application. *F*, Six hours, nine minutes after the application, when the contours had returned essentially to their original state (compare with *A*). *G*, Map of the changes in potential from before the application to two minutes following the application. These data are derived by subtracting the values in *A* from those in *B*.

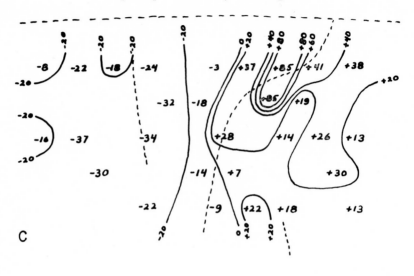

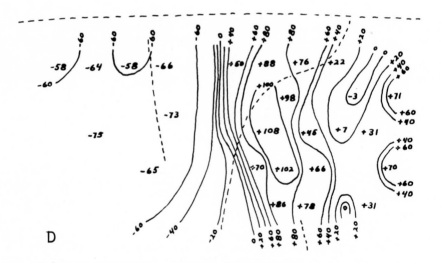

WAVEFORMS

If the potential of a single nickel electrode is recorded on a strip chart recorder as if it were an ordinary EEG, two very interesting phenomena may be demonstrated. One phenomenon may be described as a moderate voltage (1-2 mV) waveform synchronized with the intertrial interval of the learning problem. The second

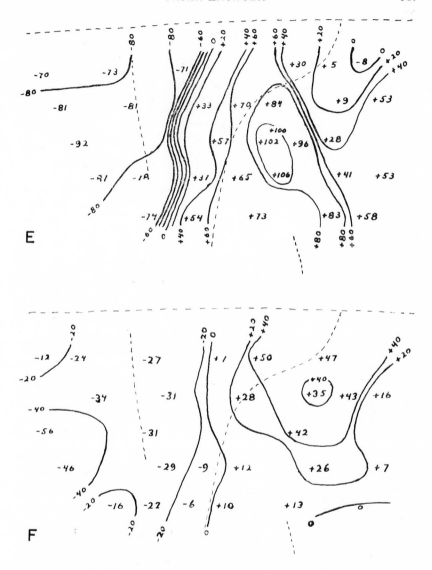

phenomenon, apparently restricted to prefrontal cortex, is an aperiodic, high voltage (often 100 mV) voltage fluctuation which appears to be correlated with a highly emotional state.

The nickel waveforms were recorded by connecting the Bausch and Lomb V.O.M. 5, and later, three Heath EUW-20a recorders directly to the nickel electrodes. The amplitude of these waveforms

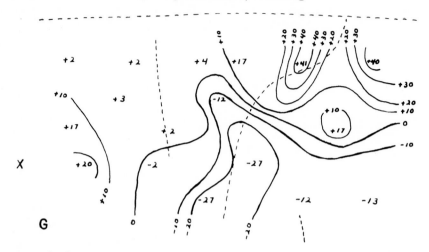

is such that no preamplifiers are needed. In the first experiment I was able to record from only one electrode at a time. After the Heath recorders were added, I was able to record from four electrodes simultaneously. Even so, the coverage was obviously very incomplete, and it is likely that significant data were missed.

The first usable records were obtained from Cebus 23, a cooperative female with extracranial nickel electrodes over the left hemisphere. Records were taken from fifteen electrodes distributed over the hemisphere as shown in Figure 59. It is immediately apparent that the periodic waveforms are largely confined to motor cortex, with some low amplitude waves appearing in parietal, occipital, and temporal lobes. There is no indication of periodic waves from premotor frontal cortex. The fact that this monkey was well adapted and quite relaxed in the experimental situation is probably pertinent to this lack of premotor activity.

These records were obtained during sessions ten through twenty of the one-tone, one-string problem. Her behavior had reached a stable level of performance several sessions before the first record was taken, so that the data do not reflect conditions during learning. Nonetheless, the clearest periodicity outside of motor cortex is seen in the vicinity of the parieto-occipital sulcus, which other data have shown to be critical to auditory learning.

A close examination of the data show that not all the periodic waveforms are in phase. The most active point, on the anterior edge

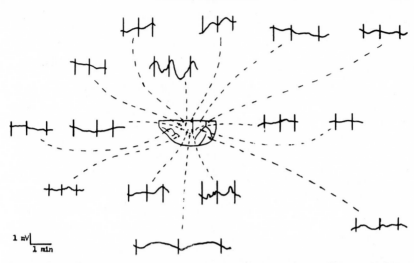

FIGURE 59. Waveforms recorded from nickel electrodes, Cebus 23, during stable performance of an operant response. Reinforcements indicated by vertical lines. Intertrial interval was varied between forty-five and ninety seconds, but each record was taken following several trials at constant spacing. Note periodic waveforms from motor cortex.

of the motor area, about 5 mm from the midline, shows responses occurring on the rising slope near the peak of the wave (positive potential upward in the figure). The region of the parieto-occipital sulcus shows the response occurring just past the peak of the wave, lateral motor cortex shows the response occurring near the trough, and other points show all intermediate phases.

The most lateral point in the motor cortex also illustrates an experimental control. The intertrial interval was deliberately varied at times during this experiment in order to be certain that it was the critical temporal variable. It may be seen that the waveform remains locked to the intertrial interval, even when it is approximately double the usual time.

Having found this interesting phenomenon, I was anxious to obtain similar data during learning to see if these waveforms related to the other data showing a critical role for the "learning-specific response" areas during auditory and visual learning. When the additional d.c. recorders were in operation, I started with a naive animal, Cebus 28, who had extracranial nickel electrodes over the right hemisphere. By recording from two different sets of electrodes on alternate days, I was able to obtain reasonably complete records from eight cortical points. The experiment was somewhat vitiated by a serious error in estimating the electrode locations, so that my choice of points from which to record was not optimal. Despite this, the data showed some very interesting facts (see Figure 60).

During the acquisition of an operant response to a visual cue (one-light, one-string problem), the monkey showed clear periodic waveforms over the occipital pole and the genu of the arcuate sulcus. The waveform over the occipital pole disappeared promptly when she was changed to an auditory (one-tone, one-string problem) task, but that over the arcuate sulcus faded out gradually, suggesting that it is more closely related to state of adaptation than to the particular problem in use. Unfortunately, I did not record from the electrode over the visual learning area on the parietal lip of the sylvian fissure. Records from closely adjacent electrodes showed no significant waveforms. This does not, however, indicate that the visual learning area would have proved negative had I recorded from it, since several examples may be seen in the data of adjacent electrodes which showed very different waveforms. The occipital pole, for instance, displayed a very consistent waveform during the visual learning problem, yet records taken from adjacent electrodes were completely negative. The same phenomenon may be seen in comparing the waveform from the genu of the arcuate sulcus, which was consistently in phase with the intertrial interval from the third session of the visual problem through the second session of the auditory problem, with records taken from an adjacent electrode over the medial limb of the sulcus, which were just as consistently negative.

When the learning problem was changed from a visual to an auditory cue, the waveforms over the occipital pole promptly disappeared, and clear periodic waves appeared from electrodes over medial parietal cortex and the intra-occipital sulcus, both of which had been consistently negative during the visual problem. Both of these locations are on the edge of the auditory learning area surrounding the parieto-occipital sulcus. Unfortunately, electrodes over primary auditory cortex were not sampled.

The shift in anatomical locus of this periodic activity as the learning and adaptation changed is most clearly seen by comparing the

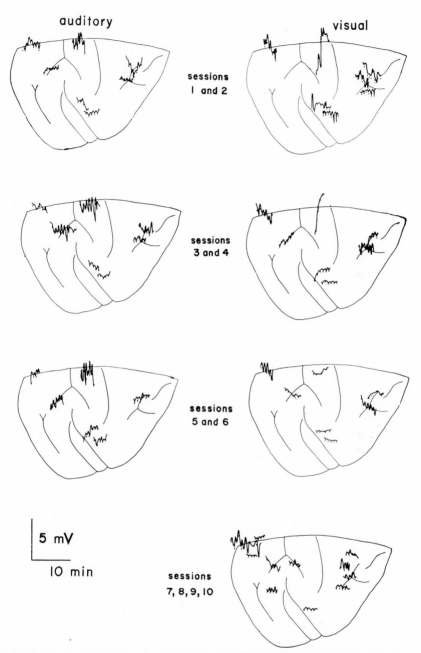

FIGURE 60. Nickel waveforms recorded from Cebus 28 during the learning of a visual and an auditory problem. The left-hand column shows data collected during auditory learning, the right-hand column data collected during visual learning. The small arrows beneath each waveform indicate occurrence of reinforcement.

data for visual problem, sessions five and six with those for auditory, sessions three and four. These are actually about equivalent points in the two learning problems, as the auditory learning was somewhat faster, undoubtedly because the monkey was better adapted to the experimental situation by that time.

A careful comparison of the waveforms with the contour maps recorded from this monkey over the same period shows no apparent relationship. The nickel potential contour maps from this animal show the usual positive peak over the arcuate sulcus (maximum +50 mV on session three of the visual problem) which fade gradually as she adapts. This correlates only very roughly with the disappearance of periodic activity from the same region, since the contours are quite flat by session one of the auditory problem, whereas the periodic activity is still visible. Furthermore, the clear periodic waveform recorded from the medial parietal region during auditory session five was from an electrode which was 7 mV negative to the average reference in a region free of steep voltage gradients.

Obviously, the investigation of these nickel potential contours and waveforms is only beginning. At present, the contour patterns and the moderate amplitude, periodic waveforms seem to be uncorrelated, and only the latter correlate meaningfully with the other toposcopically recorded data during learning. Another phenomenon, however, shows some promise of connecting the nickel potential contours, periodic waveforms, and the a.c. and d.c. toposcopic patterns during learning.

The reader has certainly observed the frequent appearance of prefrontal cortex near the arcuate sulcus in these studies. The a.c. toposcopic data implicated this region in situations calling for suppression of a response, and this finding was confirmed by the d.c. patterns found. The nickel potential contours seem to suggest that the arcuate cortex is involved in behavior patterns related to catatonia, or extreme timidity, and periodic nickel waveforms seem to appear here during the early experimental life of a preparation, before he has fully adapted to the situation.

In Cebus 27 (Satan), my "neurotic" monkey, a new and rather startling phenomenon was recorded from this same arcuate cortex. It will be recalled (see Fig. 53) that the nickel potential contours

in this animal consistently displayed steep gradients in the vicinity
of the arcuate sulcus, usually composed of sharp positive peaks just
lateral to the sulcus, frequently accompanied by smaller negative
troughs within the curve of the sulcus. I discovered that when
electrodes in this area were connected to the chart recorders, very
large, aperiodic waves were seen. Some of these fluctuations are
shown in Figure 61. Movement artifact is not a factor, since the
monkey sat immobile throughout most of the recording sessions,
and the waveforms were clearly restricted to the region around the
arcuate sulcus.

The fastest fluctuations seen amount to some 2 mV/sec, sometimes traversing 20 mV at this rate before abruptly reversing direction. They show only a crude synchrony between homotopic points
on the two hemispheres or between adjacent electrodes (8 mm
spacing) on the same hemisphere. The only certain conclusion that
can be drawn from this one animal is that whatever the biochemical system may be which is affecting the nickel electrodes, it is in a

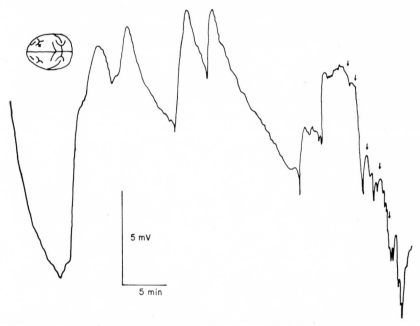

5 mV

5 min

FIGURE 61. Aperiodic waves recorded from a nickel electrode in Cebus 27
(Satan) during attempted adaptation. Electrode location shown by X in inset
at top left.

highly unstable state in that cortex surrounding the arcuate sulcus in this animal at this time. The implication of this fact for the effects of prefrontal lobotomy on human psychotics is interesting, but requires a very shaky extrapolation from very sketchy data. The obvious next step in this line of investigation is to determine the effect of psychotomimetic drugs on the nickel potentials from this area of cortex. Since the research grant has been terminated, this experiment must wait.

Chapter VII

ABLATIONS

A_{LL} the preceding data from various toposcopic techniques point toward the importance of particular areas of neocortex in visual and auditory operant learning and problem solving. The question naturally arises: What would happen if these areas were destroyed? It would appear, from the facts presented above, that selective ablation of the cortex around the parieto-occipital sulcus should be highly detrimental to learning involving auditory cues, but not to any other form of learning or behavior, and that ablation of the visual learning area on the anterior lip of the sylvian fissure should interfere only with visual learning. Ablation of the cortex just medial to the arcuate sulci should have some effect on any behavior requiring the suppression of response but should not affect learning per se.

I approached this experiment with some trepidation. Since the results of ablation experiments are notoriously hard to interpret, positive findings from this experiment may add some weight to the total evidence presented but could not be conclusive. Negative findings, on the other hand, would have set me back about four years, to the point where I had no clear idea as to the significance for normal learning processes of the toposcopically measured activity. Needless to say, the findings were not negative, or I would not be writing this book.

Since the procedures used were somewhat different for each animal, I will describe each preparation separately and in chronological sequence. A total of seven animals were used, two *Cebus albifrons* and five *Saimiri sciureus* (squirrel monkeys).

The first two preparations in this experiment were Cebus 32 and 33, both adolescent females. At this time I was experimenting with techniques for creating the desired lesions, a new type of electrode array, a new variation on the operant conditioning paradigm, and histological techniques for reconstructing the lesions. I am not feeling masochistic enough to detail all the mistakes I made, but the data from these two animals are of limited utility.

These lesions were made by thermocoagulation under direct vision. No histological reconstructions are available, but there is little question but that they were sufficiently extensive and that there was no overlap between the two sets of lesions.

Cebus 32 received bilateral ablations of the cortex in and surrounding the parieto-occipital sulci; the auditory learning area as defined by the toposcopic data. The lesions extended at least 2 mm beyond the boundaries of this learning area in every direction except medially, where they extended to the midline. No part of the lesion encroached within 1 cm of the visual learning area in the parietal lobe. This method of ablation, however, tends to interfere with blood supply and encourages the formation of dural adhesions around the ablated area, thus disrupting cerebrospinal fluid circulation. Furthermore, because of difficulties with the electrode array used, she developed an infection within a few days, and had to be maintained on penicillin throughout most of her experimental lifetime.

Cebus 33 received bilateral ablations of the visual learning areas on the anterior lip of the sylvian fissure. The location of these learning areas may be seen in Figures 36 and 38 (Chap. IV). As in Cebus 32, no histological data are available, but the cortical landmarks here are quite clear, and there is little doubt that the lesions extended 2 to 3 mm beyond the visual learning area in all directions, with some damage to the adjacent temporal cortex. This animal also developed postoperative infection, because of the type of electrode array used, and was maintained on penicillin throughout her experimental lifetime.

Cebus 32 and 33 were both run on the one-tone, two-string problem, followed by the one-light, two-string problem. I soon learned that these operant conditioning paradigms are very poor. It is possible for the animal to develop either an alternation response to the two strings, or to pull both strings simultaneously, obtaining the reward quite efficiently without having to learn the significance of the cues.

Cebus 32, with auditory ablations, fortunately adopted a strong position preference for the first one hundred trials. This actually makes the problem identical to the one-tone, one-string problem, which a normal Cebus should learn in about thirty trials. After one hundred trials with no sign of learning, she discovered the alternation response. I gave up after a total of 210 trials. The only conclusion that may be drawn from this is that she was deficient in auditory learning, but I cannot judge the extent of the deficiency.

Cebus 33, with visual area ablations, showed clear signs of learning the auditory problem after sixteen trials, but then, in the next session, discovered the technique of pulling both strings simultaneously. This works so well that there was no reason for her to learn anything further. I cannot be certain that she had no deficit in auditory learning.

Both animals began the one-light, two-string problem with well-practiced methods for cheating. Cebus 33 died of respiratory disease after ninety-eight trials with no clear signs of learning, but, of course, this tells us nothing. Cebus 32 retained her simple alternation response through seventy trials when I stopped the experiment to remove her electrode array. After her head had healed (so that she no longer needed penicillin), I trained her on the one-light, one-string problem. She showed signs of learning after sixty trials; she pawed at the light between stimulus presentations. Normally, this response is promptly followed by the development of a stable, efficient response to light onset. In her case, however, she did not reach such a stable state until after an additional one hundred trials. This result strongly suggests that ablation of the auditory learning areas causes a deficit in visual as well as auditory learning. Her previous experience with the one-light, two-string problem, however, which developed a well-practiced response which was unrelated to any cue stimulus, makes the conclusion uncertain.

Several changes were made in techniques and procedures for the next two animals, squirrel monkeys 47 and 48. The lesions were created with a radio frequency lesion maker, Grass model LM-3. The lesioning technique was calibrated on egg white, the parameters adjusted to create a lesion about 4 mm in diameter. The

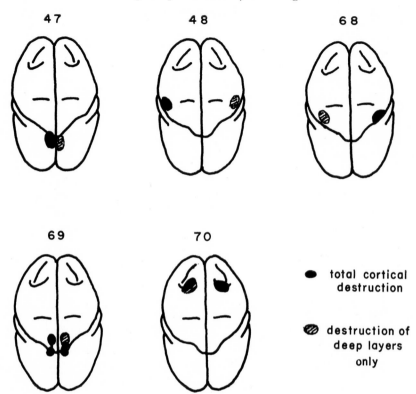

FIGURE 62. Reconstruction of cortical lesions in squirrel monkeys 47, 48, 68, 69 and 70.

technique used with these two animals was to locate the desired locations on the scalp by reference to a plastic model of the squirrel monkey brain. The model had been cast from the brain of an animal of similar size and weight. Two holes were then drilled through scalp and skull about 3 mm apart so that the two lesions would overlap. The electrode was inserted by hand to the desired depth, and the radio frequency current was passed for two minutes at each location. This creates a roughly oval volume of destruction, about 7 mm long by 4 mm across. The procedure is fast and simple, and the animals recover immediately. Postoperative infection has never occurred.

At the conclusion of the experiments, the animals were sacrificed, and the brains were removed and preserved in absolute alcohol after passing through a graded series. Alcohol was used rather than the usual formaldehyde fixative so that the sections could be stained with a picric acid and methylene blue stain with which I am experimenting. Formalin fixation prevents the use of this technique. I do not have all the problems out of the staining procedure yet, but even the failures are quite good enough for reconstruction of the lesion. When the stain works properly, as it occasionally does, it yields sections of great beauty, with deep blue perikarya and red fiber tracts. I have also found that brain tissue preserved in alcohol is much easier to section than that fixed in formalin. Since I am not the world's greatest microtomist, every bit helps.

Squirrel monkey 47 was given bilateral ablations of the auditory learning area surrounding the parieto-occipital sulci. He was run first on the one-light, one-string problem. He was rather poorly adapted to the experimental situation at the beginning of this problem, and spent a good deal of time upside-down. This made it difficult to deliver the stimuli when he was facing the panel and in a position to grasp the string. He learned slowly, showing some indication of learning after thirty-six trials but no clear and consistent response to the cue until about his eightieth trial. This is clearly outside the normal range for squirrel monkeys on this problem, the slowest previously in my notes being forty trials. His gymnastics, however, may have been as important a factor as his ablations.

Following the one-light problem, he was started on the one-tone, one-string problem. By this time, he was well adapted to the situation. He sat fairly quietly in the apparatus, appeared alert, and pulled the string vigorously for grapes. I gave up after 126 trials, when he still showed no indication that the tone had any significance whatsoever. Well-adapted, intact squirrel monkeys previously run on this problem have learned it in from 12 to 27 trials. Although the degrees of freedom are too few for a statistical test, I am quite satisfied that this preparation showed a severe deficit in auditory learning. He may also have had a visual learning deficit, but his behavior makes this conclusion uncertain.

Squirrel monkey 48 proved to be an important control animal. I intended to ablate her visual learning areas, but the postmortem data showed that I aimed too far laterally, missing them altogether. Since she underwent the same surgical procedure as the other squirrel monkeys used, she provides a "sham-operated" control. Since I believed her to be an experimental animal, with lesions of the visual learning areas, she also serves as a control for possible bias on my part. In effect, this accident converts the experimental procedure into a "double blind" design, in which neither the experimenter nor, presumably, the subjects, knew whether they were experimentals or controls at the time of data collection. Thus we rationalize our errors.

Her behavior in the apparatus was rather similar to that of squirrel monkey 47, but she ran the two problems in opposite sequence; that is, she started with the one-tone, one-string problem, during which she was rather poorly adapted, taking about sixty trials to learn. She then started the one-light, one-string problem, well adapted to the situation, and panicked the experimenter by learning it in thirty trials.

The postmortem examination of squirrel monkey 48 reassured me of the accuracy of my hypotheses but not of my methods for locating the lesions. I therefore modified the procedure for the remaining three squirrel monkeys. I used another squirrel monkey of the same size and weight which had reached the end of its experimental career, placed it in my stereotaxic instrument, and exposed its cortex over one entire hemisphere. I then adjusted the instrument until the electrode was in the desired location (this is quite unequivocal under direct vision) and noted the stereotaxic coordinates. These coordinates were then used to determine the location of the lesions for the three remaining squirrel monkeys in this series.

These last three squirrel monkeys, numbers 68, 69 and 70, were run as a group, taking considerable care to see that they all received comparable treatment. This replication of the experiment is an island of logical positivism in a slough of free-form research. If I were so inclined, I could even operationally define my hypotheses. I must immediately confess, however, that the results which I found most interesting were not the number of trials to criterion, but the manner in which each animal approached the solution of the problems presented it. For the benefit of those readers with orderly minds, if any such have persevered this far, I will first present the data in schematic, tabular form, then discuss the more interesting aspects of each animal's behavior in turn.

Squirrel monkey 68 had bilateral lesions of the visual learning areas, squirrel monkey 69 had bilateral lesions of the auditory learning areas, squirrel monkey 70 had bilateral lesions of the "response suppressor" areas just medial to the arcuate sulci. Four learning situations were used: the one-tone, one-string problem, the one-light, one-string problem, the simultaneous light-tone problem (these three are described in Chap. III), and a newly devised visual discrimination task, patterned after the Wisconsin general test apparatus. All animals completed the problems in the above order.

The results are summarized in Table II.

TABLE II

Subject	*Learning Problem*			
	One-Tone	*One-Light*	*Light-Tone*	*Visual Discrimination*
68 (visual ablations)	100	108	20	216
69 (auditory ablations)	126	133	30	30
70 ("suppressor" ablations)	57	10	160	78

The statistic used was number of trials to criterion, not including criterion trials. The one-tone and one-light problems were given in daily sessions of five reinforcements each, so that the number of trials per session was at least five, but might be more if the subject did not respond on some trials. The average number of trials per session was about 5.5. The light-tone problem was given in daily sessions of ten trials, six of which were positive (light and tone simultaneously), two were light alone, and two were tone alone. The visual discrimination problem was given in daily sessions of six trials each.

The visual discrimination task was not described in chaper three, since it has only been used with these three squirrel monkeys and is not original. The animal was placed in a wire cage, a 15-inch cube, covered with cardboard except on the front and the small access door in the rear. She was unrestrained within the cage. The cage wire was a 1-inch by 2-inch mesh, through which the monkey could easily reach. Two food cups were formed by drilling 1½-inch holes through an 18-inch length of 1-inch by 4-inch lumber, then covering the under side with Masonite.™ The wells were spaced 13 inches apart on centers. When the board was placed against the wire front of the cage, the two food cups were at opposite sides of the cage front, with the centers of the cups 2 inches from the wire. The cups were covered by sheet aluminum, bent at an acute angle so that one side of the aluminum covered the cup and the other side sloped at a 30 degree angle from the vertical, or about normal to the line of sight of a squirrel monkey standing near the front of the cage. This upright portion of the aluminum covers was painted flat black with a white figure in the center. One cover had an equilateral triangle, 1 inch on each side, the other, a 1-inch diameter circle.

The reward was always placed under the cover with the triangle. Right-left position was randomized within the limitation that it appear three times on each side during each six-trial session, and that a random sequence of RRRLLL or LLLRRR or RLRLRL or vice versa was not accepted. The reward was a red grape during most of the problem. Toward the end, however (in March), red grapes became absolutely unobtainable. I was forced to switch to white grapes. Since squirrel monkey 70 made it very clear that she did not care for white grapes, I broke faith with the logical positivists and used raisins for her. (Squirrel monkey 68 did not like raisins. Philosophers seldom have to deal with opinionated subjects.)* The covers were placed over the cups in such a position that the cue surface was turned toward the usual position of the monkey near the front center of the cage.

The food cup was baited out of the animal's view, then the board was placed against the wire front of the cage. On the first trial of each session, the monkey usually responded promptly. On the remaining five trials, however, she was typically still working on the last grape, so that she had twenty or thirty seconds to examine the covers while she masticated before making her next response. Correction procedure was used, so the monkey was reinforced on each trial. The primary datum was the first cover moved on each trial. Criterion of learning was one perfect session together with some evidence of deliberate choice. This was usually evidenced by the monkey's looking back and forth between the two covers before

---

*Squirrel monkey 69 did not care; she had already finished the experiment and her brain was pickled in ethyl alcohol, a rather enviable situation in some respects.

reaching for one. Squirrel monkey 69, however, showed evidence of choice behavior by reaching for the wrong cover, then stopping before she had touched it, looking over at the other side, then shifting to the correct side and grasping the cover with no hesitation. In addition to these requirements, I also ran the monkey for one additional session, looking for further evidence that she knew what she was doing, but I did not require perfect performance on a second session, as long as the errors appeared to be due to carelessness rather than ignorance.

My rat-running readers may consider this criterion to be inadequate, since six correct trials out of six could be achieved by chance on one out of sixty-four sessions. A monkey's behavior, however, is never random. The animal may consistently respond first to the left cup, or may consistently respond first to the cup which contained the grape on the last trial, or may, rarely, consistently alternate. Sometimes a monkey will shift strategy in the middle of a session, giving rise to a sequence that looks random. If you watch the animal closely, however, it is almost always clear what strategy is being followed, and random responses very rarely occur. Since I rejected any sequences of left-right position that might coincide with one of these strategies, the monkeys tended to be correct on three trials each session, no matter what strategy they adopted. In fact, out of fifty sessions on which I judged the animal had not yet learned the discrimination (that is, all sessions excluding criterion sessions), I found only one session with five correct and two with one correct. All other sessions were two, three, or four correct. Of these three atypical sessions, the one with five correct was rather clearly a partial and temporary solution, and one of the two sessions with only one correct response was apparently a reversed solution, that is, she appeared to be responding to the cue patterns, but had it all backward. There is, therefore, only one session out of fifty in which the monkey "randomly" achieved a score other than two, three, or four. This one case was a session in which she switched strategies in midstream and happened to hit upon the worst possible approach to that particular sequence.

A partial exception to this rule of nonrandomness was squirrel monkey 70, with lesions in the "response suppressor" region. She usually followed a simple position tendency but would occasionally respond to the other side if she happened to be facing that way when I put the board in place. More about her behavior below.

Squirrel monkeys 68 and 69, with lesions of the visual and auditory learning areas, respectively, showed no differential effects of the two different lesions throughout the series of operant conditioning tasks. Both animals appeared to have serious impairments in learning both the one-tone, one-string problem and the one-light, one-string problem. Once they had succeeded in learning these responses, neither had any difficulty in suppressing both these responses and learning to respond only to light and tone together. Their behavior throughout appeared fairly normal. They adapted to the apparatus at about the normal rate. Squirrel monkey 68 actually adapted somewhat more quickly than the average squirrel monkey, squirrel monkey 69 adapted somewhat more slowly; both were within the normal range.

The fact that squirrel monkeys 68 and 69 appeared to be affected similarly by two very different ablations puzzled me. One possible explanation that occurred to me is that the one-string problems thus far used actually contain both visual and auditory components aside from the cue stimuli. The sound of the solenoid which delivers the grape may serve an important mediating role in learning, as may the sight of the string. The primary reason for using the visual discrimination task was to set up a situation which had no auditory components. As may be seen from Table II, this task clearly differentiated between squirrel monkeys 68 and 69. It appears likely that if a situation were devised which had no visual components whatsoever, it too would discriminate between the two lesions.

The most interesting aspect of this series of experiments, however, was the effect of the frontal lobe lesions in squirrel monkey 70. It should be borne in mind that these were quite restricted lesions, involving only about 25 mm^2 of neocortex on each hemisphere, or less than 1 percent of the total neocortex of the squirrel monkey. A change in her behavior was obvious the morning following surgery when I removed her from the incubator. She showed almost no fear of me and remarkably little tendency to fight the harness and leash, which she had never experienced before. This placidity was in marked contrast to her behavior prior to surgery, which had been normally wild. Except for one brief lapse into wild, emotional behavior, this placidity lasted throughout the five months of her experimental life. It was clearly outside the normal range; I have never handled a squirrel monkey of such docility.

When she was first placed in the apparatus, she made practically no effort to escape from the restraint. In contrast to every other squirrel monkey I have adapted to this situation, she did not urinate or defecate during her first trips into the apparatus. Her movements had a curious, rhythmic quality. She went through motions which were somewhat related to the normal struggles of a monkey when first encountering this restraint, but her movements lacked emotion or variety. She would frequently repeat a simple motion over and over again for thirty to sixty seconds.

She was obviously unable to suppress inappropriate behavior. During her second adaptation session, she started to reach for a grape in the cup with her mouth, rather than with her hand. There was too little slack in the leash to let her reach the cup, yet she continued to make rhythmic swaying motions, reaching toward the cup with her mouth and then straightening again, for several seconds before she finally picked up the grape by hand. As she learned to pull the string, she would occasionally reach for it and miss, then repeat this "stroking" motion in the air for ten to twenty times, missing the string each time.

Adaptation in her case was not a matter of overcoming the emotional reaction to the situation, as it is with other monkeys, but of learning techniques by which she could compensate for her poor control of motor behavior. These stereotyped movements became gradually less prominent as she learned to compensate for them. Eventually, she spent most of her time sitting quite still, the string grasped in one or both hands, ready to respond when appropriate. Her performance was never really reliable, though, because it might be disrupted at any time by some irrelevant behavior, which, once started, could not be stopped.

Not all of her problems appeared to be due to lack of suppression of behavior. During some sessions her motor behavior appeared to be generally inhibited. At a point in the one-tone problem, for instance, where she had clearly learned the contingency, she would perform very well on some sessions and very poorly on others. The cause of her poor performance was a "freezing" in response to the onset of the tone, which markedly increased the latency of the response and sometimes outlasted a ten-second stimulus so that the trial was missed altogether. On one session late in the one-light problem, she seemed to go into a catatonic state which lasted throughout the session. She literally did not move a muscle throughout the five-minute session; as nearly as I could tell, she did not even blink. When I opened the apparatus door to remove her, she suddenly screamed in terror, whereas she had shown no fear of me before. The following day her behavior was back to normal (for her). She frequently displayed less extreme forms of inhibited behavior, such as responding to the cue stimulus with a gentle tug on the string, too weak to close the microswitch. Such an inadequate response might then be repeated ten or twenty times without pause, an interesting case of uninhibited inhibited motor behavior.

In summary, her problem was not an inability to inhibit or suppress motor activity, but rather a lack of control over such suppression, so that it often appeared inappropriately or failed to appear when needed.

The same explanation appears appropriate for her performance on the visual discrimination problem. She showed rather clear signs of learning after forty-eight trials and performed perfectly after sixty trials. On the session following this criterion session, however, she behaved as if she had never seen the stimuli before. Her difficulty here was clearly due to lack of restraint. As soon as the food cups were moved within reach, she rushed toward the wire, reaching frantically for whichever happened to be nearer. I tried placing the cups just outside her reach for a few seconds, hoping to force her to look at them. However, she would look at one, and immediately reach through the wire for it. Unable to grasp the cover, she would look over at the other one, then immediately dash over and reach through the wire for that one. It seemed as if the act of looking could not be separated from the act of reaching, as it was in the other monkeys. Only occasionally, when for some unknown reason her behavior was under better control, could she demonstrate that she knew the significance of the triangle.

To summarize the results of this series of experiments, the data are all compatible with the basic hypotheses that the visual learning area is essential to visual learning and the auditory learning area to auditory learning. The results of the visual discrimination experiment demonstrate that the auditory learning area is not essential to learning this problem. I cannot conclude from these data that the visual learning area is not essential to auditory learning, but that is probably because I have not devised a purely auditory learning problem.

Ablation of the "suppressor" cortex medial to the arcuate sulci does not interfere with either auditory or visual learning, but does interfere with performance in the simultaneous light-tone problem and causes obvious behavioral alterations as well. I conclude that the effect of this ablation is a lack of control over motor inhibition.

Chapter VIII

INTERPRETATIONS

ADMITTEDLY, these data leave a great many questions unanswered. Certain rather general trends, however, are so consistent through the various experiments that they would seem to be established beyond any reasonable doubt. Discrete loci in the cerebral cortex play a critical role in specific operant conditioning situations and in the utilization of immediate memory. The location of this critical area depends upon the sensory modality of the major information source. Specifically, during auditory operant conditioning, the focal area (in Cebus or squirrel monkeys) straddles the parieto-occipital sulcus, whereas in visual learning, the critical area is on the anterior lip of the sylvian fissure.

During the active phase of learning, the electrical activity of these critical loci is distinguishably different from normal, whether examined by a.c. or d.c. toposcopy. The a.c. change is ephemeral; it cannot be described in unequivocal, quantitative terms. The d.c. change, as recorded by long-term d.c. toposcopy, is highly distinctive and consistent. It consists of a 5 to 10 mV positive shift over the cortical area involved, appearing coincident with or slightly before the first observable signs of learning, and maintained for several days, or until learning is reasonably complete. When the learning is well established, the cortical activity appears identical to that before learning began.

Similar activity appears during a delayed-response problem, during the time periods when the location of the reward is presumably being held in the animals' memory. In this case, the activity does not disappear upon completion of learning but is maintained indefinitely. It appears to be closely associated with the use and even the contents of memory.

In the monkey this focal activity is usually unilateral, typically more concentrated in the left than in the right hemisphere. It appears to be more intense and varied in the frontal lobe than in any other major subdivision of the brain; however, neither the occipital lobe nor the inferotemporal region were adequately sampled by the electrode arrays used. There appears to be a qualitative difference between the psychological phenomena accompanying focal activity in the parietal area and that in the frontal lobe. This difference was borne out by the differential effects of ablating the cortical regions concerned. The focal regions of the parietal lobe seem to affect only specific learning abilities and have no apparent effect on other behaviors. Ablation of the frontal focal regions, however, caused very obvious and pervasive changes in behavior. It appears safe to conclude that the focal activity found in the frontal lobe was not concerned with learning per se but with alteration in previously learned behavior.

The only other set of organized data with which these may be directly compared is that produced by Livanov and his co-workers using the 50- and 100-channel electroencephaloscope. They have investigated the course of classical conditioning in the rabbit as well as conditioning and problem solving in humans. Of the phenomena they describe, the one that appears most closely related to the foci found in my research is the "local high-amplitude oscillation of potential," usually abbreviated LHOP. The phenomenon is also referred to as a "focus of enhanced bioelectrical activity," "stationary focus of excitation," or, if it was too stationary, a "stagnant focus of excitation," a term with a most unpleasant odor.

Such a focus is defined by high amplitude, usually around 500 μV, small area, usually one or two electrodes at a spacing of about 2 mm, and low frequency. The most common form seems to be a monotonic negative shift which drifts back toward the base line, probably as a function of the time constant of the a.c. coupled amplifiers. Shul'gina was able to record several instances of such LHOP through d.c. electrodes and amplifiers and found them to be d.c. step-functions, usually negative, although both polarities were found. Investigation with electrodes spaced .7 mm apart showed the LHOP to be usually confined to a single electrode or at least greatly attenuated at adjacent ones. Such extreme localization suggests that with a normal electrode spacing of 2 to 3 mm, most instances of LHOP would be missed.

The electrophysiology of this LHOP bears only slight resemblance to that of the foci I found in my monkeys. The rabbit, however, bears little resemblance to a Cebus; nor does the simple, classical conditioning with acute preparations resemble the operant conditioning paradigms I used. There are, however, certain relationships between these two examples of focal activity.

Livanov's group reports very little spontaneous focal activity at the beginning of an experiment, with a marked increase in such activity as the conditioned response is formed. Furthermore, the increase occurs primarily in areas of cortex surrounding the primary receiving area for the conditioned stimulus in use. These facts are closely parallel to the parameters of my focal activity. The smaller physical dimensions of the foci found by Livanov are very probably related to the smaller size of the rabbit brain. The fact that LHOP do not disappear upon completion of conditioning is interesting and, I think, teaches something well beyond the confines of electrophysiology.

Any mature mammal, even a rabbit, must necessarily have learned many things during its lifetime. Livanov's data and mine agree that the focal activity found is not correlated with the occurrence of either stimulus or response but only generally with the progress of learning. One may therefore reasonably ask, if such focal activity increases during the early stages of learning or conditioning, but does not then decrease when learning is complete, why is the mature animal not convulsed by the accumulated focal activity of its months or years of learning? Obviously, any grossly observable indices of learning must disappear as learning is completed, otherwise such electrophysiological changes would be cumulative over the animal's lifetime. Why, then, does the focal activity persist in the case of classical conditioning or delayed response?

If we think of learning in terms of problem solving, I think the answer to this question is fairly obvious. In the case of a delayed response, each trial constitutes a new problem, since the essential cue to the correct response is not present at the time the response is to be made. The response cannot become habitual or automatic. Similarly, the classical conditioning paradigm may be viewed as a problem-solving situation which cannot be solved. It seems reasonable to assume that the cortical activity of a rabbit being painfully shocked at frequent intervals would be directed toward finding a way to avoid the shocks. Since the shock is unavoidable in the Pavlovian paradigm, the problem has no solution. An acutely prepared rabbit strapped into a framework is not likely to find other matters with which to distract its neural processes until something resembling apathy terminates it. It is well known that Pavlovian conditioning is primarily useful as a device for producing experimental neurosis.

With a few reasonable assumptions, therefore, Livanov's data agree with mine in general location (association regions), temporal duration (active problem solving) and in the importance of d.c. processes. They appear to differ in spatial extent and in the details of electrophysiological description, but considering the different preparations used, and the great difference in speed of recording, this is not surprising.

If I may drop the thinly disguised term *focus* in favor of the more pregnant *dominant focus*, another point of agreement between my data and Livanov's is worth discussion. The Moscow group assumes that the focal activity they have found is the electrophysiological symptom of a dominant focus. The primary basis for this assumption is the fact that similar LHOP activity has been recorded from presumptive dominant foci established by mechanical pressure or strychnine. My own reason for assuming a relationship is both more tenuous and more direct.

The definitive model of a dominant focus is cortex polarized by the passage of about 5 μA/mm^2 anodal current. Since my learning foci are characterized by a surface positivity of 5 to 10 mV, it seems at least reasonable to assume, despite the dangers of predicting current flow through as complex a substance as cerebral cortex, that there must necessarily exist a current flow under such a focus of rather similar amperage and concentration. If the source of the potential is in the uppermost layer of cortex, then the current flow as conventionally represented must be downward and should be in the general range of a few microamperes per square millimeter. Such would not be the case if the source of the positive potential were actually somewhat below the cortical surface, but such an event seems unlikely in view of Aladjalova's measurements, which showed the depths of the cortex consistently negative to the surface.

If these assumptions are correct, that the source of the positive potential is very near the cortical surface, and that the resulting current flow is about 5 μA to 10 μA, then the effects of such a d.c. focus should be very similar to the effects of artificially applied polarization. Rusinov, Morrell, and many others have established the effects of such polarization in considerable detail. During the time that such a current is passing, a previously neutral stimulus becomes able to elicit the response represented by the bit of cortex being polarized. After the polarization is discontinued, such a stimulus is still able to elicit that reponse for a period of minutes or hours, but another neutral stimulus remains neutral. In other words, while the current is flowing, the cortical point "learns"; after the current is stopped, the cortical point "remembers."

One naturally wonders why this should be so. The first approach to a theoretical mechanism for such a change of state usually starts with the fact that the apical dendrites of the cortical pyramidal cells are vertically oriented and are therefore polarized along their major axis by such an inward-flowing current. Explanations based on this fact, however, overlook both the basal dendrites, which actually constitute more dendritic surface than do the apical dendrites, and the fact that a dominant focus can apparently be established by passage of anodal current through an electrode placed in thalamus or hypothalamus or even the reticular formation, where there is obviously no such neat arrangement of neurons relative to the electrode.

The solution probably lies in the tangled forest of electrochemistry, wherein I am hardly competent to serve as guide. In aqueous solution an electric current means a flow of ions. The neural effects of such a current probably stem from the altered ionic populations in the vicinity of the electrode. That is about as specific as I would care to be in a field so far removed from psychology. Leaving biochemistry to the biochemists, however, it is clear that the positive foci recorded by the d.c. toposcope behave in much the same way as an externally imposed anodal current. What is "learned," however, is not a specific movement in response to a specific stimulus, as would presumably be the case if the dominant focus were over motor cortex. In this case, the dominant focus is over parietal cortex, generally assumed to be an area for secondary elaboration of somesthetic information. The most reasonable assumption, then, is that the acquired association is between the cue stimulus and a somesthetic pattern. I would further assume, with no other support than that it seems reasonable, that the region of the parieto-occipital sulcus is a cortical point in which a particular somesthetic pattern, specifically that of pulling, overlaps with auditory information, and that the anterior lip of the sylvian fissure is an area where the same somesthetic pattern overlaps with visual information. When a dominant focus occurs in the former region, ambient auditory "stimuli" become able to elicit a representation of the act of pulling a string. When it occurs in the latter region, visual "stimuli" become capable of eliciting the same representation.

If the animal is hungry, or at least willing to eat grapes (inferred from his reaction when a grape drops in the cup), he will perform a motor action which corresponds to the somesthetic representation, that is, he will pull the string.

With most electrophysiological phenomena we cannot tell whether we are measuring a cause of a change in functional state or merely a symptom. In this case we appear to be more fortunate. The phenomenon is simple enough that it may effectively be imitated. Morrell has performed the relevant research, using anodal and cathodal polarization of different cortical regions in chronically prepared rats. He found that when cathodal polarization was applied to the sensory area, the rats appeared to learn nothing. When anodal polarization was applied to the same points, learning seemed to be accelerated, although this effect did not reach statistical significance, probably because of a restricted range. Interestingly, polarization of motor cortex had no effect. It would appear that d.c. currents in the range of 5 μA-10 μA/mm^2 are a casual agent in the mechanisms of learning, not simply a symptom of some other underlying mechanism.

To extend the argument to other mental processes in a somewhat more complex mammal, the influence of d.c. currents on human perception and emotion has been examined by several investigators. The initial datum, so far as I have been able to determine, was recorded by Kohler and Wallach in 1944. In a footnote to their massive report on figural aftereffects, they say:

> We once tried to establish electrotonus in the visual cortex from the outside. Two points of the skull—above one occipital lobe—were connected with the poles of a direct-current source. When, with one subject, fairly strong currents were used the visual field seemed to be affected on the opposite side. But we give no weight to this observation because it ought not to be repeated. For two weeks afterwards the subject suffered from a persistent headache and a disturbing state of depression.

Twenty years later, Lippold and Redfearn, less timorous than Kohler and Wallach, collected data from 171 subjects on the effects of polarization of the frontal lobes. Undeterred by such data from early subjects as "nausea," "confused speech," "loud complaints of pain," "nausea, pallor, could not speak," "talk of suicide," and so forth, they pressed on to determine, finally, that they could distinguish the effects of anodal current from those of cathodal, at the .001 level of significance. Anodal polarization through the eye sockets tends to produce elevation of mood and increased involvement with the environment, cathodal polarization produces withdrawal and quietness.

There seems to me little question but that d.c. potentials are a potent causal agent in controlling the functional state of cortical tissue and almost certainly subcortical tissue as well. The most interesting questions appear to be: What is the informational, or psychological function of a localized d.c. potential? and What structure, or structures control the distribution of d.c. potentials across the cortical surface?

In considering the first question, we can immediately see some things that the d.c. shift is *not*. It is not a memory. It is not temporally related to a specific stimulus situation, it does not have the detailed information-carrying capacity, and it remains quite constant during a period in which it is reasonable to assume that the animal's memories concerning the experimental situation are changing. It is constant over too long a period to be related to short-term memory, and disappears too soon to represent long-term memory.

It is not a facilitation of a particular pattern of motor activity. The d.c. shift shows only a most general correlation with the emission of responses. It is present in some animals whose response rate is decreasing. It remains constant while the specific manner of string pulling undergoes wide variation. It remains after an animal, full to overflowing with grapes and bored with my games, refuses to have anything further to do with the manipulanda provided him.

It is not a state of selective attention (as I once thought). It remains constant for several hours after the animal is removed from the experimental apparatus, when he is obviously attending to many things, but not to the conditioned stimuli.

The localized d.c. shift does not seem to correspond precisely to any familiar psychological variable. It appears to be closely associated with learning, but this may be due to the fact that I have been studying learning, and have therefore given the phenomenon little opportunity to appear in any other context. It certainly appears to be prerequisite to learning or, in the case of the premotor frontal cortex, to a change in learned behavior, and yet is not correlated with attention, drive, contiguity, or any of the other psychological terms which are thought to constitute the prerequisites of learning. The best that can be said at this point is that the d.c. polarization brings about a change of state in a particular bit of cortical tissue which is a necessary prerequisite to learning.

That such a mechanism should exist is eminently reasonable. If learning is to aid survival, it must be restricted to significant situations rather than being turned on continually so that every bit of trivia that comes our way is learned and gravely stored with the same care given to those bits of information that may one day save our lives. Some part of the brain must be able to recognize what constitutes a problem. As my wife chatters on at me about the day's happenings, some part of my brain must remain sufficiently involved to distinguish the fact that the car is developing an ominous knock from all the other flow of irrelevant information requiring no action on my part. If this selective mechanism is working properly, the next morning I will remember to get the car in to the garage, although I will have no memory of the marital difficulties of my wife's third cousin twice removed.

Such selective memory, or learning, is not the same thing as selective attention, although it obviously requires attention. Such a mechanism must be relatively fast in order to start the learning function before immediate memory fades. It need not be highly selective, since selective attention, obviously a separate function, can serve to screen the information presented to the learning mechanism.

Once a problem has been satisfactorily solved, this learning mechanism would presumably turn off, thus protecting the solution from disruption by the varied flow of information and behavior which goes on continually. Since there is probably no part of the brain which is not almost continually involved in normal, ongoing behavior, any theoretical mechanism of learning must explain the preservation of such learned patterns of neural activity in the face of continual, irrelevant activity.

Finally, one naturally asks the question: What brain structure controls the distribution of d.c. potential, and therefore, by inference, the process of problem solving? Here it is very easy to be set off on another search for the seat of the soul. Since consciousness is unitary, it is natural to look for a small, centralized structure to support it, such as the pineal gland, or the reticular formation.

Since Adametz and Kesner and others (including DeMott, unpublished observations) have made the midbrain reticular formation an uncomfortable seat for the soul by destroying it with no apparent ill effects, attention naturally shifts to the midline and anterior thalamus, which appears small enough, and is certainly central enough, to make a cozy home for the conscious soul. There is even a certain amount of experimental evidence to support such a thesis.

Since Morrison and Dempsey's discovery of the recruiting response, several investigators have shown that stimulation of the medial thalamus produces d.c. changes in the cortex. Furthermore, ablation of medial thalamic nuclei has been shown to retard learning.

It would seem, then, that the nonspecific thalamus and closely related striatum is a reasonable place to continue the search for the "Holy Grail." I would expect to find that stimulation of these nuclei caused enduring d.c. shifts in the cortex, as measured by chronically implanted electrodes, and that lesions reduced the lability of cortical d.c. potential to the same extent that they interfered with learning or behavioral modification. The fact that there is an anatomical separation of the thalamic nuclei projecting to the prefrontal lobe in primates and those nuclei projecting to other parts of the cortex is consonant with the different functional significance of the d.c. foci in these cortical areas.

The few data from nickel electrodes also support this functional distinction between frontal lobe and posterior lobes. The waveforms recorded from parietal, temporal, and occipital lobes were correlated only with the time course of the learning problem. The distinctive aperiodic changes recorded from the region of the arcuate sulcus, however, seemed more closely correlated with something which, if you will pardon the anthropomorphism, might be called mood. Since such controversial matters come close to the realm of theology, however, further discussion will be put off to the next chapter, wherein I shall say everything that is really interesting and therefore inappropriate in a scientific report.

References

ADAMETZ, J.H.: Rate of recovery of functioning in cats with rostral reticular lesions. *J. Neurosurg.*, 16:85-98, 1959.

KESNER, R.P., FIELDER, P., and THOMAS, G.J.: Function of the midbrain reticular formation in regulating level of activity and learning in rats. *J. Comp. Physiol. Psychol.*, 63:452-457, 1967.

KOHLER, W., and WALLACH, H.: Figural after-effects. *Proc. Amer. Phil. Soc.*, 88:269-357, 1944.

LIPPOLD, O.C.J., and REDFEARN, J.W.T.: Medical changes resulting from the passage of small direct currents through the human brain. *Brit. J. Psychiat.*, 110:768-772, 1962.

MORRISON, R.S., and DEMPSEY, E.W.: A study of thalamo-cortical relations. *Amer. J. Physiol.*, 135:281-300, 1942.

Chapter IX

ECCLESIASTES

In ADDITION to recording the vagaries of the electrochemical contours across the crania of my experimental subjects, I have watched them as they learned the strange behaviors I have required of them, as they remonstrated with me over working conditions, as they played and fought with each other. Occasionally I have even discussed the sorry state of our world with them. They were always sympathetic.

The thing that has impressed me most, as I watched these carefree, yet intent, simians, was the inadequacy of terminology in contemporary experimental psychology. To take one example from the richly varied behavior of Cebus 26, whose name was Spice to those who counted him among their friends (and was any one of a variety of epithets to those who had to clean up the wreckage he continually managed to create), I would frequently stand in front of his cage, talking to him about various topics of mutual interest after I had finished the daily chores of feeding and medicating the animals. Usually, as I stood there conversing with him, I was loading my pipe with tobacco, tamping it down, then applying the lighter and polluting the air with clouds of smoke. I noted that the Cebus characteristically squints whenever he sees a flame at close range.

On one occasion after extinguishing the lighter, I held it near the cage for his inspection. He reached out, felt it all over rather gingerly, then grasped the spark wheel and attempted to turn it. As he did so, he squinted. I find such behavior difficult to describe in terms of stimuli and learned responses. Spice had never before touched the lighter. To say that the stimulus of his touching the lighter was sufficiently similar to that of my having done so to elicit a common response is stretching the concept of stimulus to the breaking point. Spice's fingers do not really look very much like mine (mine are cleaner, for one thing). The most compelling sensory aspect of the situation was almost certainly the tactual texture of the rough spark wheel, but this was something he had never experienced before.

The only clear relationship between Spice's attempted manipulation and his previous observation of my using the lighter is a functional one. He obviously expected that when the wheel was turned by whatever means, the lighter would burst into flame, and so he squinted. A functional relationship between two situations nearly always implies an expectation of some sort of common outcome. Expectation, however, is a naughty word in most psychological theorizing. It smacks of vitalism.

If we pick up any issue of the *Journal of Experimental Psychology*, we can find examples of the use of a one-tailed or two-tailed test based on the psychologist's prediction of the direction of some experimental statistic. Psychologists may make predictions, but they do not permit such behavior on the part of their subjects.

A computer may be programmed to accept information, to make predictions, to chose between alternative courses of action on the basis of predicted outcomes and relative values. Computers are immune to charges of vitalism because they are made of transistors and diodes. Anything constructed of neurons, however, must restrict itself to absorbing stimuli and emitting responses, lest it be accused of harboring a soul. (Apparently this is some sort of dread disease which psychologists are attempting to wipe out by means of quarantine.)

If a friend of yours is absorbed in reading, and you stab him in the buttock with a largish pin, he will have absorbed a stimulus and will almost certainly emit a response. When this basically reflex and emotional response has subsided, however, he will very likely continue with more complex forms of goal-directed behavior. The goal will not be difficult to discern; it will be to effect an immediate and long-lasting change in your future behavior. The methods he may choose to achieve this goal, however, will depend upon many factors. They will be affected by his values, the kinds of behavior he finds acceptable in himself. They will be influenced by his store of information concerning you and by his predictions as to how you might react to various alternative behaviors on his part. His behavior will certainly be too complex and too loosely tied to the stimulus situation to be realistically described by the term *response*.

Stimulus-response psychology then, might accurately be described as a "pain in the buttock" psychology. It permits us to predict only in situations so simple that commonsense prediction works equally well.

In the sort of behavorial situations used in the present research, stimulus-response psychology would permit me to predict that the animal would learn to pull the string, granted a certain amount of "spontaneous" string pulling which could be reinforced, and might even, by invoking the concept of retroactive inhibition, explain the fact that when learning was complete, an animal frequently stopped responding after the first three or four trials of each session. How does it then explain the fact that he spent the rest of the session making faces at himself in the mirror or peering out at me through chinks in the apparatus to see what I was up to? How does one possibly explain the fact that a monkey will consistently work for ten trials per session at a difficult problem like the hypothesis problem long after "retroactive inhibition" would have ended his active participation in a simpler problem, such as the one-string?

It seems that we need a behavioral language more closely related to real organisms and real behavior. I think we might start by eliminating the word "response" altogether. It implies an isolated action which is produced by immediate inputs, as is the behavior of a billiard ball. Such atomistic reductionism, although it may be true in a final, philosophical sense (I said "may be"), is most unhelpful in the analysis of real behavior. The term "response" is only appropriate at the level of single neurons. When referring to organisms, and particularly organisms as complex as mammals, terms like *attempt* and *seek* and *strive* are more accurate than *respond*.

Similarly, the term *stimulus* is inappropriate. It implies a discrete change of state in energy impinging on receptors which may usefully be considered apart from the continual stream of information pouring in through every modality. Such discrete changes occur, of course, but almost exclusively in the context of psychological experiments. If we use terms such as *information*, we are less likely to overlook the fact that our subjects have many sources of information besides the stimuli we provide and that most of those sources are not under our control. The behavior of a college sophomore is not produced by our stimulus situations but is behavior he has selected to accomplish some purpose (gain credit for research participation? impress the professor?) in light of all the information available to him, including what his friends have said about psychologists, his estimate of what this professor wants, and so on.

Even my monkeys do not perform because of the stimulus situations I construct. They only behave if they "want" to behave. In most animal experiments, we make them want to behave by the clever and subtle means of starving them. In human experiments, we bribe them with research credits or hard cash. In one way or another, we must make it to the subject's advantage to cooperate. Psychologists can hardly take credit for the discovery of this most ancient law of those who would manipulate.

The only serious problems that arise in trying to construct such a realistic language of behavior have to do with teleology. We cannot permit the present to be determined by the future. A prediction, of course, is not teleological but is a present event, firmly rooted in the past. If, then, we can visualize a mechanism by means of which the mammalian brain might reasonably generate predictions, the rest is easy, since Tolman showed the way.

I do not pretend to be a neurophysiologist. My approach to this problem has been that of a gadgeteer attempting to construct something that would make predictions without violating any of the better established facts of cerebral anatomy and physiology. The overwhelming fact with which I begin is that of the cerebral cortex. No matter how bemused we may become with the reticular formation, septum, hypothalamus, or wherever the current fad may carry us, it is still true that the cortex, together with white matter and striatum which are integral parts of the cortex, constitutes well over 80 percent of the mass and volume of the primate brain. Modern western physiology gives the impression that this mass of tissue exists to insulate the diencephalon from the skull.

The second fact that impresses me is that the cortex is a two-dimensional structure. Hubel and Wiesel have shown that the visual area, at least, is functionally divided into columns of cells, with cross-sectional areas of about one square millimeter. Using this as a first approximation and applying it to the human brain (I am sure this is not quantitatively valid, but it does not matter). I visualize a two-dimensional array of about one million little gadgets. Each gadget contains some ten thousand neurons, so we can expect some pretty sophisticated performance from it.

The third fact that impresses me about the cortex is the degree of interconnectivity. The thick layer of white matter underlying the cortex consists largely of association fibers which outnumber afferent fibers four or five to one. Furthermore, the afferent fibers are largely restricted to specialized sensory cortex, so that the great majority of primate cortex is served almost exclusively by associational fibers. It seems fair to say, then, that whatever these million gadgets are doing requires a great deal of information about what other gadgets in the array are up to as compared with the amount of information coming in from sense organs.

I spent one interesting summer playing games with electronic and paper analogues of such a matrix of gadgets, although my matrix fell short of a million by several orders of magnitude. I found one very interesting thing that I could do with it.

Take an array of forty-eight little gadgets, start them all off at an intermediate level of something or other, which we will refer to as 5. Now apply an input pattern to the array. An input pattern consists of plus or minus one something or other applied to each gadget. All the gadgets receiving a plus one input will be considered the plus side of that pattern, all those receiving a minus input will be considered the minus side of that pattern. The pattern shown (*A*) was determined by tossing a coin. If a map of the array is shaded in accordance with these inputs, the spatial pattern is made clear (see Fig. 63).

If we now look at the values of the *A*+ gadgets as compared with the *A*— gadgets, we find, of course, a net difference of +38. (It would have been +48 if the pattern had happened to divide evenly.)

Now, let us apply a second input (*B*) on top of the first. If the two are unrelated, the *B* pattern will be clearly legible, even though

A 01 02 03 04 05 06 07 08

09 10 11 12 13 14 15 16

17 18 19 20 21 22 23 24

25 26 27 28 29 30 31 32

33 34 35 36 37 38 39 40

41 42 43 44 45 46 47 48

A+	A-	B+	B-	C+	C-
01	02	02	01	01	03
04	03	04	03	02	04
07	05	07	05	05	07
09	06	09	06	06	10
13	08	11	08	08	14
14	10	15	10	09	15
16	11	16	12	11	18
17	12	19	13	12	21
20	15	20	14	13	26
23	18	21	17	16	29
24	19	22	18	17	30
30	21	23	24	19	32
31	22	26	25	20	34
32	25	29	27	22	38
34	26	31	28	23	42
36	27	32	30	24	43
37	28	38	33	25	44
40	29	39	34	27	45
42	33	40	35	28	47
44	35	41	36	31	48
45	38	43	37	33	
46	39	44	42	35	
48	41	46	45	36	
	43	47	48	37	
	47			39	
				40	
				41	
				46	

FIGURE 63. Illustration of the superimposition of three patterns on a memory-predictor matrix. *A*, Random selection of three patterns; *B*, successive application of the three patterns to an initially neutral matrix; *C*, representation of the same three patterns in terms of the voltage code used in toposcopy (compare with FIGURE 16).

```
A pattern        6 4 4 6 4 4 6 4      A+  =  138
                 6 4 4 4 6 6 4 6      A-  =  100
                 6 4 4 6 4 4 6 6      diff   +38
                 4 4 4 4 4 6 6 6
                 4 6 4 6 6 4 4 6
                 4 6 4 6 6 6 4 6


A+B pattern      5 5 3 7 3 3 7 3      A+  =  137
                 7 3 5 3 5 5 5 7      A-  =  101
                 5 3 5 7 5 5 7 5      diff   +36
                 3 5 3 3 5 5 7 7
                 3 5 3 5 5 5 5 7      B+  =  142
                 5 5 5 7 5 7 5 5      B-  =   96
                                     diff   +46


A+B+C pattern  6 6 2 6 4 4 6 4        A+  =  140
               8 2 6 4 6 4 4 8        A-  =  106
               6 2 6 8 4 6 8 6        diff   +34
               4 4 4 4 4 4 8 6
               4 4 4 6 6 4 6 8        B+  =  144
               6 4 4 6 4 8 4 4        B-  =  102
                                     diff   +42

                                      C+  =  164
          B                           C-  =   82
                                     diff   +82
```

it is applied to a noisy background. The fact that struck me as curious, although it is intuitively obvious that it must be true, is that the *A* pattern is essentially unaffected. In fact, we can add as many additional patterns as we wish, as long as we do not run into either end of the possible values of something or other, without degrading the earlier patterns at all. It is sort of a magic blackboard on which one can continue to write indefinitely without ever having to erase.

C

A pattern

A + B pattern

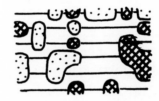

A + B + C pattern

Eventually, of course, we must run into the ends of the continuum and begin to lose information. How soon this happens depends upon the size of the input signal compared with the total length of the continuum. I assume that the nervous system could function with a pretty small ratio, so that only a small percentage of gadgets would be unable to respond to an input. Curiously enough, this loss of information would be greatest for the pattern being inserted. If we take the class of all gadgets that could not respond to the current input because they were at the upper end of their range, these must necessarily all be members of the class of plus members of the current input. This is not true for any past input pattern.

If we assume, for the sake of assuming something, that an input increment is one-twentieth, the total available range, then with the matrix in an equilibrium state, one-twentieth of the gadgets would be in their maximum plus position and one-twentieth in their maximum minus position at any given time. This means that for the current input one-twentieth of the gadgets would be unable to respond. The act of "writing in" a pattern, then, involves a loss of 5 percent of its information. Each subsequent input destroys another 2½ percent of the remaining information. Following this out to the end of our patience, we find that after ninety-nine new patterns have been written on top of it, our original pattern still contains 8 percent of its information. This would probably be somewhere around the threshold of utility. Spinning this quantitative fantasy just a bit further, if we assume that input patterns were coming in at a rate of five per second (this is about as fast as stimuli can be counted, which is probably the simplest manipulation one can do), then our magic blackboard would represent a time span of twenty seconds.

Getting away from the pseudo-mathematics and back to pseudo-neurophysiology, let us now assume that this matrix has the property of tending to complete patterns that have appeared before, given part of that pattern. Such a property would explain the great degree of interconnectivity. In fact, this pattern completion would be the major function of the matrix which in the preceding discussion has been quite passive. Such a function does not seem too much to ask of a ten-thousand-cell gadget with input lines which keep it informed as to the condition of almost every other gadget in the cortex (as a psychologist, I can be grandly vague as to just how it does this) and will give our array of gadgets most of the properties discovered by the Gestalt school of psychology.

Returning to the very limited model represented in Figure 63, we may see that with our new postulate any time patterns A and B recur, the matrix will complete the pattern $A + B + C$. The appearance of C is, however, a prediction.

Our magic blackboard, then, is a compulsive predictor. For any given state of input information, it will tend to complete the pattern which has most frequently, in the past, contained that input information. The time span represented, then, will be partly past information and partly prediction of future inputs. In fact, it should tend to center itself on the present instant, extending about equally into the past and future. Our hypothetical matrix would thus represent a time span of information extending roughly ten seconds into the future and into the past. This total pattern would be corrected with every new input, or every 200 msec; it would be a running "best estimate" of a twenty-second sequence of events centered on the now.

Ordinarily, the ten seconds extending into the past would be actual past events. If, however, for some reason or other, an input pattern appeared in isolation from its normal context, the matrix would reconstruct the events normally leading up to that input just as readily as it would those which normally follow it. In other words, the same matrix is a memory storage as well as a predictor. Given any recognizable part of a total situation, it would tend to redintegrate the whole.

How long could such a matrix retain a "memory?" Clearly, it would depend upon how frequently the same input patterns, or similar patterns appeared in other contexts. If conflicting information about similar patterns appeared frequently (proactive and retroactive inhibition), retention would be poor. If a given pattern recurred in the same context (rehearsal), retention would be good. If it did not recur at all, the functions interrelating the matrix of gadgets (about which I have been grandly vague) would undoubtedly be subject to a gradual erosion.

For important imformation to be stored for a lifetime, these interrelating functions would have to be protected against continual change. They would normally be immune to new contexts, persisting in making the same predictions no matter how often proved wrong, rather like an astrologer or the weather bureau. Only when a problem was perceived, a goal unreachable, would the functional state of at least part of the matrix be switched to a "correction" or "learn" mode. I believe this is accomplished, in the living brain, by the application of a d.c. bias.*

Both types of matrix would have their uses. A matrix which was continually "learning" would represent the most frequent and recent contexts of a particular bit of information; it would function as a short-term memory. Since part of the pattern would have to be supplied in order to redintegrate the whole, it would be a recognition type of memory, not recall. I will refer to this type of cortex (sorry, I meant matrix) by the randomly chosen title of inferotemporal. The type of matrix which only learns when learning appears necessary I will call parieto-occipital. It would have as its primary function the generation of short-term predictions. In most mammals it would also provide information to the neural structures which rouse and shape emotions. Part of the prediction generated would concern sensations from the animal's own body. That is, in addition to predicting sights and sounds and smells, the parieto-occipital matrix would also be predicting the position of its own limbs, sounds generated by its own larynx, and so on. Ordinarily, these predictions would be self-confirming, that is, owing to the close connection of the parieto-occipital matrix with the motor matrix, the prediction of an arm movement would automatically cause such an arm movement. Exceptions to this rule would occur whenever the emotion aroused by the predicted sequence of events was unpleasant. Such unpleasant emotion would block motor outflow, which in turn would interrupt the sequence of input information, thus altering the prediction. If the new sequence of predictions were emotionally acceptable, motor outflow would resume, but it would be, of course, the motor activity predicted under the new conditions (see Fig. 64 A).

An animal possessing such a machine would show goal-directed behavior and foresight, but of a temporally limited nature. Unfortunate consequences occurring more than a few seconds after an

---

*I will not go into the means by which this d.c. bias is applied, not simply because I am lazy, but more because I am a coward. I hesitate to crawl farther out on a limb which is already swaying and creaking beneath me. In avoiding this question, I leave a little green man still firmly entrenched within the cranium. I have placed my homunculus in the striato-thalamic "system." I have no very good excuse for so doing, other than that most other subcortical structures are now so crowded that I was afraid he might suffocate; only Buchwald seems interested in the striatum, and he only occupies the anterior end. Anyone who wants to pursue this particular will-o'-the-wisp will find a fairly thorough documentation of current confusion in the bibliography.

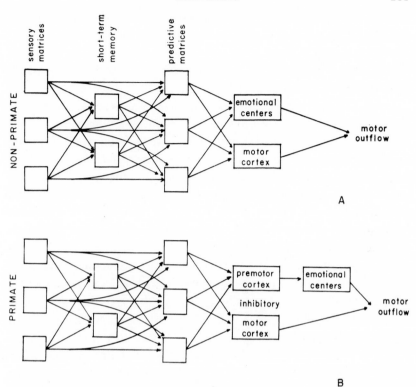

FIGURE 64. Schematic representation of the author's theory of cortical function.

act would have no more effect on its behavior than if it possessed only a primitive, switchboard type of brain. It could perform detour behavior, provided the detour required only a few seconds to accomplish. We would expect that one of the most obvious behavioral differences between such a brain and a more primitive brain would be that it could acquire an avoidance response in one or two trials, and that such a response would be fairly resistant to new learning (extinction), provided, of course, that the signal of approaching punishment occurred only a few seconds in advance of the fact.

A greater degree of foresight would certainly be useful. Suppose we were to construct another matrix of gadgets, but have it take as its input some abstraction of the total pattern of the first matrix. Its input would then be a representation of a time span of twenty seconds. By correcting its pattern less frequently, and being satisfied with a less detailed representation of events, such a matrix could represent a time span of some thirty minutes; a rather tremendous gain in foresight. I have chosen to refer to this matrix as premotor, and machines possessing it as primates.

It would not do to have this premotor matrix directly control behavior as the parieto-occipital matrix has been doing. We cannot have the representation of a movement some fifteen minutes in the future automatically producing that movement now. On the other hand, we definitely want the most distant consequences of an action to be instrumental in determining whether or not it may occur. The premotor matrix, then, will have only an inhibitory effect on motor outflow. Emotions, of course, should be based entirely on the long range prediction (Fig. 64 B).

A bonus advantage of such a matrix will be a greatly extended period during which a past event can be recalled rather than merely recognized. It should be possible for a primate to guide his behavior on the basis of cues which have been absent for several minutes, rather than only a few seconds as in the case of nonprimates.

It may be recalled that our parieto-occipital matrix requires a quantized input. A device for converting incoming visual, auditory, and so forth information into a matrix of binary bits can rather easily be constructed from another two-dimensional array of gadgets. Let the interconnectivity be primarily short range so that each gadget is connected mainly with nearby gadgets; furthermore, let the interconnections be inhibitory. We now have sort of a 2^n power flip-flop. Any gadget must always be either full "on" or full "off." Incoming sensory patterns would act as triggers, "flipping" about one-half the gadgets, whose inhibitory output would "flop" the remaining half. Assuming that this inhibitory output decayed with time, as seems to be almost universally true in the nervous system, after a finite length of time the system would be ready to be reset by the impinging sensory pattern. The output would thus be a series of patterns, coming at fairly regular time intervals, each pattern consisting of a two-dimensional array of information bits.

To summarize this bit of fantasy, I am suggesting four kinds of matrix, differing in time factor and kind of interconnection as follows:

TABLE III

MATRIX

	Sensory	Parietal	Temporal	Premotor
Time factor	msec	ca. 20 sec	ca. 20 sec	ca. 30 min
Interconnection	lateral inhibition	protected against learning	continually learning	protected against learning
Function	digitalize information	immediate prediction, immediate memory (recall), directs behavior	short-term memory (recognition)	long-term prediction, recall, selects behavior, directs emotion

This classification of cortical functions leaves no room for long-term memory. To the extent that such memory is really redintegration of constellations of past events triggered by the input of some part of that constellation, then long-term memory is the major function of the entire cortex. To the extent that it is a genuine storage of engrams, lying inert in some dusty file until needed again, I have left no room for it in the neocortex. It will have to be pushed off onto hippocampus or reticular formation or pineal gland. My cortex is far too busy with now and the next few minutes to serve as the repository for years gone by.

What would be the effect of destroying part or all of these various matrices? The sensory matrix is obvious. Lesions in the parieto-occipital matrix would have a serious effect on behavior. It must be noted, however, that the high degree of interconnectivity makes the area largely equipotential. If part of it is destroyed, we essentially have a smaller matrix to work with. The effect of this would be to decrease the amount of information contained in a pattern, and therefore to make it less resistant to erasure by subsequent patterns. In other words, lesions of the parieto-occipital (and probably anterior temporal) cortex would decrease the effective time span of prediction and immediate recall as well as decreasing the amount of detail in the patterns. The effect of this on behavior would perhaps best be described by the encompassing term *loss of intelligence*. Total extirpation of all cortex other than inferotemporal and frontal cortex would be equivalent to complete decortication.

Destruction of inferotemporal cortex alone would be expected to affect recognition and short-term memory. Again, lesions within the matrix would be equipotential, and partial destruction would affect the time span and detail of recognition.

Lesions of the premotor cortex would show the same equipotentiality, the same effect upon time span and detail. Complete destruction of the premotor region, as in lobotomy, would have the interesting effect of isolating emotion from perception. It would also leave behavior at the mercy of short-term prediction, that is, it would be impulsive and poorly controlled.

It would be fun to ramble on for a few more pages, pointing out the correspondence between such a matrix of gadgets and the two-dimensional patterns my toposcope records from the living brain. Such a ramble would prove nothing, since my ideas obviously grew out of the toposcopic data. Besides, this sermon has already outlasted any reasonable demands that one may make upon a congregation. Those readers who dislike dusty bookshelves as much as do I may leave me here, for I have left to last the task of compiling lists of titles with which to impress those who are impressed with that sort of thing.

Chapter X

BIBLIOGRAPHY

I REALIZE that it is not conventional to consider the bibliography as a chapter, but I am not particularly concerned with making this book conventional. This bibliography is not simply a list of works to which I have referred in the text. It contains more titles which I have not mentioned in the text than ones that I have mentioned. Furthermore, a few works to which I have referred in the text are not listed, for example, the cortical mapping experiments of Woolsey *et al.* Everyone who is likely to be reading this book knows that Woolsey and his collaborators map cortical evoked potentials. His data are not pertinent to anything I am saying in the book, but were used only as an example of the kind of topological research with which I am not presently concerned. I trust he will not take it amiss if I do not pad this bibliography with the very long list of papers he has published.

On the other hand, many of the titles in this bibliography are not mentioned in the text. In fact, some of them I have not even read. In cases where a reference appeared to be of peripheral interest and was not available at local libraries, I have included the reference for readers who may be more fortunate in their library facilities, even though I did not wish further to delay the publication of this book by trying to locate difficult titles. I have tried to include in this chapter a fairly comprehensive sampling of research in certain problem areas which appear to be pertinent to the toposcopic study of learning. I believe that if a student were to look up everything I have listed in one of these areas, he would have a fairly accurate idea of the status of research in that area as of this writing.

In only two areas have I attempted to be exhaustive, and I am quite certain I have failed in each. I have included everything I found in the topics of toposcopy and cortical d.c. phenomena. Much of this literature is in Russian, however, and here I have a slight handicap. Although I can translate Russian text into improbable-sounding English phrases at the rate of about one hundred words per day, they are the same hundred Russian words every day, only the English words are different. I have therefore had to rely heavily on translations and on secondary sources. This bibliography would be even less complete than it is, were it not for the timely appearance of Louttit and Hanik (1967) bibliography of Russian-English translations from the golden age of translations, 1950 to 1960.

Since our Russian colleagues did us the favor, in October of 1957, of launching Sputnik I, a blizzard of translations of anything Russian and vaguely scientific has appeared. The panic tapered off, however, during the first few years of this decade, so that most of these translations are dated between 1958 and 1963, causing the phenomenon of ready availability of Russian works published between 1950 and 1960. I note that more recent Russian publications are difficult to find in English. Another Sputnik would be appreciated.

Professor Livanov, whose mastery of English dwarfs my feeble knowledge of Russian, has begun publishing significant research twice, once in Russian and again in English. For example, after having laboriously waded through Livanov *et al.* ("The application of electronic computing techniques to the analysis of cortical biopotentials in man and in animals, with multichannel toposcopic recording"), I then discovered Livanov's contribution to the 23rd International Congress of Physiological Science, entitled "The significance of distant brain potential synchronization for realization of temporal connections," which includes the same information as well as some other work, but, curiously, does not refer to the earlier Russian paper, or, for that matter, to any other Russian work—sort of a reversed provincialism. Other similar instances have helped to reassure me that I have not missed much that is significant in the Russian literature, although I am sure that individual titles have been overlooked.

Because of this heavy reliance on translations, I have frequently referred to Russian articles in terms of their English translations;

that is, using the journal titles, page numbers, and dates of the English version, rather than of the Russian original. For example, Anan'yev V.M.: Methods of physiological investigations: electroencephaloscope. *Sechenov J. Physiol, USSR, 42*:511-522, 1956, originally appeared in *Fiziol. Zh. SSSR im. Sechenova, 42*:981-988. The latter form of reference would be more technically correct, but if one is trying to locate the English version, the former is easier to follow. In some cases, even the year of publication differs. In each instance, I have tried to use the form of reference that seemed to me most likely to ease the path of someone who does not read Russian. If you read Russian fluently, gentle reader, I am sure you can make up a better bibliography than this one, anyway.

The reader should be warned about one source of confusion that has been built into the literature in this area. Five different volumes were produced by a series of three symposia, with titles and dates so similar that one may easily gain the impression that they are all variants of the same reference. The Josiah Macy, Jr., Foundation is primarily responsible, with some collusion from the United States Department of Health.

The first volume is Brazier, M.A.B. (Ed): *The Central Nervous System and Behavior.* New York: Josiah Macy, Jr., Foundation, 1959.

This contains the report of the first conference on this topic, held from February 23-26, 1958. In the bibliography below, I have referred to this as 1958, although it was actually published the following year.

The second volume is BRAZIER, M.A.B. (Ed.): *The Central Nervous System and Behavior.* New York: Josiah Macy, Jr., Foundation, 1959.

As may be seen, this is rather difficult to distinguish from the first, although this reports a second conference on the topic, held from February 22-25, 1959.

Naturally, the third volume in the series was entitled BRAZIER, M.A.B. (Ed.): *The Central Nervous System and Behavior.* New York: Josiah Macy, Jr., Foundation, 1960.

If this were the end, the situation would be tolerable, since the conferences were largely a rehash of existing literature and could be safely ignored. Unfortunately, the United States Department

of Health compiled some pertinent translations of Russian literature for the use of participants in the second and third conferences.
These are by anonymous editors and are entitled helpfully *The
Central Nervous System and Human Behavior*. Bethesda: U. S.
Dep't of Health, Education and Welfare, 1959. *The Central Nervous System and Behavior*. Bethesda: U. S. Dep't. of Health, Education and Welfare, 1959.

Lots of luck, dear reader!

PART I: GENERAL AND REVIEW ARTICLES
Toposcopy

Only two reviews of toposcopy other than this have been written: RÉMOND, A.: Orientations et tendances des méthodes topographiques dans l'étude de l'activité électrique du cerveau. *Rev.
Neurol. (Paris)*, *93*:399-432, 1955; Livanov, M.N., and Anan'yev,
V.M.: Electroencephaloscopy. JPRS 9752, 1961, TT 61 27274
(photocopy from OTS, $9.60).

D.C. Potential Phenomena

This area was very thoroughly reviewed in 1964 by the two
authors who have contributed about one-half the literature in the
field: O'Leary, J.L., and Goldring, S.: D-C potentials of the
brain. *Physiol. Rev.*, *44*:91-125, 1964.

One of the more enjoyable forms of one-upmanship is the searching out of references five or ten years older than those found by the
last reviewer of a field. I have several nineteenth century references
in each area of knowledge wherein I may occasionally have an opportunity to display my erudition. These are polished and displayed
on appropriate occasions much as is the family silver to awe the
yokels. In the case of d.c. phenomena, however, Mary Brazier has
ruined the game by reviewing the most ancient history of d.c.
recordings, complete with photographs, no less. Since this is an area
in which one cannot hope triumphantly to dredge up a quotation
from Aristotle, one can only graciously admit defeat: Brazier,
M.A.B.: The discoverers of the steady potentials of the brain. Caton
and Beck. In Brazier, M.A.B. (Ed.): *Brain Function, vol. 1. Cortical Excitability and Steady Potentials; Relations of Basic Research
to Space Biology*. Berkeley and Los Angeles: Univ. of Calif. Press,
1963.

One of the investigators referred to in this section, Shvets, consistently found much higher voltage changes than anyone else has reported, or than I have found in my own research. Shvets, however, used platinum electrodes. My own tests of platinum showed that it is impossible to record genuine d.c. potentials through it because it polarizes to infinite resistance. It is quite possible, however, that platinum chronically implanted would tend to adsorb hydrogen, thus becoming a pH electrode, as happened in my own work with gold. This would explain the uniquely high voltages.

Dominant Focus

The intriguing mystery of the dominant focus was excellently reviewed by Morrell in 1961. In fact, this review occupies a central position in my own bibliographic toils, since Morrell also covered most of the literature on the electrophysiology of learning and conditioning, including a very good coverage of the Russian literature, which most reviewers barely touch: Morrell, F.: Electrophysiological contributions to the neural basis of learning. *Physiol. Rev.*, *41*:443-493, 1961.

Some additional facts about the dominant focus may be gleaned from reviews by Beritov: Beritov, I.: Development of physiology of the central nervous system in the Soviet Union during the recent 40 years. Translation in *The Central Nervous System and Human Behavior*. Bethesda: National Institutes of Health, 1959, pp. 11-31; and by Rusinov and Rabinovich: Rusinov, V.S. and Rabinovich, M.Y.: *EEG Researches in the USSR. Electroenceph. Clin. Neurophysiol. (Suppl.)*, 8, 1958.

John's review of higher nervous functions: John, E.R.: High nervous functions: brain functions and learning. *Ann. Rev. Physiol.*, *23*:451-484, 1961, covers most of the major facts of the dominant focus, although not as completely as Morrell or Rusinov and Rabinovich. The chapter purports to review the neural bases of learning but unfortunately treats learning as synonymous with conditioning. One gains the impression that, although the author is very sophisticated in electrophysiological techniques, his comprehension of the psychology of learning ends with Pavlov. This Pavlovian tunnel vision is characteristic of all Soviet-oriented learning research, regardless of the nationality of the scientists involved. Since those

Western researchers who show some knowledge of learning theories are apparently oblivious to the facts of the dominant focus, the very correlation which is most crucial to this book has not yet been made.

I cannot refrain from saying a few words about one piece of research turned up in this part of my bibliographic work. Budylin and Levshunova (1959) injected bile into the sciatic nerve of dogs, creating a chronic abcess which, from their report, must have been excruciatingly painful. They found, to no one's surprise but their own, that this disrupted previously learned reflexes and retarded new learning. They interpret the results in terms of a presumed dominant focus induced by the constant pain.

They managed to milk this bit of sadism for two publications, as I found an essentially identical reference in the *Sechenov Physiological Journal*, which I did not include in the below bibliography, feeling that one such article is more than enough. Of course, any scientific establishment will have a few sadists and misfits, but the fact that such behavior was rewarded to the extent of two publications does not speak well for the editorial policy of the two major Russian journals in this field.

Physiological Bases of Learning

A considerably more adequate review of the physiological bases of learning may be found in Thomas, G.J.: Neurophysiology of learning. *Ann. Rev. Psychol., 13*:71-106, 1962.

Together with the review by Morrell, mentioned above under "dominant focus," this gives a fairly comprehensive view of the state of knowledge in this area at the beginning of this decade. I have not found any more recent reviews that I feel were worth reading.

Actually, since the current fads in the physiology of learning involve such activities as feeding educated planaria to ignorant ones or administering ECS, anesthetics, or one of a variety of subtle poisons to mice as soon as they start to learn something, we seem more concerned with the prevention of learning than with its encouragement. My own, highly biased, impression is that knowledge of the physiology of learning has not really advanced significantly in this decade, anyway.

Contingent Negative Variation

This curious phenomenon, largely the property of W. Grey Walter, is distinctive enough to warrant a listing separate from d.c. phenomena in general, even though it is apparently a modulation of cortical d.c. potential. Walter himself has summarized the data to date in Walter, W.G.: Electrical signs of association, expectancy and decision in the human brain. *Electroenceph. Clin. Neurophysiol. (Suppl.)*, 25:258-263, 1967.

Hemispheric Dominance

A few references on this specialized topic have been included, only because it appears pertinent to the one-sided nature of the d.c. patterns found during learning. I have listed only a small fraction of the many references found, and I am sure I only found a small fraction of the literature that exists. The most readable article in this area is not included in the bibliography below because it is a *Scientific American* article, and such are generally considered to be not quite scientifically respectable. (I have often wondered about this almost universal tendency to omit *Scientific American* articles from bibliographies. Such articles are usually just as authoritative as anything in the more respectable journals, are far more pleasant to read, and have magnificent illustrations. I suspect the reason we tend to sneer at them is that they are understandable to the "intelligent layman," a fact which strikes at the roots of scientific mystique.) Since it is a delightful and thought-provoking article, I shall risk the tattered shreds of my scientific respectability by referring the interested reader to Gazzaniga, M.S.: The split brain in man. *Sci. Amer., 217* (2):24-29, (August) 1967.

Localization of Function

This classical area of research is highly pertinent to the present data but is simply too extensive to list in detail. I have confined the bibliography almost exclusively to primates, since I get nervous at the casual identification of homologous cortex in cats and humans. In particular, I find no cortical area in any animal other than a primate which appears to me to be a legitimate analogue of the premotor frontal lobe. It is here that the primate research is particularly voluminous. It is almost shocking, in view of the numbers of monkeys running around with large holes in their frontal lobes, to discover how little is really known about this brain tissue that distinguishes the primates from all other biological inventions. Since it is the relative size and complexity of the premotor cortex which also distinguishes the higher primates from the lower (the temporo-parieto-occipital area of a wooley monkey, for example, is difficult to distinguish from your own, dear reader), it is clearly a matter of great interest and urgency to understand its functions.

Fairly recent reviews of the state of confusion in this area include: Meyer, D.R., and Meyer, P.M.: Brain functions. *Ann. Rev. Psychol.*, *14*:155-174, 1963, and Warren, J.M., and Akert, K. (Eds.): *The Frontal Granular Cortex and Behavior.* New York: McGraw-Hill, 1964.

Striato-Thalamic "System"

I blush at endorsing another "system," since we have far too many now. Concepts such as the "limbic lobe" or the "centrencephalic system" have done nothing to advance our understanding of brain functions, but probably much to retard it. The fact is, of course, that one can find connections between any two randomly selected points in the central nervous system, given enough patience and a goodly research grant. The conceptual difficulty with such systems is not that they imply connections which are not real, but that they encourage us to think of a certain group of structures as though they could, in any meaningful sense, be separated from the whole. It is with considerable diffidence, then, that I have listed a group of references dealing with the interrelations among striatum, nonspecific thalamus, and cortex, and with the behavioral effects of interference with the former two.

The bibliography leads off with Adametz, because of his father's foresight in the spelling of his name, and because his careful extirpation of the mesencephalic reticular formation has done us the favor of exorcizing one of the most pernicious of these "systems," the reticular activating system.

I found no review of striato-thalamic relations, undoubtedly because it is not worth reviewing. One article, however, seemed to cover the major facts in a single, well-designed experiment: Buchwald, N.A., Hull, C.D., and Trachtenberg, M.C.: Concomitant behavioral and neural inhibition and disinhibition in response to subcortical stimulation. *Exp. Brain Res.*, *4*:58-72, 1967.

Miscellaneous

This inevitable result of any effort to classify contains two general kinds of references: those dealing with bibliography, and titles to which I wanted to refer, but which did not seem to fit elsewhere.

PART II: BIBLIOGRAPHY PROPER
Toposcopy

ANAN'YEV, V.M.: Methods of physiological investigations: electroencephaloscope. *Sechenov Physiol. J. USSR*, 42:981-988, 1956.

BARLOW, J.S.: A simple time-division multiplexing system for low-frequency bioelectric signals. *IEEE Trans. Biomed. Engig.*, 13:195-199, 1966.

COHN, R.: A simple method for cerebral toposcopy. *Electroenceph. Clin. Neurophysiol.*, 2:97-98, 1950.

COOPER, R., and MUNDY-CASTLE, A.C.: Spatial and temporal characteristics of the alpha rhythm: a toposcopic analysis: *Electroenceph. Clin. Neurophysiol.*, 12:153-165, 1960.

DEMOTT, D.W.: An inexpensive, multi-channel, electrophysiological recording system. *Electroenceph. Clin. Neurophysiol.*, 13:467-470, 1961.

DEMOTT, D.W.: Cortical micro-toposcopy. *Med. Res. Engin.*, 5(4):23-29, 1966.

DUDA, J.M.: Electrotoposcopy of Auditory Cortex Responses to Acoustic Stimulation in the Lightly Anesthetized Squirrel Monkey. Ph.D. Dissertation, University of Rochester, 1969.

FRIEDE, R.L.: *Topographic brain chemistry*. New York: Academic Press, 1966.

GAVRILOVA, N.A.: The relation between the initial state of the cortical bioelectric pattern and its changes during reflex elaboration. Works of the Institute of Higher Nervous Activity, *Physiol. Ser.*, 7:21-32, 1963 (orig. 1962).

GERSHUNI, G.V.: International colloquium on the electroencephalography of higher nervous activity. *Sechenov Physiol. J. USSR*, 45:189-199, 1959.

GLIVENKO, E.V., Korolkeva, T.A., and KUZNETZOVA, G.D.: Integral pattern of relations among potentials in the rabbit's cerebral cortex. *Sechenov Physiol. J. USSR*, 48:384-388, 1962.

GOLDMAN, D.: The clinical use of the "average" reference electrode in monopolar recording. *Electroenceph. Clin. Neurophysiol.*, 2:209-212, 1950.

GOLDMAN, ST., VIVIAN, W.E., CHIEN CH. K., and BOWES, H.N.: Electronic mapping of the activity of the heart and the brain. *Science*, 108:720-723, 1948.

HARRIS, J.A., and BICKFORD, R.G.: Spatial display and parameter computation of the human epileptic spike focus by computer. *Electroenceph. Clin. Neurophysiol.*, 24:281, 1968.

KNIPST, I.N.,: Spatial changes of bioelectric cortical and subcortical activity in rabbits. Works of the Institute of Higher Nervous Activity, *Physiol. Ser.*, *6*:250-259, 1963 (orig. 1961).

LILLY, J.C.: A method of recording the moving electrical potential gradients in the brain: the 25-channel Bavatron and electroiconograms. Conference on electrical instruments in nucleonics and medicine, New York, 1949. (Amer. Inst. of Elect. Engin.)

LILLY, J.C.: Equipotential maps of the posterior ectosylvian area and acoustic I and II of the cat during responses and spontaneous activity. *Fed. Proc.*, *10*:84, 1951.

LILLY, J.C.: Forms and figures in the electrical activity seen in the surface of the cerebral cortex. In Millbank Memorial Fund: *The Biology of Mental Health and Disease: Twenty-seventh Annual Conference of the Millbank Memorial Fund*. New York: Hoeber, 1952.

LILLY, J.C.: Instantaneous relations between the activities of closely spaced zones on the cerebral cortex. *Amer. J. Physiol.*, *176*:493-504, 1954.

LILLY, J.C.: Correlations between neurophysiological activity in the cortex and short term behavior in the monkey. In Harlow, H.F. and Woolsey, C.N. (Eds.): *Biological and Biochemical Bases of Behavior*. Madison: Univ. of Wisconsin Press, 1958.

LILLY, J.C., and CHERRY, R.B.: Traveling waves of action and of recovery during responses and spontaneous activity in the cerebral cortex. *Amer. J. Physiol.*, *167*:806, 1951.

LILLY, J.C., and CHERRY, R.B.: Criteria for the parcellation of the cortical surface into functional areas. *Electroenceph. Clin. Neurophysiol.*, *4*:385, 1952.

LILLY, J.C. and CHERRY, R.B.: New criteria for the division of the acoustical cortex into functional areas. *Fed. Proc.*, *11*:94-95, 1952.

LILLY, J.C., and CHERRY, R.B.: Surface movements of click responses from acoustical cerebral cortex of cat: leading and trailing edges of a response figure. *J. Neurophysiol.*, *17*:521-532, 1954.

LILLY, J.C., and CHERRY, R.B.: Surface movements of figures in spontaneous activity of anesthetized cerebral cortex. Leading and trailing edges. *J. Neurophysiol.*, *18*:18-32, 1955.

LIVANOV, M.N.: Concerning the establishment of temporary connections. *Electroenceph. Clin. Neurophysiol. (Suppl.)*, *13*:185-198, 1960.

LIVANOV, M.N.: Spatial analysis of electrical activity of the brain. *Pavlov J. Higher Nerv. Act.*, *12*:399-409, 1962.

LIVANOV, M.N.: Spatial analysis of the bioelectric activity of the brain. In Gerard, R.W., and Duyff, J.W. (Eds.): *Information Processing in the Nervous System, Proc. Int. Union Physiol. Sci., XXII Congr., Leiden.* Amsterdam: Excerpta Medica, 1962.

LIVANOV, M.N.: *The Significance of Distant Brain Potential Synchronization for Realization of Temporal Connections. Proc. Int. Union Physiol. Sci. IV: Lectures and Symposia, XXIII Cong., Tokyo.* Amsterdam: Excerpta Medica, 1965.

LIVANOV, M.N., and ANAN'YEV, V.M.: An electrophysiological study of spatial distribution of activity in the cerebral cortex of a rabbit. *Sechenov J. Physiol, USSR, 41*:461-469, 1955.

LIVANOV, M.N., and ANAN'YEV, V.M.: *Electroencephaloscopy.* Moscow, 1960. (English translation from O.T.S. No. TT61 27274).

LIVANOV, M.N., ANAN'YEV, V.M., and BEKTEREVA, N.P. A study of the bioelectric mosaics of the cortex in patients with brain tumors and traumas by means of electroencephaloscopy. *Zh. Nevropat. psikhiat. korsakol, 56*:778-790, 1956. (English abstr. in *Biological Abstracts, 35*, entry 13226, 1960.)

LIVANOV, M.N., CAVILOVA, N.A., and ASLANOV, A.S.: Cross-correlation between various cortical points in man during mental work. *Pavlov J. Higher Nerv. Act., 14*:185-194, 1964. (English abstr. in *Electroenceph. Clin. Neurophysiol., 19*:420, 1965.)

LIVANOV, M.N., GAVRILOVA, N.A., and ASLANOV, A.S.: Intercorrelations between different cortical regions of human brain during mental activity. *Neuropsychologia, 2*:281-289, 1964.

LIVANOV, M.N., GAVRILOVA, N.A., EFREMOVA, T.M., KOROLKOVA, T.A., and ASLANOV, A.S.: The application of electronic computing techniques to the analysis of cortical biopotentials in man and in animals with multichannel toposcopic recording. *Med. Electron. Biol. Engig., 3*:137-144, 1965.

LIVANOV, M.N, and RYABINOVSKAYA, A.M.: The problem of the localization of changes in the electrical processes of the rabbit's cerebral cortex in the development of a conditioned reflex to rhythmic stimulus. *Sechenov J. Physiol. USSR, 33*:523-534, 1947.

LIVANOV, M.N., ZHADIN, M.N., KREITSER, G.P., and TRUSH, V.D.: Employment of a digital computer for setting up a controlled electrophysiological experiment. *Biofizika, 11*:306-313, 1966.

MARKO, A., and PETSCHE, H.: The multivibrator toposcope; an electronic polygraph. *Electroenceph. Clin. Neurophysiol., 12*:209-211, 1960.

MONAKHOV, K.K.: "Transfers," a particular form of spatial distribution of cortical bioelectric activity. Works of the Institute of Higher Nervous Activity, *Physiol. Ser., 6*:260-270, 1963 (orig. 1961).

OFFNER, F.F.: The EEG as potential mapping: the value of the average monopolar reference. *Electroenceph. Clin. Neurophysiol., 2*:213-214, 1950.

PETSCHE, H.: An understanding of form and behavior of potential fields on the cortical surface through a combined method of EEG and toposcopy. *Wien Z. Nervenheilk., 25*:373-387, 1967.

PETSCHE, H., and MARKO, A.: Das Photozellentoposkope. *Arch. Psychiat. Zschr. Neurol., 192*:447-462, 1954.

PETSCHE, H., and STUMPF, CH.: Topographic and toposcopic study of origin and spread of the regular synchronized arousal pattern in the rabbit. *Electroenceph. Clin. Neurophysiol., 12*:589-600, 1960.

RÉMOND, A: Directions and trends in topographic methods in the study of electrical activity of the brain. *Rev. Neurol (Paris)*, 93:399-432, 1955.

RÉMOND, A.: Search for meaning in the EEG. I: The problem of spatial reference. *Rev. Neurol. (Paris)*, 102:412-415, 1960.

RÉMOND, A.: Integrated topological analysis of the EEG. *Rev. Neurol. (Paris)*, 104:204-212, 1961.

RÉMOND, A.: Chronological and topographical problems posed by responses to photic stimulation. *Electroenceph. Clin. Neurophysiol.*, 21:616, 1966.

RÉMOND, A., et OFFNER, F.: Études topographiques de l'activaté E.E.G. de la région occipitale. *Rev. Neurol. (Paris)*, 87:182-189, 1952.

RYABININA, M.A.: Some characteristics of the cortical and subcortical electroencephalographic pattern in rabbits during increased excitability of the motor analysor. Works of the Institute of Higher Nervous Activity, *Physiol., Ser.*, 7:51-58, 1963 (orig. 1962).

SHAW, J.C.: Potential distribution analysis of the EEG. *Proc. Electrophysiol. Technol. Assoc.*, 5:10-16, 1954.

SHAW, J.C., and ROTH, M.: Potential distribution analysis: I. A new technique for the analysis of electrophysiological phenomena. *Electroenceph. Clin. Neurophysiol.* 7:273-284, 1955.

SHIPTON, H.W.: An improved electrotoposcope. *Electroenceph. Clin. Neurophysiol.*, 9:182, 1957.

SHUL'GINA, G.I.: Study of local bioelectric phenomena in the cerebral cortex during conditioned reflex elaboration and during internal inhibition. Works of the Institute of Higher Nervous Activity, *Physiol. Ser.*, 5:12-18, 1962 (orig. 1960).

SHUL'GINA, G.I.: Local bioelectric phenomena in the cerebral cortex during conditioned reflex activity. Works of the Institute of Higher Nervous Activity, *Physiol. Ser.*, 6:230-249, 1963 (orig. 1961).

SNEZHNEVSKY, A.V.: Psychopharmacology, the pathophysiology of higher nervous activity, and clinical psychiatry. New York, Acad. Sci., "Pavlovian Conference on Higher Nervous Activity," 1960.

TUNTURI, A.R.: Masking of cortical responses in middle ectosylvian auditory area of dogs. *Amer. J. Physiol.*, 184:321-328, 1956.

TUNTURI, A.R.: Localized responses in auditory cortex to brief tones in high level noise. *Amer. J. Physiol.*, 195:779-786, 1958.

TUNTURI, A.R.: Statistical properties of near threshold responses to brief sounds in the MES auditory cortex of the anesthetized dog. *Amer. J. Physiol.*, 196:1168-1174, 1959.

TUNTURI, A.R.: Statistical properties of spontaneous electrical activity in the MES auditory cortex of the anesthetized dog. *Amer. J. Physiol.*, 196:1175-1180, 1959.

TUNTURI, A.R.: Effect of spontaneous activity on afferent response in the MES auditory cortex of the dog. *Amer. J. Physiol.*, 197:1141-1146, 1959.

TUNTURI, A.R.: Components of the evoked potential in the MES auditory cortex. *Amer. J. Physiol.*, 199:529-534, 1960.

TUNTURI, A.R.: Effect of thalamic lesions on spontaneous electrical activity in MES auditory cortex. *Amer. J. Physiol.*, *201*:845-854, 1961.

TUNTURI, A.R.: Frequency arrangement in anterior ectosylian auditory cortex of dog. *Amer. J. Physiol.*, *203*:185-193, 1962.

TUNTURI, A. R.: Statistical analysis of afferent potential in the auditory cortex. *Amer. J. Physiol.*, *213*:597-612, 1967.

WALTER, W.G.: Toposcopy. Third Int. EEG. Congr., *Electroenceph. Clin. Neurophysiol.* (*Suppl.*), *4*:7-16, 1953.

WALTER, W.G.: Intrinsic rhythms of the brain. In Field, J., and Magoun, H.W. (Eds.): *Handbook of Physiology*. Washington: Amer. Physiol. Soc., 1959, Vol. I.

WALTER, W.G., and SHIPTON, H.W.: A toposcopic display system applied to neurophysiology. *J. Brit. IRE*, *2*:260-284, 1951.

WALTER, W.G., and SHIPTON, H.W.: A new toposcopic display system. *Electroenceph. Clin. Neurophysiol.*, *3*:281-292, 1951.

WALTER, W., and SHIPTON, J.: La presentation et l'identification des composantes des rythmes alpha. *Electroenceph. Clin. Neurophysiol.* (*Suppl.*) *6*:177-184, 1957.

D.C. Potential Phenomena

ALADJALOVA, N.A.: Superslow rhythmic changes in the electrical potentials of the brain. *Biofizika*, *1*:127-135, 1956.

ALADJALOVA, N.A.: *Slow Electrical Processes in the Brain. Progress in Brain Research*. Amsterdam: Elsevier, 1964, Vol. 7.

ALADJALOVA, N.A.: Some indices of a slow controlling brain system. *Biofizika*, *6*:1076-1082, 1965. Reviewed in Kambarova, D.K.: A review of Soviet papers. *Electroenceph. Clin. Neurophysiol.*, *22*:579-586, 1967.

ALADJALOVA, N.A., and KOSHTOIANTS, O.Kh.: The quasi-constant potential in different levels in the cerebral cortex and its infra-slow rhythmic changes studied using a microelectrode technique. *Biofizika*, *2*:327, 1956.

ALBERT, D.J.: The effect of spreading depression on the consolidation of learning. *Neuropsychologia*, *4*:49-64, 1966.

ANTHONY, L.U., GOLDRING, S., O'LEARY, J. L., and SCHWARTZ, H.G.: Experimental cerebrovascular occlusion in dog. *Arch. Neurol.* (*Chicago*), *8*:515-527, 1963.

ARDUINI, A.: Slow potential changes evoked by sensory and reticular stimulation. In SHEER, D.E. (Ed.): *Electrical Stimulation of the Brain*. Houston: Univ. of Texas Press, 1961.

ARDUINI, A.: Enduring potential changes evoked in the cerebral cortex by stimulation of brain stem reticular formation and thalamus. In JASPER, H.H., *et al.* (Eds.) *Reticular Formation of the Brain*. Boston: Little, Brown, 1958.

ARDUINI, A., MANCIA, M., and MECHELSE, K.: Slow potential changes during electrocorticographic arousal elicited by reticular stimulation. *Proc. Intern. Physiol. Congr.*, XX, Brussels, 1956.

ARDUINI, A., MANCIA, M., and MECHELSE, K.: Slow potential changes elicited in the cerebral cortex by sensory and reticular stimulation. *Arch. Ital. Biol.*, *95*:127-138, 1957.

ASAHINA, K., and YAMANAKA, M.: The relationship between steady potential and other electrical activities of cerebral cortex. *Jap. J. Physiol.*, *10*:258-266, 1960.

BABSKY, E.B., and MINAJEV, P.F.: Changes in the activity of cholinesterase of nervous tissue under the influence of constant current. *Nature (London)*, *158*:343, 1946.

BECK, A.: Die Bestimmung der Lokalisation der Gehirund Ruckenmarksfunctionen vermittelst der elektrischen Erscheinungen. *Zbl. Physiol.*, *4*:473-476, 1890.

BECKER, R.O.: Search for evidence of axial current flow in peripheral nerves of Salamander. *Science, 134*:101-102, 1961.

BECKER, R.O.: The direct current field: A primitive control and communications system related to growth processes. *Proc. Intern. Congr. Zool.*, *16*:179-183, 1963.

BECKER, R.O., BACKMAN, C.H., and FRIEDMAN, H.: The direct current control system. *New York J. Med.*, *62*:1169-1176, 1962.

BERITOV, I.S.: On the origin of infraslow potentials of the brain. *Proc. Gagra Symp., Tbilisi, 1*:209, 1949.

BESSON, J.M., and ALÉONARD, P.: Modifications du potentiel continu cortical avec les variations de pression artérielle. *J. Physiol. (Paris), 58*:207, 1966.

BEUTNER, R.: Bioelectricity. In Glasser, O., (Ed.): *Medical Physics.* Chicago: Year Book Publ., 1947, Vol. I.

BISHOP, G.H.: Potential phenomena in thalamus and cortex. *Electroenceph. Clin. Neurophysiol., 1*:421-436, 1949.

BRAZIER, M.A.B. (Ed.): *Brain Function: Cortical Excitability and Steady Potentials.* Berkeley: U. of Calif., 1963.

BRAZIER, M.A.B.: Historical Introduction. The discoverers of the steady potentials of the brain: Caton and Beck. In Brazier, M.A.B. (Ed.): *Brain Function: Cortical Excitability and Steady Potentials.* Berkeley: U. of Calif., 1963.

BROOKHART, J.M., ARDUINI, A., MANCIA, M., and MORUZZI, G.: Sustained cortical potential changes induced by thalamic stimulation. *Fed. Proc.*, *16*:15, 1957.

BROOKHART, J.M., ARDUINI, A., MANCIA, M., and MORUZZI, G.: Thalamocortical relations as revealed by induced slow potential changes. *J. Neurophysiol., 21*:499-525, 1958.

BROOKHART, J.M., and BLACHLY, P.H.: The influence of DC potential fields on cerebellar unit activity. Proc. XIX Intern. Physiol. Congr., Montreal, 1953.

BUREŠ, J.: Direct potential difference between the cerebral hemispheres during the depression of EEG activity in anesthetized and nonanesthetized rats. *Physiol. Bohemoslov., 3*:272, 1954.

BUREŠ, J.: The relation between the depression of EEG activity brought about by electrotonus and the narcotic effect of a direct current. *Physiol. Bohemoslov.*, *4*:98, 1955.

BUREŠ, J.: The ontogenetic development of steady potential differences in the cerebral cortex in animals. *Electroenceph. Clin. Neurophysiol.*, *9*:121-130, 1957.

BUREŠ, J., and BUREŠOVÁ, O.: Die anoxische Terminaldepolarisation als Indicator der Vulnerabilität der Groshirnrinde bei Anoxie und Ischämie. *Pflüger. Arch. Ges. Physiol.*, *264*:325-334, 1957.

BURGE, W.E., WICKWIRE, G.C., and SCHAMP, H.M.: A study of the effect of different anesthetics on the electrical potenial of the brain cortex. *Curr. Res. Anesth. Analg.*, *15*:261-267, 1936.

BURNS, B.D.: The production of after-bursts in isolated unanesthetized cerebral cortex. *J. Physiol. (Paris)*, *125*:427-446, 1954.

BURNS, B.D.: The mechanism of after-bursts in cerebral cortex. *J. Physiol. (Paris)*, *127*:168-188, 1955.

BURNS, B.D.: *The Mammalian Cerebral Cortex.* London: Edward Arnold and Co., 1958.

BURR, H.S.: Variables in D.C. measurement. *Yale J. Biol. Med.*, *17*:465-478, 1944.

BURR, H.S.: Potential gradients in living systems and their measurements. *Med. Physiol.*, *2*:90, 1950.

BURR, H.S., and HARMAN, P.J.: Voltage gradients in the nervous system. *Trans. Amer. Neurol. Assn.*, *65*:11-14, 1939.

CARRERAS, M., MANCIA, D., and MANCIA, M.: Centrifugal control of the olfactory bulb as revealed by induced DC potential changes. *Brain Res.*, *6*:548-560, 1967.

CASPERS, H.: Über die Beziehungen zwischen Dendritenpotential und Gleichspannung an der Hirnrinde. *Pflueger Arch. Ges. Physiol.*, *269*:157-181, 1959.

CASPERS, H.: Changes of cortical d-c potentials in the sleep-wakefulness cycle. In Wolstenholme, G.E.W., and O'Connor, M. (Eds.): *Ciba Foundation Symposium: The Nature of Sleep.* Boston: Little, Brown, 1961.

CASPERS, H.: The cortical DC potential and its relation with the EEG. *Electroenceph. Clin. Neurophysiol.*, *13*:651, 1961.

CASPERS, H.: Relations of steady potential shifts in the cortex to the wakefulness-sleep spectrum. In Brazier, M.A.B. (Ed.): *Brain Function. Cortical Excitability and Steady Potentials:* Berkeley: U. of Calif. Press, 1963.

CASPERS, H., und SCHULZE, H.: Die Veranderungen der corticalen Gleichspannung wahrend der naturlichen Schlaf-Wach-Perioden beim freibeweglichen Tier. *Pflueger. Arch. Ges. Physiol.*, *270*:103-120, 1959.

CASPERS, H., und STERN, P.: Die Wirkung von Substantz P auf das Dendritenpotential und die Gleichspannungskomponente des Neocortex *Pflueger. Arch. Ges. Physiol.*, *273*:94-109, 1961.

COHN, R.: D.C. recordings of paroxysmal activity from the intact human head. *Electroenceph. Clin. Neurophysiol.*, *6*:692-693, 1954.

COWEN, M.A.: Elementary functional correlates of the transcephalic d.c. circuit. *Psychophysiology (Berlin)*, *3*:262-272, 1967.

COWEN, M.A., and McDONALD, R.: Some behavioral correlates of the transcephalic d.c. potential in cats. *Nature (London)*, *207*:530-532, 1965.

COWEN, M.A., and ROSS, J.: Some biochemical factors that modify the transcephalic d.c. potential. *Psychophysiology (Berlin)*, *4*:90-98, 1967.

COWEN, M.A., ROSS, J., and McDONALD, R.: Some aspects of the transcephalic DC circuit. *Psychophysiology (Berlin)*, *4*:207-215, 1967.

CREUTZFELDT, O.D., FROMM, G.H., and KNAPP, H.: Influence of transcortical d-c currents on cortical neuronal activity. *Exp. Neurol.*, *5*:436-452, 1962.

DENNEY, D., and BROOKHART, J.M.: The effects of applied polarization on evoked electro-cortical waves in the cat. *Electroenceph. Clin. Neurophysiol.*, *14*:885-897, 1962.

DEWSON, J.H., CHOW, K., and ENGEL, J.: Bioelectrical activity of isolated cortex—II. Steady potentials and induced surface-negative cortical responses. *Neuropsychologia*, *2*:167-175, 1964. (Also *Fed. Proc.*, *23*:209, 1964.)

DONDEY, M., and SNIDER, R.S.: Slow potential shifts following cerebellar stimulation. *Electroenceph. Clin. Neurophysiol.*, *7*:265-272, 1955.

DUBNER, H.H., and GERARD, R.W.: Factors controlling brain potentials in the cat. *J. Neurophysiol.*, *2*:142-152, 1939.

DUSSER DE BARENNE, J.G., and McCULLOCH, W.S.: Factors for facilitation and extinction in the central nervous system. *J. Neurophysiol.*, *2*:319-355, 1939.

EIDELBERG, E., KOLMODIN, G.M., and MEYERSON, B.A.: Effect of asphyxia on the cortical steady potential in adult and fetal sheep. *Acta Physiol. Scand.*, *69*:257-261, 1967.

VON EULER, C.: Slow "temperature potentials" in the hypothalamus. *J. Cell. Comp. Physiol.*, *36*:333-350, 1950.

FRANK, G.B.: Nature of steady potential across mammalian cerebral cortex. *Fed. Proc.*, *17*:48, 1958.

FRIEDMAN, H., BECKER, R.O., and BACHMAN, C.H.: Direct current potentials in hypnoanalgesia. *Arch. Gen. Psychiat. (Chicago)*, *7*:193-197, 1962.

FROMM, G.H., and BOND, H.W.: Slow changes in the electrocorticogram and the activity of cortical neurons. *Electroenceph. Clin. Neurophysiol.*, *17*:520-523, 1964.

FROMM, G.H., and BOND, H.W.: The relationship between neuron activity and cortical steady potentials. *Electroenceph. Clin. Neurophysiol.*, *22*:159-166, 1967.

GERARD, R.W.: Factors controlling brain potentials. *Sympos. Quant. Biol.*, *4*:292-304, 1936.

GERARD, R.W., and LIBET, B.: The control of normal and "convulsive" brain potentials. *Amer. J. Psychiat.*, *96*:1125-1152, 1940.

GLOETZER, F., Intracellular potentials, EEG, and cortical DC potentials in the sensorimotor cortex of the cat in acute hypoxia. *Arch. Psychiat. Nervenkr.*, *210*:274-296, 1967 (German).

GLOTZNER, F., and GRUSSER, O.J.: Cortical DC potential, EEG and membrane potential during seizure activity and hypoxia. *Electroenceph. Clin. Neurophysiol.*, *23*:379, 1967.

GOLDENSOHN, E.S., SCHOENFELD, R.L., and HOEFER, P.F.A.: The slowly changing voltage of the brain and the electroencephalogram. *Electroenceph. Clin. Neurophysiol.*, *3*:231-236, 1951.

GOLDRING, S.: Negative steady potential shifts which lead to seizure discharge. In Brazier, M.A.B. (Ed.): *Brain Function. Cortical excitability and steady potentials*. Berkeley: U. of Calif. Press, 1963.

GOLDRING, S., and O'LEARY, J.L.: Summation of certain enduring sequelae of cortical activation in the rabbit. *Electroenceph. Clin. Neurophysiol.*, *3*:329-340, 1951.

GOLDRING, S., and O'LEARY, J.L.: Experimentally derived correlates between ECG and steady cortical potential. *J. Neurophysiol.*, *14*:275-288, 1951.

GOLDRING, S., and O'LEARY, J.L.: Correlation between steady transcortical potential and evoked response. I. Alterations in somatic receiving area induced by veratrine, strychnine, KCL and novocaine. *Electroenceph. Clin. Neurophysiol.*, *6*:189-200, 1954.

GOLDRING, S., and O'LEARY, J.L.: Correlation between steady transcortical potential and evoked response. II. Effect of veratrine and strychnine upon the responsiveness of visual cortex. *Electroenceph. Clin. Neurophysiol.*, *6*:201-212, 1954.

GOLDRING, S., and O'LEARY, J.L.: Cortical D.C. changes accompanying recruiting responses. *Electroenceph. Clin. Neurophysiol.*, *9*:381, 1957.

GOLDRING, S., and O'LEARY, J.L.: Cortical DC changes incident to midline thalamic stimulation. *Electroenceph. Clin. Neurophysiol.*, *9*:577-584, 1957.

GOLDRING, S., and O'LEARY, J.L.: Effects of convulsive and anesthetic agents on steady cortical potentials. *Epilepsia (Amst.)*, *1*:86-94, 1959.

GOLDRING, S., O'LEARY, J.L., and HUANG, S.H.: Experimental modification of dendritic and recruiting processes and their DC after-effects. *Electroenceph. Clin. Neurophysiol.*, *10*:663-676, 1958.

GOLDRING, S., O'LEARY, J.L., and KING, R.B.: Singly and repetitively evoked potentials in human cerebral cortex with DC changes. *Electroenceph. Clin. Neurophysiol.*, *10*:233-240, 1958.

GOLDRING, S., O'LEARY, J.L., WINTER, D.L., and PEARLMAN, A.L.: Identification of a prolonged post-synaptic potential of cerebral cortex. *Proc. Soc. Exp. Biol. Med.*, *100*:429-431, 1959.

GOLDRING, S., ULETT, G., O'LEARY, J.L., and GREDITZER, A.: Initial survey of slow potential changes obtained under resting conditions and incident to

232   *Toposcopic Studies of Learning*

convulsive therapy. *Electroenceph. Clin. Neurophysiol., 2*:297-308, 1950.

GORMAN, A.L.F.: Surface versus intracellular polarization of cortical cells. *Nature (London), 216*:288-289, 1967.

GUMNIT, R.J.: DC potential changes from auditory cortex of cat. *J. Neurophysiol., 23*:667-674, 1960.

GUMNIT, R.J.: The distribution of direct current responses evoked by sounds in the auditory cortex of the cat. *Electroenceph. Clin. Neurophysiol., 13*:889-895, 1961.

GUMNIT, R.J., and GROSSMAN, R.G.: Potentials evoked by sound in the auditory cortex of the cat. *Amer. J. Physiol., 200*:1219-1225, 1961.

HARMAN, P. J.: Anesthesia and the E.M.F. of the nervous system. *Yale J. Biol. Med., 14*:189-200, 1941.

HELD, D., FENCL, V., and PAPPERHEIMER, J.R.: Electrical potential of cerebrospinal fluid. *J. Neurophysiol., 27*:942-959, 1964.

HILD, W., CHANG, J.J., and TASAKI, I.: Electrical responses of astrocytic glia from the mammalian central nervous system cultivated *in vitro. Experientia, 14*:220-221, 1958.

IWASE, Y., and TSUKAGOSCHI, Y.: On the dendritic potential and d-c shift produced by the repetitive stimulation of the guinea pig's cortex. *Seitai No Kagaku, 10*:208-211, 1959.

KANAI, T., and KATZMAN, R.: Late D.C. changes following reticular stimulation. *Electroenceph. Clin. Neurophysiol., 12*:267, 1960.

KATZMAN, R., and GOLDENSOHN, E.S.: Effect of CO2 on steady cortical potentials in dogs. *Arch. Neurol. Psychiat., 80*:454-455, 1958.

KAWANURA, H., and SAWYER, C.H.: DC changes in rabbit brain during slow-wave and paradoxical sleep. *Amer. J. Physiol., 207*:1379-1386, 1964.

KEATING, J.B.A., and KEMPINSKY, W.: The electrical field produced by a focal brain injury: relation to experimental cerebral infarction. *Electroenceph. Clin. Neurophysiol., 12*:875-886, 1960.

KEMPINSKY, W.H.: Steady potential gradients in experimental cerebral vascular occlusion. *Electroenceph. Clin. Neurophysiol., 6*:375-388, 1954.

KOHLER, W., and HELD, R.: The cortical correlate of pattern vision. *Science, 110*:414-419, 1949.

KOHLER, W., HELD, R., and O'CONNELL, D.N.: An investigation of cortical currents. *Proc. Amer. Philos. Soc., 96*:290-330, 1952.

KOHLER, W., NEFF, W.D., and WEGENER, J.: Currents of the auditory cortex in the cat. *J. Cell. Comp. Physiol., 45 (Suppl. 1)*:1-24, 1955.

KOHLER, W., and O'CONNELL, D.N.: Currents of the visual cortex of the cat. *J. Cell. Comp. Physiol., 49 (Suppl. 2)*:1-43, 1957.

KOHLER, W., and WALLACH, H.: Figural after-effects. *Proc. Amer. Phil. Soc., 88*:269-357, 1944.

KOHLER, W., and WEGENER, J.: Currents of the human auditory cortex. *J. Cell. Comp. Physiol., 45 (Suppl. 1)*:25-54, 1955.

KRIVÁNEK, J., BUREŠ, H., and BUREŠOVÁ, O.: Evidence for a relation between creatine phosphate level and polarity of the cerebral cortex. *Nature (London), 182*:1799, 1958.

KUFFLER, S.W.: Excitation and inhibition in single nerve cells. *Harvey Lect.*, 54:176-218, 1958-1959.

LANDAU, W.M., BISHOP, G.H., and CLARE, M.H.: Analysis of the form and distribution of evoked cortical potentials under the influence of polarizing currents. *J. Neurophysiol.*, 27:788-813, 1964.

LANDAU, W.M., CLARE, M.H., and BISHOP, G.H.: Effects of polarizing currents on certain evoked potentials in cerebral cortex. *Trans. Amer. Neurol. Assoc.*, 87:72-75, 1962.

LASHLEY, K.W., CHOW, K.L., and SEMMES, J.: An examination of the electrical field theory of cerebral integration. *Psychol. Rev.*, 58:123-135, 1951.

LAURSEN, A.M.: Higher functions of the central nervous system, *Ann. Rev. Physiol.*, 29:543-572, 1967.

LEÃO, A.A.P.: The slow voltage variation of cortical spreading depression of activity. *Electroenceph. Clin. Neurophysiol.*, 3:315-321, 1951.

LEÃO, A.A.P.: Further observations on the spreading depression of activity in the cerebral cortex. *J. Neurophysiol.*, 10:409-414, 1947.

LI, CHOH-LUH, and SALMOIRAGHI, G.C.: Cortical steady potential changes and extracellular microelectrode studies. *Nature (London)*, 198:858-859, 1963.

LIBERSON, W.T., and CADILHAC, G.: Further observations on DC potentials during electrically induced seizure discharge activity in guinea pig. *Electroenceph. Clin. Neurophysiol.*, 5:320, 1953.

LIBET, B., and GERARD, R.W.: Steady potential fields and neurone activity. *J. Neurophysiol.*, 4:438-455, 1941.

LIBET, B., and GERARD, R.W.: An analysis of some correlates of steady potentials in mammalian cerebral cortex. *Electroenceph. Clin. Neurophysiol.*, 14:445-452, 1962.

LIBET, B., and KAHN, J.B., JR.: Steady potentials and neurone activity in mammals. *Fed. Proc.*, 6:152, 1947.

LICKEY, M.E., and FOX, S.S.: Localization and habituation of sensory evoked DC responses in cat cortex. *Exp. Neurol.*, 15:437-454, 1966.

LIPPOLD, O.C.J.,., and REDFEARN, J.W.T.: Mental changes resulting from the passage of small direct currents through the human brain. *Brit. J. Psychiat.*, 110:768-772, 1964.

LOESCHCKE, H.H.: Über den Einfluss von C02 auf die Bestandspotentiale der Hirnhäute. *Pflueger. Arch. Ges. Physiol.*, 262:532-536, 1956.

LOW, M.D., BORDA, R.P., FROST, J.D., and KELLAWAY, P.: Surface-negative, slow-potential shift associated with conditioning in man. *Neurology (Minneap.)*, 16:771-782, 1966.

MAHNKE, J.H., and WARD, A.A.: Standing potential characteristics of the epileptogenic focus. *Epilepsia (Amst.)*, 2:161-169, 1961.

MARSHALL, W.H.: Spreading cortical depression of Leão. *Physiol. Rev.*, 39:239-279, 1959.

MARSHALL, W.H., OMMAYA, A.K., RICHTER, H., THOMPSON, H.K., and WOODY, C.D.: Relation of brain injury to slow potential changes accompanying H-ion concentration changes in the blood. *Electroenceph. Clin. Neurophysiol.*, 24:190, 1968.

McILWAIN, H.: Metabolic and electrical measurements with isolated cerebral tissues: their contributions to study of the action of drugs on cortical excitability. In Brazier, M.A.B. (Ed.): *Brain Function. Cortical Excitability and Steady Potentials.* Berkeley: U. of Calif. Press, 1963.

MURRAY, R.W.: The response of the lateralis organ of Xenopus laevis to electrical stimulation by direct current. *J. Physiol. (London)*, 134:408-420, 1956.

NAKAMURA, Y., OHYE, C., and MANO, N.: Cortical polarization and experimentally produced delta waves in the cat. *Electroenceph. Clin. Neurophysiol.*, 24:42-52, 1968.

NEGISHI, K., SELVIN DE TESTA, A., HERNANDEZ, J.A., and DIAZ BORGES, J.M.: Transcortical steady potential; its interpretation in terms of metabolic glial neuronal interaction. I. Sleep and wakeful states. *Acta Cient. Venez.*, 14 (Suppl. 1):154-162, 1963.

NELSON, P.G., and FRANK, K.: Anomalous rectification in cat spinal montoneurons and effect of polarizing currents on excitatory postsynaptic potential. *J. Neurophysiol.*, 30:1097-1113, 1967.

NORTON, S., and JEWETT, R.E.: Frequencies of slow potential oscillations in the cortex of cats. *Electroenceph. Clin. Neurophysiol.*, 19:377-386, 1965.

OIKAWA, I.: Steady potential of the cerebral cortex. Part VII. Studies of sleep induced by electric stimulation. *No to Shinkei*, 8:625-628, 1956.

O'LEARY, J.L.: Brief survey of direct current potentials of the cortex. In Moruzzi, G. (Ed.): *Progress in Brain Research.* Amsterdam: Elsevier, 1963, Vol. I.

O'LEARY, J.L., and GOLDRING, S.: Changes associated with forebrain excitation processes: d.c. potentials of the cerebral cortex. In Field, J., and Magoun, H.W. (Eds.): *Handbook of Physiology.* Washington: Amer. Physiol. Soc., 1959, Vol. I.

O'LEARY, J.L., and GOLDRING, S.: Slow cortical potentials: their origin and contribution to seizure discharge. *Epilepsia (Amst.)* 1:561-574, 1960.

O'LEARY, J.L., and GOLDRING, S.: D-C potentials of the brain. *Physiol. Rev.* 44:91-125, 1964.

PEARLMAN, A.L.: Evoked potentials of rabbit visual cortex: Relationship between a slow negative potential and excitability cycle. *Electroenceph. Clin. Neurophysiol.*, 15:426-434, 1963.

PEARLMAN, A.L., GOLDRING, S., and O'LEARY, J.L.: Visually evoked slow negativity in rabbit cortex. *Proc. Soc. Exp. Biol. Med.*, 103:600-603, 1960.

PURPURA, D.P.: Observations on the cortical mechanism of EEG. Activation accompanying behavioral arousal. *Science, 123*:804, 1956.

PURPURA, D.P.: Review and critique. In Brazier, M.A.B. (Ed.): *Brain Functions. Cortical Excitability and Steady Potentials.* Berkeley: U. of Calif. Press, 1963.

Purpura, D.P, and McMurty, J.G.: Effects of transcortical polarization on intracellular potentials and evoked responses. *Fed. Proc. 23*:209, 1964.

Purpura, D.P., and McMurty, J.G.: Intracellular activities and evoked potential changes during polarization of motor cortex. *J. Neurophysiol., 28*:166-185, 1965.

Rabinovitch, M.Ia.: The electrical activity in different layers of the cortex of the motor and acoustic analysers during the elaboration of conditioned defensive reflexes. *Pavlov, J. Higher Nerv. Act., 8*:507-519, 1958.

Ranck, J.B., Jr.: Synaptic "learning" due to electroosmosis: A theory. *Science, 144*:187-189, 1964.

Ravitz, L.I.: Standing potential correlates of hyponosis and narcosis. *Arch. Neurol. Psychiat., 65*:413-436, 1951.

Roitbak, A.I.: Electrical potentials generated in the cerebral cortex by d.c. stimulation. *Proc. Conf. Georgian Soc. Physiologists*, 1950.

Roitbak, A.I.: On the glial origin of the slow negativity of the cortex. In *Sovremennye problemy deiatelnosti i stroenia tsentralnoi nervoi sistemy,* Mezniereba, Tbilisi, 1965, pp. 67-87. Ref. in Kogan, A.B., and Choraian, O.G.: A review of Soviet papers. *Electroenceph. Clin. Neurophysiol., 22*:487-492, 1967. Also Abstract in *Psych. Abstr., 41*:13157, 1967.

Rowland, R.V.: Simple non-polarizable electrode for chronic implantation. *Electroenceph. Clin. Neurophysiol., 13*:290-291, 1961.

Rowland, V., Bradley, H., School, P., and Deutschman, D.: Cortical steady-potential shifts in conditioning. *Conditional Reflex, 2*:3-22, 1967.

Rowland, V., and Goldstone, M.: Appetitively conditioned and drive-related bioelectric baseline shift in cat cortex. *Electroenceph. Clin. Neurophysiol. 15*:474-485, 1963.

Rusinov, V.S., and Smirnov, G.D.: Quelques données sur l'étude électro-encéphalographique de l'activité nerveuse supérieure. *Electroenceph. Clin. Neurophysiol. (Suppl.), 6*:9-23, 1957.

Sano, K., Miyake, H., and Mayanagi, Y. Steady potentials in various stress conditions in man. *Electroenceph. Clin. Neurophysiol. (Suppl.), 25*:264-275, 1967.

Schulze, H., and Caspers, H.: Die physiologischen Schwankungen der corticalen Gleichspannung und ihre Beziehungen zur Reticularisakivitat. *Pflueger. Arch. Ges. Physiol., 274*:55-56, 1961.

Shuranova, Zh. P.: Slow shifts of cortical potential on stimulation of medial thalamic nuclei. *Pavlov J. Higher Nerv. Act., 15*:705, 1965.

Shvets, T.B.: Slow electrical processes in the cerebral cortex of the rabbit. *Proceedings of Conference on the Electrophysiology of the Central Nervous System,* Moscow, 1958.

Shvets, T.B.: The bioelectric potentials of the cerebral cortex of a rabbit, recorded by using a direct current amplifier. Works of the Institute of Higher Nervous Activity, *Physiol. Ser., 4*:100-113, 1962 (orig. 1958).

Shvets, T.B.: Slow changes in potential in the cerebral cortex of a rabbit under the effect of pressure exerted on the motor cortical region. Works of the Institute of Higher Nervous Activity, *Physiol. Ser.,* 4:114-125, 1962 (orig. 1958).

SHVETS, T.B.: Changes of the D-C potential of the cortical surface in response to various afferent stimuli. Works of the Institute of Higher Nervous Activity, *Physiol. Ser.,* 7:73-82, 1963 (orig. 1962).

SOTIRESCU, N., and CRIGHEL, E.: Steady potential shifts and long duration wave alterations elicited by different types of neocortical epileptic foci. *Electroenceph. Clin. Neurophysiol.,* 17:599, 1964.

SPECKMANN, E.J., and CASPERS, H.: Shifts of cortical standing potential in hypoxia and asphyxia. *Electroenceph. Clin. Neurophysiol.,* 23:379, 1967.

SPECKMANN, E.J., and CASPERS, H.: Changes in cortical steady potential during respiratory arrest. *Rev. Neurol. (Paris),* 117:5-19, 1967 (French).

STARR, A., and LIVINGSTON, R.B.: Long-lasting nervous system responses to prolonged sound stimulation in waking cats. *J. Neurophysiol.,* 26:416-431, 1963.

STRUMWASSER, F., and ROSENTHAL, S.: Prolonged and patterned direct extracellular stimulation of single neurons. *Amer. J. Physiol.,* 198:405-420, 1960.

TERZUOLO, C.A., and BULLOCK, T.H.: Measurement of imposed voltage gradient adequate to modulate neuronal firing. *Proc. Nat. Acad. Sci. U.S.A.,* 42:687-694, 1956.

TSCHIRGI, R.D., and TAYLOR, J.L.: Slowly changing bio-electric potentials associated with the blood-brain barrier. *Amer. J. Physiol. 195:*7-22, 1958.

VANASUPA, P., GOLDRING, S., O'LEARY, J.L., and WINTER, D.: Steady potential changes during cortical activation. *J. Neurophysiol.,* 22:273-289, 1959.

VASTOLA, E.F.: Steady potential responses in the lateral geniculate body. *Electroenceph. Clin. Neurophysiol.,* 7:557-567, 1955.

WARD, A.A., JR. and MAHNKE, J.H.: Standing potential characteristics of the epileptogenic focus. *Trans. Amer. Neurol. Assn.,* 85:93-95, 1960.

WARD, A.A. JR., and MAHNKE, J.H.: Negative slow potential changes in cortex. *Electroenceph. Clin. Neurophysiol.,* 13:308, 1961.

WASANO, T., INOKUCHI, S., INANAGA, K., NAKAO, H., and FUCHIWAKI, H.: The slowly changing potential of the brain and electrocorticogram under the influence of anesthetics and convulsant drugs. *Kyushu J. Med. Sci.,* 3:243-251, 1953.

WEINSTEIN, W., KENDIG, J.H., GOLDRING, S., O'LEARY, J.L., and LOURIE, H.: Hypothermia and electrical activity of cerebral cortex. *Arch. Neurol. (Chicago),* 4:441-448, 1961.

WILSON, S., and SCHMIDT, R.: Steady potential, the direct cortical response and the epileptic focus. *Electroenceph. Clin. Neurophysiol.,* 17:579, 1964.

WURTZ, R.H.: Steady potential shifts during arousal and deep sleep in the cat. *Electroenceph. Clin. Neurophysiol.,* 18:649-662, 1965.

WURTZ, R.H.: Steady potential correlates of intracranial reinforcement. *Electroenceph. Clin. Neurophysiol.,* 20:59-67, 1966.

WURTZ, R.H.: Steady potential fields during sleep and wakefulness in the cat. *Exp. Neurol.*, 15:274-292, 1966.

WURTZ, R.H.: Physiological correlates of steady potential shifts during sleep and wakefulness. II. Brain temperature, blood pressure, and potential changes across the ependyma. *Electroenceph. Clin. Neurophysiol.*, 22:43-53, 1967.

WURTZ, R.H., GOLDRING, S., and O'LEARY, J.L.: Cortical A-C potentials accompanying paradoxical and slow-wave sleep in the cat. *Fed. Proc.*, 23:209, 1964.

WURTZ, R.H., and O'FLAHERTY, J.J.: Physiological correlates of steady potential shifts during sleep and wakefulness. I. Sensitivity of the steady potential to alterations in carbon dioxide. *Electroenceph. Clin. Neurophysiol.*, 22:30-42, 1967.

YAMAMOTO, C., and IWAURA, K.: Modification of electrocortical activity by D-C polarization. *Electroenceph. Clin. Neurophysiol. (Suppl.)*, 18:11-12, 1959.

Dominant Focus

ALBERT, D.J.: The effects of polarizing currents on the consolidation of learning. *Neuropsychologia*, 4:65-77, 1966.

BERITOV, I.: Development of physiology of the central nervous system in the Soviet Union during the recent 40 years. *Sechenov Physiol. J. USSR*, 43:941-955, 1957. Translated in *The Central Nervous System and Behavior*. Bethesda: U.S. Dep't. of Health, Education and Welfare, 1959.

BINDMAN, L.J., LIPPOLD, O.C.J., and REDFEARN, J.W.T.: The prolonged after-action of polarizing currents on the sensory cerebral cortex. *J. Physiol. (London)*, 162:45P-46P, 1962.

BISHOP, G.H., and O'LEARY, J.L.: The effect of polarizing currents on cell potentials and their significance in the interpretation of central nervous system activity. *Electroenceph. Clin. Neurophysiol.*, 2:401-416, 1950.

BLAGODATOVA, E.T.: Effect of constant current on the spontaneous electroencephalogram of the rabbits. *Sechenov. J. Physiol.*, 46:1106-1116, 1960.

BLAGODATOVA, E.T.: Effect of direct current (D.C.) on excitability and electrical activity of the cerebral cortex in the rabbit. *Sechenov. Physiol. J. USSR*, 48:579-586, 1962. (*Fed. Proc.*, 22:T416-T420, 1963.)

BRAZIER, M.A.B.: Long-persisting electrical traces in the brain of man and their possible relationship to higher nervous activity. *Electroenceph. Clin. Neurophysiol. (Suppl.)* 13:347-358, 1960.

BUDYLIN, V.G., and LEVSHUNOVA, N.A.: The formation and course of conditioned reflexes in the presence of a traumatic dominant in the cerebral cortex. *Pavlov J. Higher Nerv. Act.*, 9:500-505, 1959.

COWIE, D.M.A., and PEREZ-CRUET, J.: Effects of external cathodal polarization on classical motor conditioning in dogs. *Conditional Reflex*, 2:216-226, 1967.

FARBER, D.A.: *Electrical Activity in the Retina in the Presence of a Persistent*

Focus of Excitation in the Optic Nerve and Visual Region of the Cortex. Moscow, 1953.

GAVLICHEK, V.: Electroencephalographic characteristics of the conditioned reflex defensive dominant state. *Sechenov. J. Physiol.*, *44*:274-285, 1958.

GAVRILOVA, L.N.: The influence of unilateral latent focus of excitation on the course of unconditioned and conditioned alimentary reflexes. *Pavlov J. Higher Nerv. Act.*, *10*:928-933, 1960.

GRECHUSHNIKOVA, L.S.: Interfocal relationships in the presence of a dominant focus and conditioned reflexes. Works of the Institute of Higher Nervous Activity, *Physiol. Ser.*, *5*:68-75, 1961 (orig. 1960).

GRECHUSHNIKOVA, L.S.: EEG changes in the case of a motor dominant created by rhythmic fading stimulation. Works of the Institute of Higher Nervous Activity, *Physiol. Ser.*, 7:33-40, 1963 (orig. 1962).

KALININ, P.I.: Effect of polarization of lateral and medial geniculate bodies on a motor dominant focus in rabbit brain. *Sechenov. Physiol. J. USSR*, *50*:252, 1964 *(Fed. Proc. 24*, T347-350, 1965).

KALININ, P.I., and HAN-SHÊN, LIU.: The role of the midbrain reticular formation and thalamus in the elaboration of a dominant motor center. Works of the Institute of Higher Nervous Activity, *Physiol. Ser.*, 7:59-72, 1963 (orig. 1962).

KALININ, P.I., and SOKOLOVA, A.A.: The electrical activity of the midbrain reticular formation of the rabbit in the presence of a dominant focus in the cerebral cortex. *Pavlov J. Higher Nerv. Act.*, *11*:(6) 111-117, 1961.

KHAVKINA, N.N.: Functional characteristics of centres in relation to the formation of a dominant state in man. *Sechenov. J. Physiol.*, *44*:834-842, 1958.

KHODOROV, B.I.: An investigation on the process of formation of a defence motor conditioned reflex in the dog (conditioned reflex and dominants). *Pavlov J. Higher Nerv. Act.*, *8*:820-828, 1958.

KUPFERMANN, I.: Effects of cortical polarization on visual discriminations. *Exp. Neurol.*, *12*:179-189, 1965.

LOUCKS, R.B.: Preliminary report of a technique for stimulation or destruction of tissues beneath the integument and the establishment of conditioned reactions with faradization of the cerebral cortex. *J. Comp. Psychol.*, *16*:439, 1933.

MEDIANIK, I.A., and OLEINIK, IA.V.: The influence of a direct current on the excitability of the vegetative centers of the brain. *Sechenov. Physiol. J. USSR*, *43*:374-378, 1957.

MESHCHERSKIY, R.M.: The role of corticofugal influences in effecting the dominant and the conditioned reflex. *Soviet Psychology*, *5* (No. 4):23-27, 1967.

MORRELL, F.: Effect of anodal polarization on the firing pattern of single cortical cells. *Ann. NY Acad. Sci.*, *92*:860-876, 1961.

MORRELL, F.: Electrophysiological contributions to the neural basis of learning. *Physiol. Rev.*, *41*:443-494, 1961.

MORRELL, F., and NAITOH, P.: Effect of cortical polarization on a conditioned avoidance response. *Exp. Neurol.*, 6:507-523, 1962.

MORRELL, F., and ROWLAND, V.: Studies on learning. In Brazier, M.A.B. (Ed.) *Brain Function. Cortical excitability and steady potentials.* Berkeley: U. of Calif. Press, 1963.

MNUKHINA, R.S.: Electroencephalographic analysis of the mechanism of temporary connexion closure. *Pavlov J. Higher Nerv. Act.*, 11(2):359-367, 1961.

MOVCHAN, N.P.: The effect of polarity of direct electric current on positive conditioned defense motor reflexes. *Works of the Pavlov Institute of Physiology*, 10:74-81, 1963 (orig. 1962).

NAUMOVA, T.S.: The electrical activity of a cortical dominant focus during the reflex act to sound. *Sechenov. Physiol. J. USSR*, 42:361, 1956.

NAUMOVA, T.S.: Electrographic data pertaining to the problem of bilateral (paired) activity of the cerebral hemispheres. *Sechenov. Physiol. J. USSR*, 43:288-294, 1957.

NOVIKOVA, L.A., and FARBER, D.A.: Electrophysiological research on the connection between the visual and the auditory analyzer under the influence of a dominating focus in the cerebral cortex of the rabbit. *Sechenov. Physiol. J. USSR*, 42:341, 1956.

NOVIKOVA, L.A., RUSINOV, V.S., and SEMIOKHINA, A.F.: Electrophysiological analysis of the occlusive function of the cerebral cortex of the rabbit under the influence of a dominating focus. *Pavlov J. Higher Nerv. Act.*, 2:844, 1952.

PAVLYGINA, R.A. *Disturbance and restoration of higher nervous activity on the creation of a focus of excitation in the hypothalamus.* Moscow, 1955.

PAVLYGINA, R.A.: The creation of a dominant focus in the hypotholamic region and the examination of its properties. Works of the Institute of Higher Nervous Activity. *Physiol. Ser.* 2:172-192, 1960 (orig. 1956).

PAVLYGINA, R.A.: Investigation of a center of excitation created in the cerebral cortex similar in type to a "single tetanized contraction." Works of the Inst. of Higher Nervous Activity, *Physiol. Ser.*, 7:41-50, 1963 (orig. 1962).

PAVLYGINA, R.A.: Trace phenomena in a dominant state. *Pavlov J. Higher Nerv. Act.*, 17:505-512, 1967.

PAVLYGINA, R.A., and POZDNYAKOVA, R.A.: The production of a dominant focus in the motor analyzor by the application of direct current pulses. Works of the Institute of Higher Nervous Activity, *Physiol. Ser.*, 5:48-56, 1962. (orig. 1960).

PODSOSENNAYA, L.S.: A dominant to a fading electrocutaneous stimulation and its effect on defense conditioned reflexes. Works of the Institute of Higher Nervous Activity. *Physiol. Ser.*, 3:31-41, 1961 (orig. 1959).

ROITBAK, A.I.: Primary responses of the cerebral cortex to sound clicks and electrical stimulation of the medial geniculate nucleus; their changes during unconditioned stimulation. Proc. XXI Intern. Physiol. Congr., Buenos Aires, 1959.

Rusinov, V.S.: The electrophysiological analysis of the occlusive function of the cerebral cortex during existence of a dominating focus. Proc. Int. Conf. of Physiologists, Moscow, 1953.

Rusinov, V.S.: An electrophysiological analysis of the connecting functions in the cerebral cortex in the presence of a dominant area. Proc. XIX Intern. Physiol. Cong., Montreal, 1953.

Rusinov, V.S.: Electrophysiological research in the dominant area in the higher parts of the central nervous system. Proc. XX Intern. Physiol. Congr., Brussels, 1956 .

Rusinov, V.S.: Electrophysiological investigation of foci of stationary excitation in the central nervous system. *Pavlov, J. Higher Nerv. Act., 8*:- 444-451, 1958.

Rusinov, V.S.: Long lasting excitation, dominant and temporary connection. Proc. XXI Intern. Physiol. Congr., Buenos Aires, 1959.

Rusinov, V.S.: General and localized alterations in the electroencephalogram during the formation of conditioned reflexes in man. *Electroenceph. Clin. Neurophysiol. (Suppl.), 13*:309-320, 1960.

Rusinov. V.S.: The problem of stationary excitation and changes in the steady potential of the cerebral cortex in the presence of a dominant focus and in relation to the formation of a conditioned reflex. *Pavlov J., Higher Nerv. Act., 11* (5):6-19, 1961.

Rusinov, V.S.: *Problems of Lability, Parabiosis and Inhibition.* Moscow, 1962.

Rusinov, V.S.: Electrophysiological investigations during the formation of temporary connections. *Pavlov. J. Higher Nerv. Act., 12*:412-417, 1962.

Rusinov, V.S.: Electrophysiological studies during the formation of a temporary connection. In Gerard, R.W., and Duyff, J.W.: (Eds.): *Information Processing in the Nervous System. Proc. XXII, Intern. Physiol. Congr., Leiden.* Amsterdam: Excerpta Medica, 1962.

Rusinov, V.S.: Dominant and its Role in the Formation of Temporal Connections. *XXIII, Intern. Physiol. Congr., Tokyo. IV: Lectures and Symposia.* Amsterdam: Excerpta Medica, 1965.

Rusinov, V.S.: Polarization by anodal direct current of the motor area of the cerebral cortex and the motor dominant state. *Pavlov J. Higher Nerv. Act. 15*:202-216, 1965. Reviewed in Kogan, A.B., and Choraian, O.G.: A review of Soviet papers. *Electroenceph. Clin. Neurophysiol., 22*:487-492, 1967.

Rusinov, V.S., and Rabinovich, M.Y.: Electroencephalographic researches in the laboratories and clinics of the Soviet Union. *Electroenceph. Clin. Neurophysiol. (Suppl.), 8*, 1958.

Ryabinina, M.A.: A pressure-produced dominant center in the cerebral cortex of a rabbit. Works of the Institute of Higher Nervous Activity, *Physiol. Ser., 3*:42-48, 1961 (orig. 1959).

RYABININA, M.A.: Importance of various layers of the cerebral cortex in the production of a dominant center by application of a direct current. Works of the Institute of Higher Nervous Activity, *Physiol. Ser.*, 6:200-209, 1963 (orig. 1961).

SHVETS, T.B.: Comparison of the EEG observed during existence of a dominant focus, with the EEG in the generalization stage of a conditioned reflex. Proc. 18th Conf. on Higher Nervous Activity, 1958.

SHVETS, T.B.: Slow electric activity in the cerebral cortex of rabbits during fixation of a temporary connection. Works of the Institute of Higher Nervous Activity, *Physiol. Ser.*, 5:57-67, 1962 (orig. 1960).

SOKOLOVA, A.A.: *Electrical Activity of the Cortex and Subcortical Formations in the Presence of a Dominant Focus in the Cortex.* Dissertation, Moscow, 1954.

SOKOLOVA, A.A., and KHON, SEK-BU: An electrophysical investigation of a dominant focus in the cerebral cortex of a rabbit created by the action of continuous current. *Pavlov J. Higher Nerv. Act.*, 7:135-145, 1957.

SOKOLOVA, A.A.: Electrical activity in the visual and motor regions of the cerebral cortex in rabbits during reinforcement of a dominant focus in the motor region by light stimulation. *Pavlov J. Higher Nerv. Act.*, 8:549-556, 1958.

SOKOLOVA, A.A.: Electrical activity in the cortex and subcortical formations of the rabbit in the presence of a dominant focus in the cortex. *Pavlov J. Higher Nerv. Act.*, 9:664-671, 1959.

STAROBINETS. M.K.H.: Steady polarization potentials of the human brain during alertness, anesthesia and sleep. *Pavlov J. Higher Nerv. Act.*, 17:338-344, 1967.

UKHTOMSKI, A.A.: Concerning the condition of excitation in dominance. *Reflexological and Neurophysiological News*, 2:345, 1926. English Abstract in *Psychol. Abstr.*, No. 2388, 1927.

UKHTOMSKI, A.A.: *Collected Papers.* Leningrad, 1950.

Physiology of Learning

ADEY, W.R.: Brain mechanisms and the learning process. *Fed. Proc.*, 20:617-627, 1961.

ADEY, W.R.: Hippocampal states and functional relations with corticosubcortical systems in attention and learning. *Progr. Brain Res.*, 27:228-245, 1967.

ADEY, W.R.: Neurophysiological correlates of information transaction and storage in brain tissue. *Progr. Physiol. Psychol.*, 1:1-42, 1966.

ADEY, W.R., KADO, R.T., DIDIO, J., and SCHINDLER, W.J.: Impedance changes in cerebral tissue accompanying a learned discriminative performance in the cat. *Exp. Neurol.*, 7:259-281, 1963.

ADEY, W.R., WALTER, D.O., and HENDRIX, C.E.: Computer techniques in correlation and spectral analysis of cerebral slow waves during discriminative behavior. *Exp. Neurol.*, 3:501-524, 1961.

ADEY, W.R., DUNLOP, C.W., and HENDRIX, C.E.: Hippocampal slow waves; distribution and phase relations in the course of approach learning. *Arch. Neurol. (Chicago)*, 3:74-90, 1960.

ADEY, W.R., WALTER, D.O., and LINDSLEY, D.F.: Effects of subthalamic lesions on learned behavior and correlated hippocampal and subcortical slow wave activity. *Arch. Neurol. (Chicago)*, 6:194-207, 1962.

ANOKHIN, P.K.: Electroencephalographic analysis of cortico-subcortical relations in positive and negative conditioned reactions. *Ann. NY Acad. Sci.*, 92:899-938, 1961

ARTEMYEV, V.V., and BEZLADNOVA, N.I.: Electrical reaction of the auditory area of the cortex of the cerebral hemispheres during the formation of a conditioned defense reflex. *Tr. Inst. Fiziol. (Tbilisi)*, 1:228-236, 1952.

ASRATIAN, E.A.: Stable local electrophysiological manifestations of conditioned reflexes. *Pavlov J. Higher Nerv. Act.*, 17:896-908, 1967.

BALL, G.G., and ADAMS, D.W.: Intracranial stimulation as an avoidance or escape response. *Psychonomic Sci.*, 3:39-40, 1965.

BECK, E.C., DOTY, R.W., and KOOI, K.A.: Electrocortical reactions associated with conditioned flexion reflexes. *Electroenceph. Clin. Neurophysiol.*, 10:279-289, 1958.

BERITOFF (BERITASHVILI), I.S.: *Neural mechanisms of higher vertebrate behavior*. Liberson, W.T. (Trans., Ed.). Boston: Little, Brown, 1965.

BETTINGER, L.A., DAVIS, J.L., MEIKLE, M.B., BIRCH, H., KOPP, R., SMITH, H.E., and THOMPSON, R.F.: "Novelty" cells in association cortex of cat. *Psychonomic Sci.*, 9:421-422, 1967.

BREMNER, F.J.: Hippocampal activity during avoidance behavior in the rat. *J. Comp. Physiol. Psychol.*, 58:16-22, 1964.

BURÈS, J., BURESOVÁ, O., WEISS, T., FIFKOVA, E., and BOHDANECKY, Z.: Experimental study of the role of hippocampus in conditioning and memory function. In *Physiologie de l'Hippocampe*. Paris: C.N.R.S., 1962. (Colloques Internationaux du Centre National de la Recherche Scientifique. No. 107: "Physiologie de l'Hippocampe," Montpellier, 24-26 Août, 1961. Paris: Centre National de la Recherche Scientifique, 1962.)

CARLSON, K.R.: Cortical spreading depression and subcortical memory storage. *J. Comp. Physiol. Psychol.*, 64:422-430, 1967.

CHANG, H.T.: Some observations on the excitability changes of cortical and subcortical neurons and their possible significance in the process of conditioning. *Electroenceph. Clin. Neurophysiol. (Suppl.)*, 13:39-49, 1960.

CHIORINI, J.R.: Slow potential changes from cat cortex and classical aversive conditioning. *Electroenceph. Clin. Neurophysiol.*, 23:90, 1967.

CHOW, K.L., DEMET, W.C., and JOHN, E.R.: Conditioned electrocorticographic potentials and behavioral avoidance response in cat. *J. Neurophysiol.*, 20:482-493, 1957.

CHOW, K.L., RANDALL, W., and MORRELL, F.: Effect of brain lesions on conditioned cortical electropotentials. *Electroenceph. Clin. Neurophysiol.*, 20:357-369, 1966.

DELAFRESNAYE, J.R. (Ed.): *Brain Mechanisms and Learning*. Oxford: Blackwell, 1961.

DRACHMAN, D.A., and OMMAYA, A. K.: Memory and the hippocampal complex. *Arch. Neurol. (Chicago)*, *10*, 411-425, 1964.

ELAZAR, Z., and ADEY, W.R.: Spectral analysis of low frequency components in the electrical activity of the hippocampus during learning. *Electroenceph. Clin. Neurophysiol.*, *23*:225-240, 1967.

ELAZAR, Z., and ADEY, W.R.: Electroencephalographic correlates of learning in subcortical and cortical structures. *Electroenceph. Clin. Neurophysiol.*, *23*:306-319, 1967.

EHRLICH, D.J., and MALMO, R.B.: Electrophysiological concommitants of simple operant conditioning in the rat. *Neuropsychologia*, *5*:219-235, 1967.

Fourth International Congress of Electro-encephalography and Clinical Neurophysiology. Eighth meeting of the international League Against Epilepsy. Amsterdam: Exerpta Medica, 1957.

FREEMAN, W.J.: Phasic and long-term excitability changes in pre-pyriform cortex of cats. *Exp. Neurol.*, *5*:500-518, 1962.

GALAMBOS, R.: Electrical correlates of conditioned learning. In Brazier, M.A.B. (Ed.): *Central Nervous System and Behavior*. New York: Josiah Macy, Jr., Foundation, 1959.

GALAMBOS, R.: Some neural correlates of conditioning and learning. In Ramey, E.R., and O'Doherty, D.S. (Eds.): *Electrical Studies on the Unanesthetized Brain*. New York: Hoeber, 1960.

GALAMBOS, R., and MORGAN, C.T.: The neural basis of learning. In Field, J., and Magoun, H.W.: *Handbook of Physiology*, Vol. III. Washington: Amer. Physiol. Soc., 1960.

GALAMBOS, R., and SHEATZ, G.C.: An electroencephalograph study of classical conditioning. *Amer. J. Physiol.*, *203*:173-184, 1962.

GALAMBOS, R., SHEATZ, G.C., and VERNIER, V.G.: Electrophysiological correlates of a conditioned response in cats. *Science*, *123*:376-377, 1956.

GASTAUT, H.: État actuel des connaissances sur l'électroencéphalographie du conditionnement. *Electroenceph. Clin. Neurophysiol. (Suppl.)*, *6*:133-160, 1957.

GASTAUT, H., JUS, A., JUS, C., MORRELL, F., STORM VAN LEEUWEN, W., DONGIER, S., NAQUET, R., REGIS, H., ROGER, A., BEKKERING, D., KAMP, A., and WERRE, J.: Étude topographique des réactions électroencéphalographiques conditionées chez l'homme. *Electroenceph. Clin. Neurophysiol.*, *9*:1-34, 1957.

GASTAUT, H., and ROGER, A.: Les mécanismes de l'activité nerveuse supérieure envisagés au niveau des grandes structures fonctionnelles du cerveau. *Electroenceph. Clin. Neurophysiol. (Suppl.)*, *13*:13-38, 1960.

GLUCK, H., and ROWLAND, V.: Defensive conditioning of electrographic arousal with delayed and differentiated auditory stimuli. *Electroenceph. Clin. Neurophysiol.*, *11*:485-496, 1959.

GMYRIA-NOVI, V.A.: Changes in evoked potentials due to linkage of a temporary connection. *Sechenov Physiol. J. USSR,* 50:10-19, 1964. Abstract: *Electroenceph. Clin. Neurophysiol.,* 19:419, 1965.

GRASTYÁN, E., and KARMOS, G.: The influence of hippocampal lesions in simple and delayed instrumental conditioned reflexes. In *Physiologie de l'hippocampe.* Paris: C.N.R.S., 1962. (See Burès, *et al.,* above.)

GRASTYÁN, E., LISSÁK, K., MADARÁSZ, I., and DONHOFFER, H.: Hippocampal electrical activity during the development of conditioned reflexes. *Electroenceph. Clin. Neurophysiol.,* 11:409-430, 1959.

HALL, R.D., and MARK, R.G.: Fear and the modification of acoustically evoked potentials during conditioning. *J. Neurophysiol.,* 30:893-910, 1967.

HEARST, E., BEER, B., SHEATZ, G.C., and GALAMBOS, R.: Some electrophysiological correlates of conditioning in the monkey. *Electroenceph. Clin. Neurophysiol.,* 12:137-152, 1960.

HOREL, J.A., and VIERCK, C.J., JR.: Average evoked responses and learning. *Science,* 158:394, 1967.

ISAACSON, R.L., DOUGLAS, R.J., and MOORE, R.Y.: The effect of radical hippocampal ablation on acquisition of avoidance response. *J. Comp. Physiol. Psychol.,* 54:625-628, 1961.

JASPER, H.H., RICCI, G.F., and DOANE, B.: Patterns of cortical neuronal discharge during conditioned responses in monkeys. In Wolstenholme, G.E.W., and O'Connor, C.M. *Neurological Basis of Behavior.* Boston: Little, Brown, 1958. (Ciba Symp.)

JASPER, H.H., RICCI, G.F., and DOANE, B.: Microelectrode analysis of cortical cell discharge during avoidance conditioning in the monkey. *Electroenceph. Clin. Neurophysiol. (Suppl.),* 13:137-155, 1960.

JASPER, H.H., and SMIRNOV, G.D.: The Moscow colloquium on electroencephalography of higher nervous activity. *Electroenceph. Clin. Neurophysiol. (Suppl.),* 13, 1960.

JOHN, E.R.: High nervous functions: brain functions and learning. *Ann. Rev. Physiol.,* 23:451-484, 1961.

JOHN, E. R.; Chemical and electrophysiological studies of memory. In Gerard, R.W., and Duyff, J.W. (Ed.): *Information Processing in the Nervous System, Proc. Int. Union Physiol. Sci., XXII Congr., Leiden.* Amsterdam: Excerpta Medica, 288-298, 1962.

JOHN, E.R., and KILLAM, K.F.: Electrophysiological correlates of avoidance conditioning in the cat. *J. Pharmacol. Exp. Ther.,* 125:252-274, 1959.

JOHN, E.R., RUCHKIN, D.S., and VILLEGAS, J.: Signal analysis of evoked potentials recorded from cats during conditioning. *Science,* 141:429-431, 1963.

JOHN, E.R., RUCHKIN, D.S., LEIMAN, A., SACHS, E., and AHN, H.: Electrophysiological Studies of Generalization Using Both Peripheral and Central Conditioned Stimuli. *Proc. Int. Union Physiol. Sci. XXIII Congr., Tokyo. IV: Lectures and Symposia.* Amsterdam: Excerpta Medica, 1965.

JOUVET, M., and HERNÁNDEZ-PEON, R.: Méchanismes neurophysiologiques concernant l'habituation, l'attention, et le conditionement. *Electroenceph. Clin. Neurophysiol. (Suppl.)*, *6*:39-49, 1957.

KAADA, B.R., RASMUSSEN, W.E., and KVEIM, O.: Effects of hippocampal lesions on maze learning and retention in rats. *Exp. Neurol.*, *3*:333-335, 1961.

KALININ, P.I., and SOKOLOVA, A.A.: The electrical activity in the reticular formation of the midbrain in the rabbit during extinction of the activation reaction to an indifferent stimulus. *Sechenov. Physiol. J. USSR.*, *47 (5)*:2-7, 1961.

KANDEL, E.R., and SPENCER, W.A.: Cellular neurophysiological approaches in the study of learning. *Physiol. Rev.*, *48*:65-134, 1968.

KARMOS, G., and GRASTYÁN, E.: Influence of hippocampal lesions on simple and delayed conditional reflexes. *Acta Physiol. Acad. Sci. Hung.*, *21*:215-224, 1962.

KIMBLE, DANIEL (Ed.): *Learning, Remembering and Forgetting. Proceedings of N.Y. Acad. Sci. second conference on learning, remembering and forgetting.* Princeton, N.J., 27-30, Sept., 1964. (Abst. in) *Science, 146*:1605, 1964.

KIMBLE, P.D., and PRIBRAM, K.H.: Hippocampectomy and behavior sequences. *Science, 139*:824-825, 1963.

KITAI, S.T., COHEN, B., and MORIN, F.: Changes in the amplitude of photically evoked potentials by a conditioned stimulus. *Electroenceph. Clin. Neurophysiol.*, *19*:344-349, 1965.

KNIPST, I.N.: Electrical activity at different levels of the cerebral cortex during the formation of defensive conditioned reflex in rabbits. Works of the Institute of Higher Nervous Activity, *Physiol. Ser.*, *1*:391-409, 1960 (orig. 1955).

KNIPST, I.N.: Bioelectrical activity in various levels of the cerebral cortex in rabbits during the elaboration of the defensive conditioned reflex to stimuli with nonsynchronized rhythms. Works of the Institute of Higher Nervous Activity, *Physiol. Ser.*, *2*:219-247, 1960 (orig. 1956).

KNIPST, I.N.: Electrophysiological studies on the stage of generalization of conditioned defense reflexes. Works of the Institue of Higher Nervous Activity, *Physiol. Ser.*, *5*:1-11, 1962 (orig. 1960).

KOGAN, A.B.: *Electrophysiological investigations of the central mechanisms of certain complex reflexes.* Moscow, 1949. Ref. in Rusinov and Rabinovich: EEG Researches in the USSR. *Electroenceph. Clin. Neurophysiol. (Suppl.) 8*:1958.

KUPALOV, P.S.: The organization of the nervous process of the brain during the conditioned reflex activity. *Electroenceph. Clin. Neurophysiol., (Suppl.)*, *13*:3-11, 1960.

LAIRY, G.C.: Quelques remarques sur le problème "EEG et physiologie du comportement." *Electroenceph. Clin. Neurophysiol.*, *16*:130-135, 1964.

LESSE, H.: Electrographic recordings of amygdaloid activity during a conditioned response. *Fed. Proc.*, *16*:79, 1957.

LIVANOV, M.N.: Rhythmic stimuli and the interrelation of fields in the cerebral cortex, I and II. *Physiol. Zh. USSR*, 28:2-3, 1940.

LIVANOV, M.N.: *Certain results of electrophysiological investigations of conditioned connections.* Transactions of the XV conference on problems of higher nervous activity, in honor of the 50th anniversary of Pavlov's theory of conditioned reflexes. Moscow and Leningrad: 1952.

LIVANOV, M.N., and KOROLKOVA, T. A.: The influence of inadequate stimulation of the cortex with induction current on the bioelectrical rhythm of the cortex and conditioned reflex activity. *Pavlov J. Higher Nerv. Act.*, 1:332-346, 1951.

LIVANOV, M.N., KOROLKOVA, T.A., and FRENKEL, G.M.: Electrophysiological studies of higher nervous activity. *Pavlov J. Higher Nerv. Act.*, 1:521-538, 1951.

LIVANOV, M.N., and POLYAKOV, K.L.: Electrical processes in the cerebral cortex of rabbits during the formation of the defensive conditioned reflex to rhythmic stimulation. *Bull. Acad. Sci. USSR*, 3:286-307, 1945.

LUR'YE, R.N., and RABINOVICH, M.YA.: Study of electrical phenomena in the cortex ends of analysors in dogs during the formation of conditioned defense reflexes. *Pavlov J. Higher Nerv. Act.*, 6:863-871, 1956. Engl. translation in *The Central Nervous System and Human Behavior*. Bethesda: U.S. Dept. Health, Education and Welfare, 1959.

MACLEAN, P.D., FLANIGAN, S., FLYNN, J.P., KIM, C., and STEVENS, J.R.: Hippocampal function: tentative correlations of conditioning, EEG, drug and radioautographic studies. *Yale J. Biol. Med.*, 28:380-395, 1955.

MAGOUN, H.W.: Recent contributions to the electrophysiology of learning. N.Y. Acad. Sci., *"Pavlovian Conference on Higher Nervous Activity."* 1960.

MAJKOWSKI, J.: The electroencephalogram and electromyogram of motor conditioned reflexes after paralysis with curare. *Electroenceph. Clin. Neurophysiol.*, 10:503-514, 1958.

MAJKOWSKI, J.: Electrophysiological studies of learning in split brain cats. *Electroenceph. Clin. Neurophysiol.*, 23:521-531, 1967.

MARK, R.G., and HALL, R.D.: Acoustically evoked potentials in the rat during conditioning. *J. Neurophysiol.*, 30:875-892, 1967.

MARSH, J.T., McCARTHY, D.A., SHEATZ, G., and GALAMBOS, R.: Amplitude changes in evoked auditory potentials during habituation and conditioning. *Electroenceph. Clin. Neurophysiol.*, 13:224-234, 1961.

MESHCHERSKII, R.M.: Changes of electrical activity in the cortical end of visual analyzer of a rabbit during the elaboration of a conditioned defensive reflex to light stimuli. Works of the Institute of Higher Nervous Activity. *Physiol. Ser.*, 1:351-367, 1960 (orig. 1955).

MILNER, B.: Les troubles de la memoire accompagnant des lesions hippocampique bilaterales. In *Physiologie de l'Hippocampe*. Paris, C.N.R.S., 1962 (See Burès, *et al*, above.)

MORRELL, F.: Electroencephalographic studies of conditioned learning. In

Brazier, M.A.B.: *The Central Nervous System and Behavior.* New York: Josiah Macy, Jr., Foundation, 1958.

MORRELL, F.: Microelectrode and steady potential studies suggesting a dendritic locus of closure. *Electroenceph. Clin. Neurophysiol. (Suppl.), 13*:65-79, 1960.

MORRELL, F., and JASPER, H.H.: Electrographic studies of the formation of temporary connections of the brain. *Electroenceph. Clin. Neurophysiol., 8*:201-314, 1956.

MORRELL, F., and NAQUET, R.: Conditioning of generalized hypersynchronous discharges in cats with epileptogenic lesions. *Electroenceph. Clin. Neurophysiol., 8*:728, 1956.

MORRELL, F., NAQUET, R., and GASTAUT, H.: Evolution of some electrical signs of conditioning: 1. Normal cat and rabbit. *J. Neurophysiol., 20*:574-587, 1957.

NAUMOVA, T.S., POPOVA, N.S., and JULYANINA, N.N.: Dynamics of amplitudes of evoked potentials in the cortical auditory and visual projection areas of dogs in the course of defensive conditioning. *Pavlov J. Higher Nerv. Act., 16*:984-993, 1966.

PEIMER, I.A.: Local electrical responses in the cerebral cortex of man and their relationship to generalized reactions in the process of conditioned reflex activity. *Sechenov. Physiol. J. USSR, 44*:791-801, 1958. Also in *The Central Nervous System and Behavior.* Bethesda: U.S. Dept. of Health, Education and Welfare, 1959, 771-784.

PICKENHAIN, L., and KLINGBERG, F.: Behavioral and electrophysiological changes during avoidance conditioning to light flashes in the rat. *Electroenceph. Clin. Neurophysiol., 18*:464-476, 1965.

PINTO-HUMAY, T., PROCTOR, F., and KUPFERMAN, I.: Direct Current Recording and Stimulation during Learning in Rabbits. *Electroenceph. Clin. Neurophysiol., 17*:452, 1964.

ROITBAK, A.I.: Electrical phanomena in the cerebral cortex during the extinction of orientation and conditioned reflexes. *Electroenceph. Clin. Neurophysiol. (Suppl.), 13*:91-100, 1960.

RUTLEDGE, L.T.: Facilitation: electrical response enhanced by conditional excitation of cerebral cortex. *Science, 148*:1246-1248, 1965.

SCHUCKMAN, H., and BATTERSBY, W.S.: Frequency specific mechanisms in learning. *Electroenceph. Clin. Neurophysiol., 18*:45-55, 1965.

SEGUNDO, J.P., ROIG, J.A., and SOMMER-SMITH, J.A.: Conditioning of reticular formation stimulation effects. *Electroenceph. Clin. Neurophysiol., 11*:471-484, 1959.

SHUL'GINA, G.I.: Study of local bioelectric phenomena in the cerebral cortex during conditioned reflex elaboration and during internal inhibition. *Works of the Institute of Higher Nervous Activity, Physiol. Ser., 5*:12-18, 1962 (orig. 1960).

SHUMILINA, A.I.: An experimental analysis of the electrical activity of the reticular formation and cerebral cortex during the development of a conditioned food response, *Sechenov Physiol. J. USSR, 47 (1)*:1-9, 1961.

STERN, J.A., DAS, K.C., ANDERSON, J.M., BIDDY, R.L., and SURPHLIS, W.: "Conditioned" alpha desynchronization. *Science, 134*:388-389, 1961.

STORM VAN LEEUWEN, W., KAMP, A., KOK, M.L., QUARTEL, F., DeLOPES, D.A., SILVA, F.H., and TIELEN, A.M.: Relations entre les activités électriques cérébrales du chien, son comportement et sa direction d'attention. *Actualities Neurophysiol.*, 7:167-186, 1967.

THOMAS, GARTH, J.: Neurophysiology of Learning. *Ann. Rev. Psychol., 13*:71-106, 1962.

TISHANINOVA, L.V.: Excitability and reactivity of the rabbit cerebral cortex during elaboration of a conditioned defense reflex. Works of the Institute of Higher Nervous Activity, *Physiol. Ser., 6*:219-229, 1963 (orig. 1961).

TROFIMOV, L.G.: The electroencephalographical investigation of higher nervous activity. *Pavlov J. Higher Nerv. Act., 9*:552-557, 1959.

ULETT, G.: Comment on Morrell, F., and Jasper, H.: Conditioning of cortical electrical activity in the monkey. *Electroenceph. Clin. Neurophysiol.*, 7:461, 1955.

UTTAL, W.R.: Evoked brain potentials—signs or codes? Perspect. *Biol. Med. (Paris), 10*:627-639, 1967.

VORONIN, L.G.: Some results of comparative-physiological investigations of higher nervous activity. Psychol. Bull., *59*, 161-195, 1962.

VORONIN, L.G., KALYUZHNY, L.V., and ZAKHAROVA, T.N.: Electroencephalographic data on the role of lateral and ventromedial nuclei of the hypothalamus in closing food conditioned temporary connections. *Pavlov J. Higher Nerv. Act., 15*:364-373, 1965. In Kogan, A.B., and Choraian, O.G.: A review of Soviet papers. *Electroenceph. Clin. Neurophysiol., 22*:487-492, 1967.

WANG, T'AI-AN and NEZLINA, N.I.: Electrical activity of cerebral cortex during formation of conditioned reflexes in monkeys. *Pavlov J. Higher Nerv. Act., 13*:235, 1963. Fed. Proc. *23*, T260-263, 1964.

WEINBERGER, N.M., NAKAYAMA, K., and LINDSLEY, D.B.: Electrocortical recruiting responses during classical conditioning. *Electroenceph. Clin. Neurophysiol., 24*:16-24, 1968.

YOSHII, N., and HOCKADAY, W. J.: Conditioning of frequency-characteristic repetitive electroencephalographic response with intermittent photic stimulation. *Electroenceph. Clin. Neurophysiol., 10*:487-502, 1958.

YOSHII, N., PRUVOT, P., and GASTAUT, H.: Electroencephalographic activity of the mesencephalic reticular formation during conditioning in the cat. *Electroenceph. Clin. Neurophysiol., 9*:595-608, 1957.

ZUCKERMANN, E.: Effect of cortical and reticular stimulation on conditioned reflex activity. *J. Neurophysiol., 22*:633-643, 1959.

Contingent Negative Variation

BLACK, S., and WALTER, W.G.: Effects on anterior brain responses of variation in the probability of association between stimuli. *J. Phychosom. Res., 9*:33-43, 1965.

CANT, B.R., and BICKFORD, R.G.: The effect of motivation on the contingent negative variation (CNV). *Electroenceph. Clin. Neurophysiol.*, 23:594, 1967.

DONGIER, M., and BOSTEM, F.: Tentative application in psychiatry of the contingent negative variation. *Electroenceph. Clin. Neurophysiol.*, 23:282, 1967.

GUIBAL, M., and IAIRY, G.C.: Preliminary findings concerning the expectancy wave and the visually deficient child. *Electroenceph. Clin. Neurophysiol.*, 23:579, 1967.

GULLICKSON, G.R., and DARROW, C.W.: Respiratory effects on the contingent negative variation. *Electroenceph. Clin. Neurophysiol.*, 23:593, 1967.

HILLYARD, S.A., and GALAMBOS, R.: Effects of stimulus and response contingencies on a surface negative slow potential shift in man. *Electroenceph. Clin. Neurophysiol.*, 22:297-304, 1967.

IRWIN, D.A., KNOTT, J.R., McADAM, D.W., and REBERT, C.S.: Motivational Determinants of the "Contingent Negative Variation." *Electroenceph. Clin. Neurophysiol.*, 21:538-543, 1966.

IRWIN, D.A., REBERT, C.S., McADAM, D.W., and KNOTT, J.R.: Slow potential changes (CNV) in the human EEG as a function of motivational variables. *Electroenceph. Clin. Neurophysiol.*, 21:412-413, 1966.

KNOTT, J.R., and IRWIN, D.A.: Anxiety, stress and the contingent negative variation (CNV). *Electroenceph. Clin. Neurophysiol.*, 24:286-287, 1968.

KOOI, K.A., SHAFII, M., and RICHEY, E.T.: Differentiation between visually evoked F and V potentials. *Electroenceph. Clin. Neurophysiol.*, 24:482-485, 1968.

LIBERSON, W.T., and LIBERSON, C.W.: Protracted slow potentials following vertex evoked responses. *Electroenceph. Clin. Neurophysiol.*, 21:413, 1966.

LOW, M.D., BORDA, R.P., and KELLAWAY, P.: "Contingent negative variation" in rhesus monkeys: an EEG sign of a specific mental process. *Percept. Motor Skills*, 22:443-446, 1966.

LOW, M.D., COATS, A.C., RETTIG, G.M., and McSHERRY, J.W.: Anxiety, attentiveness—alertness: a phenomenological study of the CNV. *Neuropsychologia*, 5:379-384, 1967.

McADAM, D.W.: Slow potential changes recorded from human brain during learning of a temporal interval. *Psychonomic Sci.*, 6:435-436, 1966.

McADAM, D.W.: Development of the contingent negative variation during the learning of a temporal interval. *Electroenceph. Clin. Neurophysiol.*, 23:491, 1967.

McADAM, D.W.: Changes in somato-sensory evoked potentials during the contingent negative variation (CNV). *Electroenceph. Clin. Neurophysiol.*, 24:286, 1968.

REBERT, C.S., McADAM, D.W., KNOTT, J.R., and IRWIN, D.A.: Slow potential change in human brain related to level of motivation. *J. Comp. Physiol. Psychol.*, 63:20-23, 1967.

WALTER, W.G.: Effects on anterior brain responses of an expected association between stimuli. *J. Psychosom. Res.*, *9*:45-49, 1965. (See also p. 51-61.)

WALTER, W.G.: The analysis, synthesis and identification of evoked responses and contingent negative variation (CNV). *Electroenceph. Clin. Neurophysiol.*, *23*:489, 1967.

WALTER, W.G.: Electrical signs of association, expectancy and decisions in the human brain. *Electroenceph. Clin. Neurophysiol. (Suppl.)*, *25*:258-263, 1967.

WALTER, W.G., COOPER, R., ALDRIDGE, V.J., McCALLUM, W.C., and WINTER, A.L.: Contingent negative variation: an electric sign of sensorimotor association and expectancy in the human brain. *Nature (London)*, *203*:380-384, 1964.

WALTER, W.G., et al.: Contingent negative variation and evoked responses recorded by radio-telemetry in free-ranging subjects. *Electroenceph. Clin. Neurophysiol.*, *21*:616-617, 1966.

WALTER, W.G., COOPER, R., CROW, H.J., McCALLUM, W.C., WARREN, W.J., and ALDRIDGE, V.J.: Contingent negative variation and evoked responses recorded by radiotelementry in free-ranging subjects. *Electroenceph. Clin. Neurophysiol.*, *23*:197-206, 1967.

Hemispheric Dominance

ARCHIBALD, Y.M., and WEPMAN, J.M.: Language disturbance and nonverbal cognitive performance in eight patients following injury to the right hemisphere. *Brain*, *91*:117-130, 1968.

BINGLEY, T.: Mental symptoms in temporal lobe epilepsy and temporal lobe gliomas, with special reference to laterality of lesion and the relationship between handedness and brainedness. *Acta. Psychiat. Neurol. Scand.*, *33 (Suppl.)* 120:IX-151, 1958.

BUREŠ, J. and BUREŠOVÁ, O.: The use of Leao's spreading depression in the study of interhemispheric transfer of memory traces. *J. Comp. Physiol., Psychol.*, *53*:558-563, 1960.

ČERNÁČEK, J., and PODIVINSKY, F.: Late somatosensory cortical response and cerebral dominance. *Physiologia Bohemoslovenica*, *16*:256-263, 1967.

CHESHER, E.C.: Some observations concerning the relation of handedness to the language mechanism. *Bull. Neurol. Inst. NY*, *4*:556-562, 1936.

COLONNA, A., and FAGLIONI, P.: The performance of hemisphere-damaged patients on spatial intelligence tests. *Cortex*, *2*:293-307, 1966.

COSTA, L.D., and VAUGHAN, H.G.: Performance of patients with lateralized cerebral lesions. I: Verbal and perceptual tests. *J. Nerv. Ment. Dis.*, *134*:162-168, 1962.

CRITCHLEY, M.: *The Parietal Lobes*. Baltimore: Williams and Wilkins, 1953.

DARLEY, F.L.(Ed.): *Brain Mechanisms Underlying Speech and Language*. New York: Grune and Stratton, 1967.

DOWNER, J.L.deC.: Changes in visual gnostic functions and emotional behavior following unilateral temporal pole damage in the "splitbrain" monkey. *Nature (London)*, *191*:50-51, 1961.

ELITHORN, A.: Intelligence, perceptual integration and the minor hemisphere syndrome. *Neuropsychologia*, 2:327-332, 1964.

GAZZANIGA, M.S.: Effects of commissurotomy on a preoperatively learned visual discrimination. *Exp. Neurol.*, *8*:14-19, 1963.

GAZZANIGA, M.S.: Psychological properties of the disconnected hemispheres in man. *Science*, *150*:372, 1965.

GAZZANIGA, M.S., BOGEN, J.E., and SPERRY, R.W.: Some functional effects of sectioning the cerebral commissures in man. *Proc. Nat. Acad. Sci. USA*, *48*:1765-1769, 1962.

GAZZANIGA, M.S., BOGEN, J.E., and SPERRY, R.W.: Laterality effects in somesthesis following cerebral commissurotomy in man. *Neuropsychologia*, *1*:209-215, 1963.

GESCHWIND, N., and KAPLAN, E.: A human cerebral deconnection syndrome. *Neurology (Minneap.)*, *12*:675-685, 1962.

GLONING, K., and QUATEMBER, R.: Statistical evidence of neuropsychological syndromes in left-handed and ambidextrous patients. *Cortex*, 2:484-488, 1966.

GOODGLASS, H., and QUADFASEL, F.A.: Language laterality in left-handed asphasics, *Brain*, 77:521-548, 1954.

HÉCAEN, H.: Clinical symptomatology in right and left hemispheric lesions. In Mountcastle, V.B. (Ed.): *Interhemispheric Relations and Cerebral Dominance*. Baltimore: Johns Hopkins, 1962.

HÉCAEN, H., and DEAJURIAGUERRA, J:. *Lefthandedness: Manual Superiority and Cerebral Dominance*. New York: Grune and Stratton, 1964.

HÉCAEN, H., and PIERCY, M.: Paroxysmal dysphasia and the problem of cerebral dominance. *J. Neurol. Neurosurg. Psychiat.*, *19*:194-201, 1956.

HUMPHREY, M.E., and ZANGWILL, O.L.: Dysphasia in left-handed patients with unilateral brain lesions. *J. Neurol. Neurosurg. Psychiat.*, *15*:184-193, 1952.

MUSLAND, R.L.: Brain mechanisms underlying the language function. *Bull. Orton Soc.*, *17*:1-31, 1967.

McFIE, J., and ZANGWILL, O.L.: Visual-constructive disabilities associated with lesions of the left cerebral hemisphere. *Brain*, *83*:243-260, 1960.

MOUNTCASTLE, V.B. (Ed.): *Interhemispheric Relations and Cerebral Dominance*. Baltimore: Johns Hopkins, 1962.

MYERS, R.E.: Transmission of visual information within and between the hemispheres: a behavioral study. In Mountcastle, V.B. (Ed.): *Interhemispheric Relations and Cerebral Dominance*. Baltimore: Johns Hopkins, 1962.

PIERCY, M., HÉCAEN, H., and AJURIAGUERRA, J.: Constructional apraxia associated with unilateral cerebral lesions—left and right sided cases compared. *Brain*, *83*:225-242, 1960.

PIERCY, M., and SMYTH, V.O.G.: Right hemisphere dominance for certain non-verbal intellectual skills. *Brain, 85*:775-790, 1962.

Ross, R.B., and Russell, I.S.: Lateralization and one-trial interhemispheric transfer of avoidance conditioning. *Nature (London), 204*:909-910, 1964.

Russell, I.S., and Ochs, S.: One-trial interhemispheric transfer of a learning engram. *Science, 133*:1077-1078, 1961.

Russell, I.S., and Ochs, S.: Localization of a memory trace in one cortical hemisphere and transfer to the other hemisphere. *Brain, 86*:37-54, 1963.

Schaltenbrand, G., and Woolsey, N.: *Cerebral Localization and Organization.* Madison: U. of Wis., 1964.

Sem-Jacobsen, C.W.: Electrical stimulation-effects on speech in areas around the third ventricle. *Electroenceph. Clin. Neurophysiol., 14*:956, 1962.

Semmes, J.: Hemispheric specialization: a possible clue to mechanism. *Neuropsychologia, 6*:11-26, 1968.

Semmes, J., Weinstein, G.L., and Teuber, H.: *Somatosensory Changes After Penetrating Brain Wounds in Man.* Cambridge: Harvard, 1960.

Sweet, W.H.: Seeping intracranial aneurysm simulating neoplasm. *Arch. Neurol. Psychiatr., 45*:86-104, 1941.

Teuber, H.L., and Mishkin, M.: Judgment of visual and postural vertical after brain injury. *J. Psychol., 38*:161-175, 1954.

Travis, R.P., and Sparks, D.L.: The influence of unilateral and bilateral spreading depression during learning upon subsequent relearning. *J. Comp. Physiol. Psychol., 56*:56-59, 1963.

Localization of Function

Bard, P., and Mountcastle, V.B.: Some forebrain mechanisms involved in the expression of rage with special reference to suppression of angry behavior. In *The Frontal Lobes. Res. Publ. Assoc. Res. Nerv. Ment. Dis, 27*:362-404, 1947 (Fulton, J.F., Aring, C.D., and Wortis, S.B. (Eds.). Baltimore: Williams and Wilkins, 1948).

Bates, J.A.V., and Ettlinger, G.: Posterior biparietal ablations in the monkey. *Arch. Neurol. (Chicago), 3*:177-192, 1960.

Bignall, K.E., and Singer, P.: Auditory, Somatic and visual input to association and motor cortex of the squirrel monkey. *Exp. Neurol., 18*:300-312, 1967.

Blake, M.O., Meyer, D.R., and Meyer, P.M.: Enforced observation in delayed response learning by frontal monkeys. *J. Comp. Physiol. Psychol., 61*:374-379, 1966.

Blum, J.S.: Cortical organization in somesthesis: effects of lesions in posterior association cortex on somatosensory function in Macaca urulatta. *Comp. Psychol. Monogr., 20*:219-249, 1950.

Blum, J.S., Chow, K.L., and Pribram, K.H.: A behavioral analysis of the organization of the parieto-temporo-preoccipital cortex. *J. Comp. Neurol., 93*:53-100, 1950.

Blum, R.A.: The effect of bilateral removal of the prefrontal granular cortex on delayed response performance and emotionality in chimpanzee.

Amer. Psychol., 3:237-238, 1948.

BLUM, R.A.: Effects of subtotal lesions of frontal granular cortex on delayed reaction in monkeys. *Arch. Neurol. Psychiatr., 67*:375-386, 1952.

BRUSH, E.S., MISHKIN, M., and ROSVOLD, H.E.: Effects of object preferences and aversions on discrimination learning in monkeys with frontal lesions. *J. Comp. Physiol. Psychol., 54*:319-325, 1961.

BRUTKOWSKI, S., and DABROWSKA, J.: Disinhibition after prefrontal lesions as a function of duration of intertrial intervals. *Science, 139*:505-506, 1963.

BUCY, P.C. (Ed.): *The Precentral Motor Cortex.* Urbana: U. of Ill., 1938.

CHOW, K.L.: Effect of partial extirpations of posterior association cortex on visually mediated behavior in monkeys. *Comp. Psychol. Monogr., 20*:187 217, 1950.

CHOW, K.L., and BLUM, J.S.: Studies of the posterior "Associative cortex" in monkeys. *Comp. Psychol. Monogr., 20*, No. 105, 1950.

DENNY-BROWN, D.: *The frontal lobes and their functions.* In Feilding, A. (Ed.): *Modern Trends in Neurology.* New York: Hoeber, 1951.

ETTLINGER, G., MORTON, H.B., and MOFFET, A.: Tactile discrimination performance in the monkey: The effect of bilateral posterior parietal and lateral frontal ablations, and of callosal section. *Cortex, 2*:5-29, 1966.

ETTLINGER, G., and WEGENER, J.: Somaesthetic alternation, discrimination and orientation after frontal and parietal lesions in monkeys. *Quart. J. Exp. Psychol., 10*:177-186, 1958.

FRENCH, G. M.: Spatial discontiguity in monkeys with lesions of the frontal cortex. *Science, 135*:728-729, 1962.

FRENCH, G.M., BIRNBAUM, I., LEVINE, R., and PINSKER, H.: Discriminative choice in normal and prefrontal rhesus monkeys. *J. Comp. Physiol. Psychol., 59*:225-230, 1965.

FULTON, J.F., ARING, C.D., and WORTIS, S.B. (Ed.): *The Frontal Lobes. Res. Publ. Assoc. Res. Nerv. Ment. Dis.,* 27: 1947. Baltimore: Williams and Wilkins, 1948.

HARLOW, H.F., and SETTLAGE, P.H.: Effect of extirpation of frontal areas upon learning performance of monkeys. *Res. Publ. Assoc. Res. Nerv. Ment. Dis., 27*:446-459, 1947. (See Fulton, above.)

IVERSEN, D.: Tactile learning and memory in baboons after temporal and frontal lesions. *Exp. Neurol., 18*:228-238, 1967.

JACOBSEN, C.J., WOLFE, J.B., and JACKSON, T.A.: An experimental analysis of the functions of the frontal association areas in primates. *J. Nerv. Ment. Dis., 82*:1-14, 1935.

KUYPERS, H.G.J.M.: Central cortical projections to motor, somatosensory and reticular cell groups. In Tower, D.B. and Schadé, J.P. (Eds.): *Structure and Function of the Cerebral Cortex.* Amsterdam: Elsevier, 1960.

KUYPERS, H.G.J.M., SZWARCBART, M.K., MISHKIN, M., and ROSVOLD, H.E.: Occipitotemporal corticocortical connections in the rhesus monkey. *Exp. Neurol. 11*:245-262, 1965.

LASHLEY, K.S.: *Brain Mechanisms and Intelligence, a Quantitative Study of Injuries to the Brain*. Chicago: U. of Chicago, 1929.

LASHLEY, K.S.: The mechanisms of vision: XVIII. Effects of destroying the visual "associative areas" of the monkey. *Genet. Psychol. Monogr., 37*:107-166, 1948.

LICHTENSTEIN, P.E.: Studies of anxiety. II. The effects of lobotomy on a feeding inhibition in dogs. *J. Comp. Physiol. Psychol. 43*:419-427, 1950.

LURIA, A.R.: *Frontal Lobes and Regulation of Behavior*. Symp. 10, 28th. Intern. Congr. Psychol. Moscow, 1966.

LURIA, A.R.: *Higher Cortical Function in Man*. New York: Basic Books, 1966. (Reviewed by Doty, R.W.: *Electroenceph. Clin. Neurophysiol., 23*:100, 1967.)

LURIA, A.R., KARPOV, B.A., and YARBUSS, A.L.: Disturbances of active visual perception with lesions of the frontal lobes. *Cortex, 2*:202-212, 1966.

METTLER, F.A.: Physiological effects of bilateral simultaneous frontal lesions in the primate. *J. Comp. Neurol., 81*:105-136, 1944.

METTLER, F.A. (Ed.): *Selective Partial Ablation of the Frontal Cortex*. New York: Hoeber, 1949.

MEYER, D.R., and MEYER, P.M.: Brain functions. *Ann. Rev. Psychol., 14*:155-174, 1963.

MEYER, D.R., and SETTLAGE, P.H.: Analysis of simple searching behavior in the frontal monkey. *J. Comp. Physiol. Psychol., 51*:408-410, 1958.

MILES, R.C., and BLOMQUIST, A.J.: Frontal lesions and behavioral deficits in monkeys. *J. Neurophysiol., 23*:471-484, 1960.

MISHKIN, M., and PRIBRAM, K.H.: Analysis of the effects of frontal lesions in monkeys: I. Variations of delayed alternation. *J. Comp. Physiol. Psychol., 48*:492-495, 1955.

MISHKIN, M., PROCKOP, E.S., and ROSVOLD, H.E.: One-trial object discrimination learning in monkeys with frontal lesions. *J. Comp. Physiol. Psychol., 55*:178-181, 1962.

MOFFET, A., ETTLINGER, G., MORTON, H.B., and PIERCY, M.F.: Tactile discrimination performance in the monkey: the effect of ablation of various subdivisions of posterior parietal cortex. *Cortex, 3*:59-96, 1967.

ORBACH, J., and CHOW, K.L.: Differential effects of resections of somatic areas I and II in monkeys. *J. Neurophysiol., 22*:195-203, 1959.

ORBACH, J., and FISCHER, G.J.: Bilateral resections of frontal granular cortex. *Arch. Neurol. (Chicago), 1*:78-86, 1959.

OSCAR, M., and WILSON, M.: Tactual and visual discrimination learning in monkeys with frontal lesions. *J. Comp. Physiol. Psychol., 62*:108-114, 1966.

PENFIELD, W.: Bilateral frontal gyrectomy and postoperative intelligence. *Res. Publ. Assoc. Res. Nerv. Ment. Dis., 27*:519-534, 1947. (See Fulton, above.)

PINSKER, H.M., and FRENCH, G.M.: Indirect delayed reactions under various testing conditions in normal and midlateral frontal monkeys. *Neuropsychologia, 5*:13-24, 1967.

PINTO-HAMUY, T., and LINCK, P.: Effect of frontal lesions on performance of sequential tasks by monkeys. *Exp. Neurol., 12*:96-107, 1965.

POPPEN, R.L., PRIBRAM, K.H., and ROBINSON, R.S.: Effects of frontal lobotomy in man on the performance of a multiple choice task. *Exp. Neurol., 11*:217-229, 1965.

PRIBRAM, K.H.: The intrinsic systems of the forebrain. In Field, J., and Magoun, H.W. (Eds.): *Handbook of Physiology*, Vol. II. Washington: Amer. Physiol. Soc., 1960.

PRIBRAM, H.B., and BARRY, J.: Further behavioral analysis of parieto-temporo-preoccipital cortex. *J. Neurophysiol., 19*:99-106, 1956.

PRIBRAM, K.H., KONRAD, K., and GAINSBURG, D.: Frontal lesions and behavioral instability. *J. Comp. Physiol. Psychol., 62*:123-124, 1966.

PRIBRAM, K.H., and TUBBS, W.E.: Short-term memory, parsing, and the primate frontal cortex. *Science, 156*:1765-1767, 1967.

PRIBRAM, K.H., and WEISKRANTZ, L.: A comparison of the effects of medial and lateral cerebral resections on conditioned avoidance behavior of monkeys. *J. Comp. Physiol. Psychol., 50*:74-80, 1957.

PRIBRAM, K.H., WILSON, W.A., and CONNORS, J.: Effects of lesions of the medial forebrain on alternation behavior of rhesus monkeys. *Exp. Neurol., 6*:36-47, 1962.

SETTLAGE, P., ZABLE, M., and HARLOW, H.F.: Problem solution by monkeys following bilateral removal of the prefrontal areas: VI. Performance of tests requiring contradictory reactions to similar and to identical stimuli. *J. Exp. Psychol., 38*:30-65, 1948.

STAMM, J.S.: Electrical stimulation of frontal cortex in monkeys during learning of an alternation task. *J. Neurophysiol., 24*:414-426, 1961.

THOMAS, G.J., and OTIS, L.S.: Effects of rhinencephalic lesions on conditioning of avoidance responses in the rat. *J. Comp. Physiol. Psychol., 51*:130-134, 1958.

THOMAS, G.J., and OTIS, L.S.: Effects of rhinencephalic lesions on maze learning in rats. *J. Comp. Physiol. Psychol., 51*:161-166, 1958.

WARREN, J.M., and AKERT, K. (Eds.): *The Frontal Granular Cortex and Behavior*. New York: McGraw-Hill, 1964.

WEISKRANTZ, L., MIHAILOVIC, LJ., and GROSS, C.G.: Effects of stimulation of frontal cortex and hippocampus on behavior in the monkey. *Brain, 85*:487-501, 1962.

WEGENER, J.G., and STAMM, J.S.: Behavior flexibility and the frontal lobes. *Cortex, 2*:188-200, 1966.

WILSON, W.A., JR., and OSCAR, M.: Probability learning in monkeys with lateral frontal lesions. *J. Comp. Physiol. Psychol., 62*:462-464, 1966.

WOOLSEY, C.N., SETTLAGE, P.H., MEYER, D.R., SPENCER, W., PINTO-HAMUY, T., and TRAVIS, A.M.: Patterns of Localization in precentral and "supplementary" motor areas and their relation to the concept of a premotor area. In *Patterns of organization in the central nervous system. Res. Publ. Assn. Res. Nerv. Ment. Dis., 30:*238-264, 1951.

Striato-Thalamic "System"

ADAMETZ, J.H.: Rate of recovery of functioning in cats with rostral reticular lesions. *J. Neurosurg., 16:*85-98, 1959.

ADEY, W.R., and DUNLOP, C.W.: Amygdaloid and peripheral influences on caudate and pallidal units in the cat, with investigations of the effects of chlorpromazine. *Exp. Neurol., 2:*348-363, 1960.

AJMONE MARSAN, C., and VAN BUREN, J.: Functional relationship between frontal cortex and subcortical structures in man. *Electroenceph. Clin. Neurophysiol., 16:*80-87, 1964.

ALBERT, M., and BIGNAMI, G.: Effects of frontal, median cortical and caudate lesions on two-way avoidance learning by rats. *Physiol. Behav., 3:*141-147, 1968.

ALBE-FESSARD, D., OSWALDO-CRUZ, E., and ROCHA-MIRANDA, C.: Activités évoquées dans le noyau caudé du chat en résponse à des types divers d'afférences. I. Etude macrophysiologique. *Electroenceph. Clin. Neurophysiol., 12:*405-420, 1960.

ALBE-FESSARD, D., OSWALDO-CRUZ, E., and ROCHA-MIRANDA, C.: Activités évoquées dans le noyau caudé du chat en résponse à des types divers d'afférences. II. Etude microphysiologique. *Electroenceph. Clin. Neurophysiol., 12:*649-661, 1960.

ANDERSEN, P., ANDERSSON, S.A., JUNGE, K., LOMO, T., and SVEEN, O.: Physiological mechanism of the slow 10 c/sec. cortical rhythmic activity. *Electroenceph. Clin. Neurophysiol., 23:*394, 1967.

BARGMANN, W., and SCHADÉ, J.P. (Eds.): *Progress in Brain Research, Vol. 5: Lectures on Diencephalon.* Amsterdam: Elsevier, 1964.

BATTIG, K., ROSVOLD, H.E., and MISHKIN, M.: Comparison of the effects of frontal and caudate lesions on delayed response and alternation in monkeys. *J. Comp. Physiol. Psychol., 53:*400-404, 1960.

BLOCH, V., and HEBB, D.O.: Étude des phenomenes d'enrayement et d'activation du comportement par stimulation thalamique et reticulaire chez le rat non anesthesie. *Psychol. Franc., 1:*8-9, 1956.

BUCHWALD, N.A., HULL, C.D., and TRACHTENBERG, M.C.: Concomitant behavioral and neural inhibition and disinhibition in response to subcortical stimulation. *Exp. Brain Res., 4:*58-72, 1967.

BUCHWALD, N.A., WYERS, E.J., CARLIN, J., and FARLEY, R.: Effect of stimulation of the caudate nucleus on visual discrimination in cats. *Anat. Rec., 136:*172, 1960.

BUCHWALD, N.A., WYERS, E.J., LAUPRECHT, C.W., and HEUSER, G.: The "caudate spindle" IV. A behavioral index of caudate-induced inhibition. *Electroenceph. Clin. Neurophysiol., 13:*531-537, 1961.

BUSER, P., ENCABO, H., and LAMARCHE, M.: Action inhibitrice de certains noyaux thalamiques medians sur la mise en jeu reflexe du tractus pyramidal chez le chat. *Arch. Ital. Biol.*, *103*:448-468, 1965.

Butkhuzi, S.M.: Electrophysiological analysis of cortical control of caudate nucleus. *Sechenov Physiol. J. USSR: 51*:47, 1965 *(Fed. Proc. 24*:T999-1002, 1965).

Cardo, B.: Role de certains noyaux thalamiques dans l'elaboration et le conservation de divers conditionnements. *Psychol. Francaise, 10*:334-351, 1965.

Carman, J.B., Cowan, W.M., and Powell, T.P.S.: The organization of corticostriate connexions in the rabbit. *Brain, 86*:525-562, 1963.

Chiles, W.D.: Performance during stimulation of the diencephalic activating system. *J. Comp. Physiol. Psychol., 47*:412, 1954.

Chorover, S.L., and Gross, C.G.: Caudate nucleus lesions: behavioral effects in the rat. *Science, 141*:826-827, 1963.

Chow, K.L., Dement, W.C., and Mitchell, S.A., Jr.: Effects of lesions of the rostral thalamus on brain waves and behavior in cats. *Electroceph. Clin. Neurophysiol., 11*:107-120, 1959.

Coxe, W.S., Hirsch, J.F., Benjamin, R.M., Welker, W.I., Thompson, R.F., and Woolsey, C.N.: Precentral and supplementary motor areas of Ateles. *Physiologist, 1*:19, 1957.

Dean, W.H., and Davis, G.D.: Behavior changes following caudate lesions in rhesus monkey. *J. Neurophysiol., 22*:524-537, 1959.

Delacour, J., Albe-Fessard, D., and Libouban, S.: Rôle chez le rat de deux noyaux thalamiques dans le conditionnement instrumental, *Neuropsychologia, 4*:101-112, 1966.

Delacour, J., and Santacana de Martinez, M.P.: Rôle du thalamus median dans l'etablissement et la retention de conditionnements defensifs, classiques et intrumentaux. *Neuropsychologia, 5*:237-252, 1967.

Delafresnaye, J.F. (Ed.): *Brain Mechanism and Consciousness.* Springfield: Thomas, 1954.

Delgado, J.M.R.: Effect of brain stimulation on task-free situations. *Electroenceph. Clin. Neurophysiol. (Suppl.), 24*:260-280, 1963.

Demetrescu, M., and Demetrescu, M.: The inhibitory action of the caudate nucleus in cortical primary receiving areas in the cat. *Electroenceph. Clin. Neurophysiol., 14*:37-52, 1962.

Demetrescu, M., Demetrescu, M., and Iosif, G.: The tonic control of cortical responsiveness by inhibitory and facilitatory diffuse influences. *Electroenceph. Clin. Neurophysiol., 18*:1-24, 1965.

Dempsey, E.W., and Morison, R.S.: The production of rhythmically recurrent cortical potentials after localized thalamic stimulation. *Amer. J. Physiol., 135*:293-300, 1942.

Divac, I., Rosvold, H.E., and Szwarcbart, M.K.: Behavioral effects of selective ablation of the caudate nucleus. *J. Comp. Physiol., Psychol., 63*:184-190, 1967.

Dusser de Barenne, J.G., and McCulloch, W.S.: Suppression of motor response obtained from area 4 by stimulation of area 4s. *J. Neurophysiol.,* 4:311-323, 1941.

ENOMOTO, T.F.: Unilateral activation of the non-specific thalamic system and bilateral cortical responses. *Electroenceph. Clin. Neurophysiol.,* 11:219-232, 1959.

GASANOV, U., CRIGHEL, E., and KREINDLER, A.: Relationships between the relay and association nuclei of the cat thalamus. *Electroenceph. Clin. Neurophysiol.,* 22:573, 1967.

GERBER, C.J.: Effect of selected excitant and depressant agents on the cortical response to midline thalamic stimulation. *Electroenceph. Clin. Neurophysiol.,* 13:345-364, 1961.

GOLDRING, S., ANTHONY, L.U., STOHR, P.E., and O'LEARY, J.L.: "Caudate-induced" cortical potentials: comparison between monkey and cat. *Science, 139*:772, 1963.

GRINDEL', O.M., and FILIPPYCHEVA, N.A.: Reduced lability of excitation in motor analyzer in patients with focal lesions of the frontal lobes. *Pavlov J. Higher Nerv. Act.,* 9:475-483, 1959.

GROSS, C.G., CHOROVER, S.L., and COHEN, S.M.: Caudate, cortical, hippocampal and dorsal thalamic lesions in rats: alternation and Hebb-Williams maze performance. *Neuropsychologia, 3*:53-68, 1965.

HANSING, R.A., SCHWARTZBAUM, J.S., and THOMPSON, J.B.: Operant behavior following unilateral and bilateral caudate lesions in the rat. *J. Comp. Physiol. Psychol.,* 66:378-388, 1968.

HARMAN, P.J., TANKARD, M., HOVDE, C., and METTLER, F.A., An experimental anatomical analysis of the topography and polarity of the caudate-neocortex interrelationship in the primate. *Anat. Rec., 118*:307-308, 1954.

HERNÁNDEZ-PÉON, R., and STERMAN, M.B.: Brain functions. *Ann. Rev. Psychol., 17*:363-394, 1966.

HUNTER, J., and JASPER, H.H.: Effect of thalamic stimulation in unanesthetized animals. *Electroenceph. Clin. Neurophysiol., 1*:305-324, 1949.

JASPER, H.H.: Diffuse projection systems: the integrative action of the thalamic reticular system. *Electroenceph. Clin. Neurophysiol., 1*:405-420, 1949.

JASPER, H.H.: Unspecific thalamocortical relations. In Field, J., and Magoun, H.W. (Eds.): *Handbook of Physiology,* Vol. II. Washington: Amer. Physiol. Soc., 1960.

KESNER, R.P., FIELDER, P., and THOMAS, G.J.: Function of the midbrain reticular formation in regulating level of activity and learning in rats. *J. Comp. Physiol. Psychol., 63*:452-457, 1967.

KIRBY, R.J.: Avoidance and escape behavior following striatal lesions in the rat. *Exp. Neurol., 20*:215-227, 1968.

KLING, A., and TUCKER, T.J.: Effects of combined lesions of frontal granular cortex and caudate nucleus in the neonatal monkey. *Brain Res., 6*:428-439, 1967.

KNOTT, J.R., INGRAM, W.R., and CORRELL, R.E.: Some effects of subcortical stimulation on the bar press response. *Arch. Neurol. (Chicago)*, 2:476-484, 1960.

MAHUT, H.: Effects of subcortical electrical stimulation on discrimination learning in cats. *J. Comp. Physiol. Psychol.*, 58:390-395, 1964.

MANZONI, T., SAPIENZA., S., and URBANO, A.: EEG and behavioral sleep-like effects induced by the fastigial nucleus in unrestrained unanesthetized cats. *Arch. Ital. Biol.*, 106:61-72, 1968.

McLENNAN, H., EMMONS, P.R., and PLUMMER, P.M.: Some behavioral effects of stimulation of the caudate nucleus in unrestrained cats. *Canad. J. Physiol. Pharmacol.*, 42:329-339, 1964.

MENNIER, M., KALBERER, M., and KRUPP, P.: Functional antagonism between diffuse reticular and intralaminary recruiting projections in the medial thalamus. *Exp. Neurol.*, 2:271-289, 1960.

METTLER, F.A., GRUNDFEST, H., and HOVDE, C.A.: Distant electrical potentials evoked by stimulation of the caudate nucleus. *Anat. Rec.*, 112:359, 1952.

METTLER, F.A., HOVDE, C.A., and GRUNDFEST, H.: Electrophysiologic phenomena evoked by electrical stimulation of the caudate nucleus. *Fed. Proc.*, 11:107, 1952.

MORRISON, R.S., and DEMPSEY, E.W.: A study of thalamo-cortical relations. *Amer. J. Physiol.*, 135:281-300, 1942.

MOTOKIZAWA, F., and FUJIMORI, B.: Fast activities and DC potential changes of the cerebral cortex during EEG arousal response. *Electroenceph. Clin. Neurophysiol.*, 17:630-637, 1964.

NARIKASHVILI, S.P., and MONIAVA, E.S.: Interaction between thalamocortical projection systems. *Pavlov J. Higher Nerv. Act.*, 9:399-407, 1959.

NASHOLD, B.S.: HANBERY, J., and OLSZEWSKY, J.: Observations on the diffuse thalamic projections. *Electroenceph. Clin. Neurophysiol.*, 7:609-620, 1955.

NAUMOVA, T.S.: Changes in the electrical activity of the caudate nucleus on the establishment of a temporary relationship (coupling) between auditory and motor analysors. *Sechenov. Physiol. J. USSR*, 43:10-18, 1957.

POWELL, T.P.S., and COWAN, W.M.: A study of thalamo-striate relations in the monkey. *Brain*, 79:364-390 (plus plates xxxii-xxxiv), 1956.

PURPURA, D.P., HOUSEPIAN, E.M., and GRUNDFEST, H.: Analysis of caudate-cortical connections in neuraxially intact and telencephal isole cats. *Arch. Ital. Biol.*, 96:145-167, 1958.

PURPURA, D.P., McMURTRY, J.G., and MAEKAWA, K.: Synaptic events in ventrolateral thalamic neurons during suppression of recruiting responses by brain stem reticular stimulation. *Brain Res.*, 1:63-76, 1966.

PURPURA, D.P., and YAHR, M. (Eds.): *The Thalamus*. New York: Columbia, 1965.

ROSE, J.E., and WOOLSEY, C.N.: Organization of the mammalian thalamus and its relationships to the cerebral cortex. *Electroenceph. Clin. Neurophysiol.*, 1:391-402, 1949.

Rosvold, H.E., Mishkin, M., and Szwarcbart, M.K.: Effects of subcortical lesions in monkeys on visual-discrimination and single-alternation performance. *J. Comp. Physiol. Psychol., 51*:437-444, 1958.

Rougeul, A., Perret, C., and Buser, P.: Effects comportementaux et electrographiques de stimulations electriques de thalamus chez le chat libre. *Electroenceph. Clin. Neurophysiol., 23*:410-428, 1967.

Scheibel, M.E., and Scheibel, A.B.: The organization of the nucleus reticularis thalami: a Golgi study. *Brain Res., 1*:43-62, 1966.

Scheibel, M.E., and Scheibel, A.B.: The organization of the ventral anterior nucleus of the thalamus. A Golgi study. *Brain Res., 1*:250-268, 1966.

Schlag, J.D., and Chaillet, F.: Thalamic mechanisms involved in cortical desynchronization and recruiting responses. *Electroenceph. Clin. Neurophysiol., 15*:39-62, 1963.

Schlag, J.D., and Chaillet, F., and Herzet, J.P.: Thalamic reticular system and cortical arousal. *Science, 134*:1691-1692, 1961.

Schlag, J.D., Kuhn, R.L., and Velasco, M.: An hypothesis on the mechanism of cortical recruiting responses. *Brain Res., 1*:208-212, 1966.

Schreiner, L., Rioch, D.M., Pechtel, C., and Masserman, J.H.: Behavioral changes following thalamic injury in cats. *J. Neurophysiol., 16*:234-246, 1953.

Schulman, S.: Impaired delayed response from thalamic lesions. *Arch. Neurol. (Chicago), 11*:477-499, 1964.

Spiegel, E.A., and Szekely, E.G.: Prolonged stimulation of the head of the caudate nucleus. *Arch. Neurol. (Chicago), 4*:55-65, 1961.

Stevens, J.R., Kim, C., and MacLean, P.D.: Stimulation of caudate nucleus. *Arch. Neurol. (Chicago), 4*:47-54, 1961.

Teuber, H.L., and Proctor, F.: Some effects of basal ganglia lesions in subhuman primates and man. *Neuropsychologia., 2*:85-93, 1964.

Tissot, R., and Monnier, M.: Dualité du système thalamique de projection diffuse. *Electroenceph. Clin. Neurophysiol., 11*:675-686, 1959.

Vanasupa, P., Goldring, S., O'Leary, J.L., and Winter, D.: Steady potential changes during cortical activation. *J. Neurophysiol. 22*:273-284, 1959.

Vanderwolf, C.H.: Warm-up effects in the avoidance performance of rats with medial thalamic lesions. *Anim. Behav., 14*:425-429, 1966.

Velasco, M., and Lindsley, D.B.: Role of orbital cortex in regulation of thalamocortical electrical activity. *Science, 149*:1375-1377, 1965.

Velasco, M., Skinner, J.E., and Lindsley, D.B.: Blocking of electrocortical activity mediated by a thalamocortical system by lesions in the forebrain and rostral diencephalon. *Electroenceph. Clin. Neurophysiol., 22*:292,1967.

Walter, D.O., and Adey, W.R.: Spectral analysis of electroencephalograms recorded during learning in the cat, before and after subthalamic lesions. *Exp. Neurol., 7*:481-501, 1963.

Weinberger, N.M., Velasco, M., and Lindsley, D.B.: Effects of lesions upon thalamically induced electrocortical desynchronization and recruiting. *Electroenceph. Clin. Neurophysiol., 18*:369-377, 1965.

Miscellaneous

BASSETT, C.A.L.: Elecrical effects in bone. *Sci. Amer.* 213(4):18-25, Oct. 1965.

BONIN, G. VON: The cerebral cortex of the Cebus monkey. *J. Comp. Neurol.*, 69:181-227, 1938.

DeMOTT, D.W., and DAVIS, T.P.: Irradiance thresholds for chorioretinal lesions. *Arch. Ophthal. (Chicago)*, 62:653-656, 1959.

ECCLES, J.C., and McINTYRE, A.K.: The effect of disuse and of activity on mammalian spinal reflexes. *J. Physiol.*, 121:492, 1953.

GALAMBOS, R.: A glia-neural theory of brain function. *Proc. Nat. Acad. Sci. USA*, 47:129-136, 1961.

GEIGER, R.S.: The behavior of adult mammalian brain cells in culture. *Neurobiology*, 5:1-52, 1963.

GROSS, N.B., and SMALL, A.M.: Frequency correlates on the auditory cortex of the cat brain. *Exp. Neurol.*, 3:375-387, 1961.

HYDEN, H.: A microchemical study of the relationship between glia and nerve cells. In Tower, D.B., and Schadé, J.P. (Eds.): *Structure and Function of the Cerebral Cortex*. Amsterdam: Elsevier, 1960.

KLEE, M.R., OFFENLOCH, K., and TIGGES, J.: Cross-correlation analysis of electroencephalographic potentials and slow membrane transients. *Science*, 147:519-521, 1965.

KLÜVER, H.: Behavior Mechanisms in Monkeys. Chicago: U. of Chicago, 1933.

LENDE, R.A.: Cerebral cortex: a sensorimotor amalgam in the marsupialia. *Science*, 141:730-732, 1963.

VAN DER LOOS, H.: On dendro-dendritic junctions in the cerebral cortex. In Tower, D.B., and Schadé, J.P. (Eds.): *Structure and Function of the Cerebral Cortex*. Amsterdam: Elsevier, 1960.

LOUTTIT, R.T., and HANIK, M.J.: *Bibliography of Translations in the Neural Sciences 1950-1960*, Bethesda: Nat. Inst. Mental Health, 1967 (Public Health Service Publ. No. 1635).

McCULLOCH, W.S.: *Finality and Form*. Springfield: Thomas, 1952.

MORRELL, F.: Lasting changes in synaptic organization produced by continuous neuronal bombardment. In Delafresnaye, J., et al. (Eds.): *Brain Mechanisms and Learning*. Oxford: Blackwell, 1961.

ROBINS, E., SMITH, D.E., EYDT, K.M., and McCAMAN, R.E.: The quantitative histochemistry of the cerebral cortex. II: Architectonic distributtion of nine enzymes in the motor and visual cortices. *J. Neurochem.*, 1:68-76, 1956.

ROUVRAY, R., and RÉMOND, A.: Le nickel comme source d'artefacts en EEG et ECoG. *Electroenceph. Clin. Neurophysiol.*, 2:352, 1950.

RUTLEDGE, L.T., RANCK, J., and DUNCAN, J.A.: Prevention of supersensitivity in partially isolated cerebral cortex. *Electroenceph. Clin. Neurophysiol.*, 23:256-262, 1967.

SPERRY, R.W., MINER, N., and MYERS, R.E.: Visual pattern perception following subpial slicing and tantalum wire implantations in the visual cortex. *J. Comp. Physiol. Psychol.*, 48:50-58, 1955.

SPERRY, R.W., and MINER, N.: Pattern perception following insertion of mica plates into visual cortex. *J. Comp. Physiol. Psychol.*, 48:463-469, 1955.

STRAW, R.N., McADAM, D., BERRY, C.A., and MITCHELL, C.L.: A simple cable for reduction of movement artifact in electroencephalographic recordings. *Electroenceph. Clin. Neurophysiol.*, 22:90-92, 1967.

U.S. DEPT. OF HEALTH, EDUCATION AND WELFARE (Ed.): *The Central Nervous System and Human Behavior*. Bethesda: Russian Scientific Translation Program, NIH, 1959.

U.S. DEPT. OF HEALTH AND WELFARE (Ed.): *The Central Nervous System and Behavior*. Bethesda: Russian Scientific Translation Program, NIH, 1959.